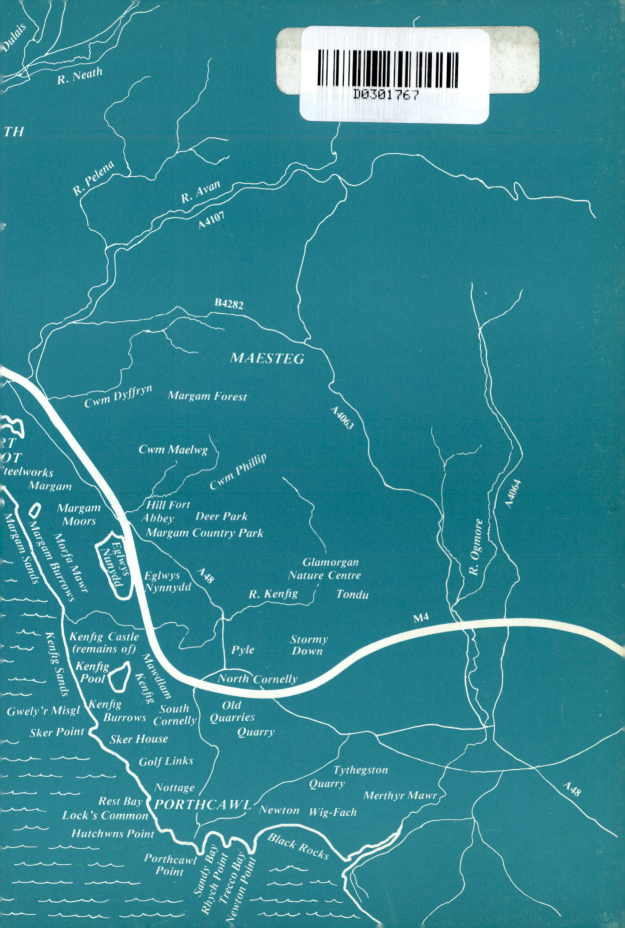

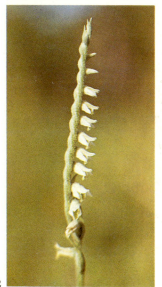

Plate 1   INDUSTRY AND WILDLIFE—*Author*

1. Flower regeneration, gravel diggings and Steelworks at Margam (Evening primrose, mullein, ragwort, hawkbit and thyme)
2. Autumn lady's tresses orchid
3. Bee orchids
4. Southern marsh orchids

Swansea Bay's Green Mantle

by

Mary E. Gillham, B.SC., PH.D.

Common shorebirds: Curlew, Tern, Black-headed gull, Dunlin, Sanderling

D. BROWN AND SONS LIMITED COWBRIDGE

First published 1982

© *Mary E. Gillham, 1982*

All photographic illustrations are the copyright of the individual photographers

ISBN 0 905928 18 0

DESIGNED AND PRINTED IN WALES BY

D. Brown and Sons Ltd., Cowbridge and Bridgend, South Wales

Colour separations by Pinegate Ltd., Cardiff

Bound by Western Book Company Limited, Maesteg

To

COLONEL MORREY SALMON, C.B.E., M.C., D.I.
Ornithologist

In recognition of more than 75 years of work
with and for Glamorgan's Wildlife

ACKNOWLEDGEMENTS

I am greatly indebted to Keri Williams and Jack Evans for providing many of the most exciting animal photographs in this volume and to Michael Collins for his aerial view of Crymlin Burrows. Roy Perry has given invaluable assistance with identification of the more obscure groups of plants and animals and by his meticulous checking of the final page proofs, and much field data was gleaned from the late Arthur Morgan. Joan Raum, Morrey Salmon, Steve Moon, John Perkins, Peter Ferns and Andrew Lees have read parts of the script and made helpful suggestions. To these and those others acknowledged in subsequent pages, I extend sincere thanks. The errors are mine.

CONTENTS

7

PART EIGHT: ROCK POOLS, HEADLANDS AND DOWNS AROUND PORTHCAWL

ILLUSTRATIONS

1. COLOUR PLATES

2. MONOCHROME PLATES

FOREWORD

BY H.R.H. THE PRINCE OF WALES, K.G., K.T., P.C., G.C.B.

BUCKINGHAM PALACE

     As Patron of The Royal Society for Nature Conservation
I am delighted to be able to contribute this foreword to Dr.
Gillham's new book. The author is Chairman of the Glamorgan
Naturalists' Trust, and I was recently lucky enough to be
able to visit the Glamorgan Nature Centre at Tondu, which
demonstrates in the most effective way the splendid work
being done by Dr. Gillham and her colleagues to conserve,
and sometimes improve, the environment in South Wales. The
Trust is also doing an immense amount to inform and assist
all those who have an interest in the wildlife of the area,
and this book, like its predeccesor "The Natural History of
Gower", will surely complement the work of the Trust and be
of the greatest help and interest to all those who are
concerned with an area which contains some of the most
diverse and extraordinary habitats in Britain.

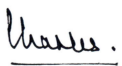

Petrochemical Works East of Crymlin Burrows

PREFACE

Conservation is the 'in thing' at present, but the word 'conservationist' is becoming synonymous with 'harbinger of gloom and doom'—and there is cause enough in this age of so much pressure on the countryside. Every year that passes sees another hundred square miles of the fair face of Britain disappearing under concrete, and many more being degraded and misused. Every DAY sees the extinction, finally and forever, of one of the world's species of plant or animal. The early 1970s saw the annual destruction of 10,000 miles of hedges—enough of those linear woodlands that make the British scene so British, to stretch from Glamorgan to Australia.

But do we overestimate the power of our own nastiness? Geologists are fond of telling us that man appeared on the world scene late on the last day of Mother Earth's calendar. We were not the first to arrive and are unlikely to be the last to go. Our existence is quite closely tied to all the rest, loath though we are to admit it. The world can well do without us if we choose to annihilate ourselves.

This book sets out to be provocative: to present the other side of the coin to those whose bookshelves are crowded with doom-watch publications on extinction of species, pollution of environment and exhaustion of resources.

While recognising the problems and acknowledging that we have made a 'right mess' of things to date, it tries to emphasise the omnipotence of the natural world and the impotence of man to impose his will on all that it contains. Gardeners who have done battle with flowers as bright as poppies and insects as graceful as white butterflies to produce a monoculture of pudgy cabbages, will appreciate the sentiments expressed.

The destruction of primaeval forest in Brazil or Peru leaves devastation in its wake, because everything is geared to life in tropical rain forest, and no other. Ours, on the other hand, is a man-made landscape of considerable diversity, with jig-sawed patches of this and that.

For centuries of use and mis-use, since the original felling and burning of the oak forest and pursuit of arable farming by men of the Iron Age, the vegetation of our islands has been recovering, adapting and changing to fit our ways. More and brighter flowers line our derelict railway tracks today than our shady woodland rides. Nature is not only forgiving, she is bountiful, returning good for evil.

15

There can be few better regions to demonstrate the sheer tenacity and recuperative powers of the wild than the 24 mile sweep of South Wales coast east of Swansea, that has scathingly been dubbed 'Swansea Bay City'.

Only here, by the sea's edge, is there sufficient flat land to build the huge establishments that modern industry demands, and the old industrial revolution was not all on the heights around Merthyr Tydfil and in the mining valleys: the Glamorgan coast has always had its share. Heavy metal industries and coal ports rose at Swansea, Neath, Briton Ferry and even Porthcawl, long before British Steel and B P Chemicals moved in.

Along this much abused stretch of sandy shore our clever, acquisitive species has been clawing its way up for generations at the expense of its fellow creatures—pushing them out, covering them over, drying them up, drowning them, poisoning them—and still they return for more.

We do not wilfully destroy, we just do not think. The angler who abhors the hunting of otters, lightly abandons his nylon line to strangle the swans and lead sinkers to be picked up as gizzard grist and cause lead poisoning in the cygnets. The housewife who decries the slaughter of whales and seals, cheerfully empties her detergent down the sink and into the rivers and sea.

The re-creation of living organisms—a craft that man has never mastered—goes on apace. When some are killed more will be born to eat the food they no longer need. When flower carpets are destroyed others will move in and, if conditions are no longer right for what was lost they will be right for something else. It is ourselves we punish: plants and animals do not have the sense of beauty with which we are endowed.

Industrial waste can make as good a nesting site for oyster catchers as beach pebbles: crabs, frogs and beetles shelter as successfully under our discarded garbage as under natural logs. It is man who has to suffer the visual eyesores and unlovely noises with which he has chosen to surround himself.

Long-abandoned scraps of the old Baglan Canal are peopled now by great-crested newts and flowering rush; hard core dumped in Baglan Bay at the coming of the main line railway is mellowed by willow-dotted marshland where sedge warbler and water rail breed.

Vesiculate slag from the steel furnaces provides nesting sites for lapwings and waste from the coke ovens tempts ringed plovers to lay. Brickbats from building sites produce crevices for wheatears, and bottles littering the dunes are used by song thrushes as anvils for breaking their snail shells.

Foxes rear cubs under railway embankments, hares frolic between gas storage tanks, water voles plop into scummy drainage dykes. Marsh

16

orchids romp across dune slacks contaminated by hydrocarbons; bumble bees pack their pollen baskets from yellow stonecrop which defies annual applications of herbicide. Painted lady butterflies come winging in from North Africa, swallows from South Africa, dunlin from Greenland and bramblings from Scandinavia.

Toads engage in their mating orgies in pools dredged out by gravel diggers and bats scoop up flies under factory ceilings. Sub-tropical crabs enjoy hot cooling waters spewed into the docks and starlings warm their feet on hot water pipes. Kestrels nest on flare stacks, gulls on workshop roofs. Crows forage over rubbish tips bright with viper's bugloss and reptilian vipers bask beside pyramidal orchids on fly ash dumps from the coal-fired power stations.

It is a major miracle of our time that so much wildscape has survived, in spite of the worst that man can do. We can take heart, but must not be complacent. Evening primrose and great mullein will cover our squalor, but there are others, more sensitive, which will need all the help they can get if we are to retain any real diversity: and everyone knows that 'variety is the spice of life'.

Apathy arises from lack of hope. The force that created and guides the universe has proved again and again that there is ample cause for hope, to counter that massive weight of unconcern. Let us up and enter into partnership with the rest instead of constantly warring with them. Industry we must have, and housing, but we have no need for the no-man's-land of dereliction in between.

Let us dispel the gloom and challenge the doom. Let us see to it that reservoirs of native countryside and all that these contain are conserved, so that there is a source of new material to flow into those areas that we have finished with. Let us stop uprooting, plundering, killing and polluting, if not for their sake, then for our own.

It is as certain as doom itself, that we cannot live without our fellow beings, even if we could tolerate the sterility of a concrete desert devoid of bird song and petal fall. Hope implies action and action reaches for success. Our children's children could still find the world a fit place to live in and lament, with the happily frustrated Welsh poet: 'Oh God, why did you make the world so beautiful and man's span so short to see it all?'

Pessimistic die-hards may tell us that we are living in cloud cuckoo land when we admit to the loveliness all around. Our answer: 'What's wrong with cloud cuckoo land if it enables human batteries to be recharged for the morrow at so little cost to the ecosystem?'.

MARY. E. GILLHAM
Cardiff, 1982

Steelworks on Margam Moors, 1972

INTRODUCTION

'In their 6,000 miles of coastline the people of Britain have inherited their most magnificent natural asset.' So wrote the compiler of 'The AA Book of the Seaside' and how very true that sentiment rings. Some find their consuming passion among the hills, others on the marshlands, but for most of our island race it is the coast which exerts an irresistible pull, and the annual jaunt to the seaside has been a ritual for the more fortunate since there has been a means to transport them thither.

110 miles of that 6,000 belongs to the triple county of Glamorgan, West, Mid and South, and is as varied in character as that of any other British shire. Floristically and faunistically it is an extension of the English Lowlands infiltrated by a rich taste of the Welsh Uplands. Yet it is also the heart of industrial South Wales and all the biggest of the economic enterprises now crowd along the coastal strip.

Amenity-wise, this coastline is called upon to cater not only for its own great conurbations but for others, whose citizens come streaming in along the M4 motorway and the rail link from London via South Wales to the Irish ferry.

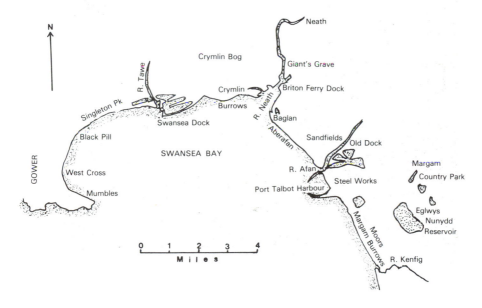

1. Map of Swansea Bay

How can one region, however diverse, reconcile so many conflicting facets and still retain a wealth of wildlife? The answer is found in compromise, as so often in our multi-purpose world. While part is still truly indigenous wildscape, much is what ecologists now classify as 'the unofficial countryside', implying the bits which man has tried to filch but which Nature is fast winning back.

Leaving aside her spacious upland moors with tight ribbon development pressed into the valley bottoms, we can divide the southern fringes of Glamorgan into four.

In the West is the magnificent 20 mile peninsula of Gower, where ancient bastions of Carboniferous mountain limestone pit their strength against the western sea. Britain's first designated 'Area of Outstanding Natural Beauty', this formed the subject of the initial book of this regional series, 'The Natural History of Gower'.

Subject of this, the second book, is the great sweep of Swansea Bay, from where the pale limestone dips beneath the sea off the tidal islands of the Mumbles to where it reappears in the rugged bluffs of Porthcawl. Its spacious acres of wind-whisked sand dunes and waterlogged alluvial flats are strung along 24 miles of coast, but such is the curvature of the shore that it is only 14 miles from end to end as the cormorant flies, and the land visible on the horizon is not always that of Devon or Somerset.

Our third region, after more sandhills, is the 27 mile stretch of less ancient cliffs dropping sheer to the sea from Ogmore to Penarth. 14 miles of the precipitous Liassic limestone cliffs are categorised as 'The Glamorgan Heritage Coast'—one of three such in Britain selected by the Countryside Commission for pilot management schemes. Eastwards are the great pebble beaches around Aberthaw and the New Red Sandstone cliffs of the Trias.

Fourthly, from the Taff-Ely Basin and Rumney Marshes at Cardiff, are the Severnside Levels, stretching on through Gwent and Gloucester to the inner end of the Bristol Channel—scoured by the second greatest tides in the world and sustaining thousands of migrant waders on remote expanses of tidal mud and sand. Drained by Romans and Augustinian monks, the coastal plain is still largely agricultural, but is under threat from all kinds of development and languishing in the intimidating shadow of the impending Severn Barrage.

But the biggest conflict between our material and aesthetic needs is being played out in our area of immediate concern, around the shore of Swansea Bay. The survival of so much of lasting indigenous value here through the tremendous pressures of the Industrial Revolution is a happy coincidence not of our making. To squander so priceless an asset in this enlightened age when conservation of natural resources is in the forefront of every thinking person's mind, would be unforgiveable.

The first stage in protecting this heritage is to learn to understand it.

To most people the book of the countryside is as closed as that of nuclear fission or the income tax laws. Those who bother to find out a little more, can scarcely fail to have their interest awakened, and, in a whole lifetime of pleasurable seeking, they will have learned only a fraction of what there is to know.

A person who has come to reverence a flower for its exquisite perfection and intricate pollination mechanism, will not trample it underfoot or dig it up. One who is not in too much of a hurry to linger awhile, may see into the secret lives of those bewhiskered furry creatures that have learned to keep out of our way so successfully that most of us do not realise they are there.

The following chapters tell something of what is still to be seen on this rich coastline, against a backcloth of fluctuating levels of land and sea during prehistoric times and of the great sandblows and drownings of the Middle Ages. They trace the course of succession on land thrown out of the tidal treadmill during the last century and on artificial surfaces fabricated by man in the last few decades.

It is a story which aims to awaken interest, and with interest sympathy and concern. The apathy which 'does nothing about it' is often a state of not knowing rather than not caring. The more people who know and care and take the trouble to advise and influence the planners who have the handling of our destiny, the more we are likely to be able to 'cleave to that which is good' before it all disappears down the maw of human ignorance.

In spite of the incredible persistence of the few, there are many wild plants and animals which will need all the aid we can supply if they are to survive. We do not need to know the life cycles of each and every one, but merely to ensure that their habitat remains inviolate. If we provide the right environment they will do the rest; so long as we have not already exterminated them.

The wise use of land is one of the facts of life which we have to come to terms with, because land supplies our all. Coastal Glamorgan, from Swansea to Kenfig, is representative of many such stretches in Britain where the issues are most crucial. If we can get to grips with these, the lessons learned should be applicable elsewhere.

Huge metallurgical industries have boomed here over the past two centuries and the Swansea Valley Rehabilitation Scheme has gone a long way in clearing up the aftermath of dereliction. Scarlet fly-caps now push up beneath yellowing birches, where once all was fumes and clamour. Other areas still await their face lift, and it is here that our new and necessary industry should be sited—not on the precious green acres that have survived all the hazards of this clamorous past.

Landscape architects feel a glow of virtue at sinking vast sums of money into the planting of rye-grass and sapling trees on once denuded acres; while others hard by are sending bulldozers into the last fragments of *real* countryside to erect more finite breeze-block buildings.

How much wiser—and cheaper—it would be to put the new enterprises on the already ruined acres and save the unruined ones for posterity! No landscape architect can create a new dunescape or fen or peat bog or put the cowslips and orchids of the old pastures back into the new. No planner can replan the landscapes that took Nature thousands of years to fashion, in the patient build-up of a living soil and the intricate web of life that depends on it. No naturalist, however dedicated, can bring back plants and animals driven to extinction by the thoughtless greed of an ill-planned past.

A nation fighting for survival in a virgin countryside has need to burn and plunder to gain a little land from the wilderness on which to earn a livelihood. Today the roles are reversed. It is the countryside which is fighting for survival in a technological age more destructive than any the world has known. It is both resilient and tolerant. Given time and opportunity, it will heal scars that seem unhealable, but it would appreciate a little more consideration from those who dismantled the original jig-saw. Man's superior intellect does not give him carte blanche to ignore the needs of others—nor does it spare him the consequences to himself and his children yet unborn if he does.

Many have known the craving to get away from it all, to the weekend cottage or the annual holiday. As the high rise blocks get higher and suburbia broader, the craving and the need increase. The people of the South Wales Valleys, however squalid their immediate environment, have 'the mountain' at their back, where they can fill their lungs.

The people of the coastal plain will find themselves smothered by the workaday world if there is not a little more forethought in the planning of their future: with no escape except to take to the hills. Yet no county is better endowed than Glamorgan with the vast expanses of sandy beaches that can accommodate thousands of holiday makers.

Do we intend to go on cutting these beaches off from the people, as by the snaking black tip spewed from the Steelworks along more than two miles of sea-washed sand bordering one of the country's richest dune systems at Margam?

It is small wonder that the Afan Naturalists' Society has emerged at Port Talbot to study the remnants of what is recognised nationwide as a superb plant and animal community, spilling from the sandhills to the water meadows, before it is irretrievably lost. Perhaps they can be instrumental in preventing its obliteration.

There have always been a few voices crying in the wilderness in the cause of conservation, but movements such as the County Naturalists' Trusts and local natural history societies are 'of the people, by the people, for the people'. With greater affluence comes greater power to destroy and greater responsibility to preserve, and the people of South Wales are not going to be more backward than the next in recognising this.

This growing band of enthusiasts from the steel and oil conurbation of Port Talbot and Baglan, have set themselves up as an action group, following in the footsteps of that other thriving band from the iron and coal conurbation of the north—The Merthyr Tydfil and District Naturalists' Society. Movements like this, from within, are the ones most likely to stir the cauldron of unconcern into an awareness of what is going on before it is too late to make amends.

This book is not about the malady but about the healthy part of the system which survives in spite of it. The picture is cheering. There is still time to effect a workable compromise so long as we act fast.

Mid Glamorgan County Council has already acted and is making a splendid job of running the local nature reserve at Kenfig Burrows. Thousands of people pass through every year and come away refreshed and stimulated. Kenfig and adjacent dunes had all the insignia of a National Nature Reserve, but encroachment of the Steelworks and rise of the local population to beyond 50,000 invalidated its claim when designation was due after the second world war. The 25 year battle for second best as a Local Nature Reserve was launched in 1953 by Colonel Morrey Salmon and finally clinched in 1978.

Other superb areas remain. There are the flowery dunes of Crymlin Burrows, which no-one has yet destroyed with a major trunk road; the spreading fen and reedbeds of Crymlin Bog, recently threatened with untold tons of Swansea city's rubbish, but which there is still time to save for the bitterns and bearded tits which show signs of wanting to move in, alongside the herons and reed warblers.

A battle has recently been waged to save a similar area at Pant-y-Sais from inundation by builders' rubble, and other sites, notably the 850 acres of Margam Country Park, have already been set aside for natural history and amenity purposes.

The Neath Valley is one of the wonders of Wales, scenically, geologically, biologically and industrially, from its mountain waterfalls to its sea-washed sands, and a goodly proportion has survived the busy turmoil of copper smelting, iron working and ship building. New jobs will be needed with the run-down of Steel in the 1980s, but there is sufficient rubble infill around Briton Ferry, Baglan and Aberafan to accommodate these without destroying more of the green acres.

Nature is on our side, adding tons of sea-borne sand to the accreting dunes at Crymlin with every tide. All the sand on Glamorgan's once mighty dune systems came from the sea, some of it catastrophically in mediaeval times. The sea may yet take it back. The 1976 drought , 1978

23

freeze-up, 1979 deluges and the arid spring and flooded summer of 1980, interspersed with ferocious gales, remind us that we are but pawns in the natural world. Things could change overnight: as they did when Kenfig Borough and its busy seaport were buried by sand in the sixteenth century.

The stewardship of the 24 miles described in this volume is in our hands, to make or mar. The 'high spots' for birds have long been recognised and jealously guarded. Members of the Gower Ornithological Society have studied the bird life of the Blackpill Sands since the inception of their organisation, in spite of the fascinations of Gower enticing them away. Members of the Cardiff Naturalists' Society make regular visits to Kenfig Pool, to record the wintering bird flocks and summer breeders. Both now converge on the waterfowl of the great Steelworks Reservoir at Eglwys Nunydd.

Port Talbot deep water harbour has added a new dimension to local ornithology in the past decade and the bird and animal life in the steelworks itself is thriving, having not yet got the message that man has taken over.

The dunes have always been a Mecca for botanists and hold a wealth of national rarities which people come long distances to see. Much has gone, but sufficient remains for parts to have been designated as Grade I sites of national biological importance by the Nature Conservancy Council.

Wetlands have fared less well and the loss of the Morfa Pools at Margam, with their flocks of wild geese and rare mudworts, was a blow only partially compensated for by the coming of the reservoir. Crymlin Bog, another Grade I site, must be saved for posterity. We have the knowledge now, and the means. To destroy even the smallest part of it would be nothing short of vandalism.

Our enlightened law-makers have made it illegal for the little old lady to potter out with her trowel and dig up a few primroses for her cottage garden. They do nothing to stop the bulldozers going in and ripping up acres of rare plants piecemeal. Somewhere along the line we have gone astray. Now is the time to make amends. Tomorrow may be too late.

Do enough of us realise this? Do enough of us go and look? Do we lie back on sandy banks 'where the wild thyme blows' and listen to the trilling song of the skylarks and the mournful call of the redshank? More. Do we decide that this is the sort of world we want and do something about ensuring that it is not lost for ever?

This book tells the story of the living tapestry of today's landscape and of its history. Please God it is not destined to become wholly history. The custodianship is ours. To understand is to love; to love is to cherish; to cherish is to conserve. So read on, and, if in the light of what you read, you realise that a corner somewhere in your hard-pressed county is under threat and worth saving, lobby your MP, or join those stalwart, merry conservationists who go out with pick and shovel at weekends, pond clearing, debris shifting, fence building, path making and tree planting.

Evolution may find its own answer eventually, but for us it could be too late. Strains of sheep's fescue and common bent grass, faced with heavy-metal poisoning, have changed their chromosomal make-up to defeat the toxins in the soil. Those which failed to evolve failed to survive—and the grass swards are duller than if the heavy-metal contamination had been tackled at source.

In 1979 the large blue butterfly, with its fascinating life cycle involving a youth spent in thyme-covered anthills, was officially declared extinct in Britain, in spite of the fact that 30 colonies were known in the 1950s and their plight recognised for over 20 years.

Let us acknowledge our place as an integral part of a larger whole and see that the others get a sporting chance. 'Conservation is the key to sustained development and the two are mutually dependent.'

Part One

Extensive Tide-Washed Shores

Shelduck and Spartina grass

Like winds and sunsets, wild things were taken for granted until progress began to do away with them.

Aldo Leopold in ''A Sand Country Almanac.''

1 ANCIENT STORY IN THE SANDS

The History of a Drowning Coast

WIDE sweeps of sea-washed sand are a valuable asset, both scenically and recreationally, in our crowded age, and Swansea City is as favoured as any in this respect. Twice daily the great tides of the Bristol Channel roll back towards misty horizons off Devon to reveal hundreds of acres of shimmering golden 'play space'. Away to the South, past the host of little sailing craft, they reach to the decorative limestone humps of The Mumbles, with the promise of Gower beyond. Eastwards the broad yellow ribbon unfurls to Baglan and Port Talbot, where the broken skyline is a reminder of the city's industrial heritage.

The sand yielded by the Bristol Channel from pulverised rock fragments is more finite than those spreading acres might suggest and that which was carted away a decade or so ago has not been fully replenished. Fortunately, the muddier silts which replace it settle out downshore where the fishermen dig for bait, and the sparkling grains are still firm underfoot for the average upshore walker. Sometimes the flats are smooth, sometimes thrown into ripples by the ebb, but always they are too much on the move for seaweeds to gain a hold. How then, do we account for those bright green beds of *Enteromorpha* scattered across the upper beach?

Many changes have occurred along the fringe of the bay since the tongue of the massive ice sheet overlying the South Wales Coalfield licked southwards to encompass the recessed lowland from Langland on South-east Gower to Pyle at the boundary of West and Mid Glamorgan. The seaweeds have not 'built their house upon the sand', but are exploiting the denuded remains of a Bronze Age forest which thrived here some six thousand years ago. They are anchored on horizontal peat banks, spawned around 4,000 B.C., subsequently buried by marine sediments, and now poking out again through a thinning cover of beach sand. Many of them are clinging to the remains of ancient trees which grew in what is the uppermost bed of an alternating series of peat, sand and silt layers, some of them formed on the sea floor and some on the land.

Way below this surface that we see today are glacial deposits left by an earlier and more extensive ice sheet than that which ground its way southwards some 70,000 to 10,000 years ago, but failed to penetrate beyond the Severn Estuary. This was the ancient Wolstonian

2. Fossilised timber on an ancient intertidal peat bed

Glaciation, which is thought to have lasted from 140,000 to 105,000 years ago.

Much of the water which was formerly part of the sea was then piled up as ice on the land, and terrestrial conditions prevailed on what is now the sea-bed.

The milder Ipswichian Interglacial Period of some 35,000 years duration which followed, saw the melting of the great ice cap and the infilling of the sea to a height of 55 feet (17 m.) above its present level, so that the land on which much of Swansea City is built was under the sea.

Then came the more recent Ice Age of the Devensian Period and sea level went down again. Later, between 20,000 and 6,000 years ago, during the Flandrian Marine Transgression, this ice, too, was melting, the melt-waters drowning the old coastline and penetrating inland up the river valleys. There were fluctuations in the general rise, so that different kinds of sediment were deposited at different times, and it was about 5,000 years ago (around 3,000 B.C.) that the sea reached to 13 feet (4 m.) above its present height. Since then the coastline of South Wales has remained fairly stable.

As the waters rose and fell, rising a little higher each time, quantities of marine and estuarine clays deposited in the low-lying phases were interbedded with terrestrial peat layers formed during periods of uplift, and became spread across Swansea Bay.

Boreholes put down by engineers in 1931 at the East end of Swansea Docks, penetrated intermittent layers of organic debris produced on old land surfaces down to one lying 64½ feet (20 m.) below O.D. (Ordnance Datum). Radio-carbon analysis dates this as being a little over 9,000 years old.

These remains show us that land plants were growing in Swansea Bay during the early post-glacial period, although the land surface was then about 60 feet below that of today.

Pollen grains preserved in the peat tell us the sort of plants that occurred. The approximate boundary between Late Glacial and Post Glacial deposits some 8,350 years ago is marked by a gradual change from the sort of pine-birch forest which fringes today's Arctic Tundra, to the mixed oak forest with hazel, elm and lime that we find in Southern Britain. The change occurs at 63 feet below O.D.

The sea stayed at around this level for the next 1,400 years or so, then proceeded to rise again during the Boreal Period. Plant communities on the land were gradually swallowed up by marine clays settling out on the new bed of the advancing sea.

Digging down into these, we find the fossilised remains of peppery furrow shells (*Scrobicularia plana*) and sea snails (*Hydrobia ulvae*). These are estuarine animals to be found much further up the Bristol Channel today, the first (a bivalve) living in the mud and the snail crawling about on its surface.

Their populations dwindled and disappeared as the sea drained away once again, and their sticky habitat was overlain in its turn by more terrestrial soils. Pines and birches grew up once more—then mixed oak forest with birch, elm and lime. Alder began increasing from about 5,500 B.C.

The remnants of these trees are now 20 feet below O.D. The submerged forest so well developed off Blackpill is more recent—probably of Atlantic or Sub-boreal age or anything from 3,000 to 7,000 years old. Tree roots penetrating the clay are likely to be those of willows—relics of the swamp woodland which colonised the margins of the estuary as the water receded. They lie in a fudge-textured matrix threaded with recognisable remains of reed stems. Although sodden, the ancient trees still show the patterning of their constituent cells when viewed under a microscope.

Birch logs with banded silvery bark almost intact, are remnants of the birch-oak forest which took over from the willow swamp as soil level built up. This submerged forest on the West Swansea Bay beach is matched by a peat bed 4-5 feet thick which extends from the Mumbles almost to the mouth of the River Tawe at a greater distance from the sea. That bed, its surface about 15 feet above O.D., rests on blue clay and is mostly overlain by sand or by man-made ground. The finding of fragments of beech among the birch, suggests that the trees may have grown on into the Iron Age, the beech very near, or even at, its most westerly limit as a native tree in Britain. There are two main peat beds on the shore at Brynmill, the lower just below O.D. and the upper about 10 feet higher.

Similar deposits occur in Crymlin Bog to the north-east, where peat has now accumulated to 18-20 feet above mean sea level. On the open coast, unprotected by the intervening dunes and sandflats which have closed the mouth of Crymlin Bog, the peat is being slowly eroded and is sometimes no more than a foot thick. It is the final remnant of land inundated during the later phases of the Neolithic submergence, in which the oscillating levels of land and sea accounted for a total overall drowning of at least 75 feet.

Samples examined by Sir Harry Godwin from Swansea Docks to the north-east showed lake deposits over the lowermost birch forest, these containing fruits of submerged lake plants such as hornwort and wefts of freshwater algae. Deeper samples were all of fen peat enriched with nutrients brought by ground waters accumulating on the surface of the estuarine silts. Samples from high levels, particularly towards Crymlin Bog, had been formed in acid, less fertile conditions, akin to those prevailing on the Coalfield bogs of the present day.

By about 3,000 B.C. the changing sea level, having reached its maximum height of 13 feet more than now, was cutting a little cliff into the glacial deposits to landward, this running from Blackpill, through Derwen Fawr at Sketty Lane and across Singleton Park. It was during this period that a shingle beach was deposited at Margam, its remains now well inland from the coast. Glacial drift carried out to sea at this time was pounded down to finer particles and may have provided much of the sand for the period of dune building which followed, and for some of today's extensive beaches.

Not much is known of prehistoric man in Swansea Bay, but in 1969 Dr. Savory excavated an early Bronze Age site at West Cross in Swansea. These people of more than 3,000 years ago were largely pastoral, tending flocks and herds, but there is evidence that they grew wheat and barley further east in the Vale of Glamorgan and their implements suggest that they still engaged in hunting. This applies also to later inhabitants in the deteriorating climate of the Iron Age. Remnants of the frugal possessions of these early South Walians have been recovered from the base of the blanketing dunes which hid them for centuries.

A Roman villa on the site of the present Oystermouth churchyard has yielded the most westerly mosaic found in Britain. Swansea probably started its urban career as a Norse settlement and trading post. Quite recent habitations have been swallowed by the encroaching sea and at very low tides it is possible to walk onto the old Green Grounds Farm which succumbed to submergence in Swansea Bay more than 300 years ago.

Most relics of the earlier communities are still buried under the sand at Blackpill and Singleton, where the main force of the waves is deflected by Mumbles Point, and the evidence is fragmentary. Eastwards, where Swansea Bay sweeps round to face into the full force of the south westerly swells, the relics coming to light during the early

1970s were more extensive and more convincing. They indicate a period of warm climate, with the remains of beetles and a variety of mammals.

Beyond Port Talbot Harbour, along the entire frontage of the Abbey Steelworks and the Margam Sand and Gravel Workings, there is more sticky blue-grey clay of the old estuarine deposits containing the brittle remains of countless peppery furrow shells and sea snails, worn thin by the 6,000 years of their incarceration.

The clay has weathered out into slabs and longitudinal ridges at right angles to the coast, exposing vertical faces ranging from 3 feet downshore to 3 inches upshore. By the winter of 1973/74 only about half of the horizontal surfaces retained their former covering of peat, the surviving deposits increasing downshore to a thickness of about 2 feet. Marine erosion was currently at work, particularly near high tide mark, and by the winter of 1977-78 the peat was much thinner. Nevertheless, it is likely that the many parallel furrows leading seawards were old creeks draining a former saltmarsh. The earlier existence of at least some of them is shown by the crowded fossilised hoof prints, all pointing in the same direction, where a bovine herd had passed across, down one side and up the other of each. They were so well preserved when found in 1974 that the soft imprinted clay must have been drifted over by sand soon after the animals had passed.

Only now are these buried remains of past communities coming to light in such profusion. Earlier in 1973 the whole beach here was sanded over, although patches of peat and clay had been appearing and disappearing during the earlier seventies. Both are penetrated by the branched underground stems of reeds and other marsh plants, those at the surface punctuated by the round scars left by severed shoots.

Tree remains are legion and are mostly of oak and pine with less of the birch which is the principal Swansea species. Branches are compressed to show oval cross sections, like those of Coal Measure plant fossils. None have been found erect, so they may have washed down from an inland forest in some catastrophic flood—just as a catastrophic sand blow may have covered the tracks of the stampeding animals. Timber is soft and sodden and some is stained deep red by iron compounds—partly from natural bog iron ore, but mostly from effluents draining out of the Steelworks refuse tip.

There are thought to be copper residues from copper smelting as well as ferric ones chelated onto the organic material. Iron-rich solutions seeping from wastes on the man-made land above oxidise to form 'rivers of blood' as they emerge onto the sands and this particulate material is washed back and forth by the tides to dye both fossil wood and bones. And there are plenty of old bones—too many to represent the decease of a population under normal conditions and possibly the fruits of some disaster, but more likely the accumulation from an

5

6

7

8

Plate 2   WADERS—*Keri Williams*

5. Redshank
6. Greenshank
7. Common sandpiper
8. Pectoral sandpiper
9. Little stint

9

33

10

11

12

13

14

Plate 3   ACCRETING SAND AT CRYMLIN BURROWS—*10 Michael Collins, rest Author*

10. Aerial view of Crymlin Burrows from North-east: Baglan pipeline left at mouth of River Neath, March 1975. Greener area of marsh enclosed by two main dune ridges, (the more seaward three-pronged at the (eastern) growing end) with greener foredune in front. By July 1980 a new dune ridge had progressed several hundred yards eastwards along the beach from the 'Tank Farm'

11. View West to Crymlin 'Tank Farm' along curve of main seaward dune ridge to show lower, parallel dune (separated by bluish sea holly in depression) and new eastward growth of dune along foreshore. 1980.

12. Lesser broomrape at Crymlin is parasitic on sea holly, **13 & 14** in sand couch zone.

34

3. Fossilised antler, horn and bones on an ancient intertidal clay bed

ancient kitchen midden which has been spread around by the sea. Dr. Barbara Noddle has been identifying bones collected by fossickers and a fascinating picture is emerging.

Among the oldest finds are the massive bones and horns of the late Caenozoic aurochs (*Bos primigenius*) which is the ancestor of the domestic cow but larger than any now living. Aurochs were the wild cattle of Europe, Asia and North Africa and remains may be pre-glacial, particularly if compresssed, but the breed survived until the seventeenth century and genetic traces are still present in domestic breeds of Camargue, Spanish and Corsican cattle, though Shetland cattle are closest on bone conformation. The Margam relics are heavily mineralised, weighing much more than newer bones, which are porous. Those from the grey clays retain their pale colour unless iron-stained; those from the peats are dyed black.

Commoner than these are the smaller, later bones of Celtic cattle (*Bos taurus*)—probably domestic animals from Iron Age farms because the cortex of the bone is thinner than that of the thickset animals brought to Western Britain by the Romans. These heavier animals may not have reached Margam, however, so the remains could be from later survivors of the indigenous Celtic stock. Other bones found include those of the Celtic horse (*Equus calabus* ?) and wild boar (*Sus scrofa*).

Bones and antlers of red deer (*Cervus elaphus*) were present in quantity in 1974, half embedded in clay and half in peat. They are from large animals, some of them six pointers with antlers over 3 feet long. These were not such giants as the deer of the old Scottish forests, but may be from earlier in time, because beasts got larger and then smaller again through the ages.

35

They are bigger than average for their period (though not so big as those from just West of the R. Loughor on the further side of Swansea). This suggests that they were not hunted very much, possibly because there were not many people to hunt them. Human exploitation nearly always selects out the better animals and leaves a poorer breeding stock, resulting in loss of size.

Dating of finds in relation to level can be complicated by animals or bones falling into the deep ditches by which the Romans drained the coastal marshes. Long since covered over as the ditches silted up, the remains can get related to a lower layer of sediments which were actually deposited much earlier. Fossil antlers and the like are not confined to Margam beach but have been coming to light from Aberafan Sands in the north to Kenfig Sands and Sker Point in the south, with a single specimen in 1974 from Aberthaw away to the east.

Exposure of the Margam bone beds in the first half of the seventies was undoubtedly helped by the taking of sand and gravel from the foreshore, but is thought to result also from the building of the Port Talbot Harbour in the late sixties. The new breakwater altered the course of the longshore currents so that sand was no longer deposited here except well downshore and as tongues which drifted up into the old salt marsh gullies. Ironically much sand now gets deposited in the harbour itself and has to be removed by dredging.

The sparsity or absence of green *Enteromorpha* on the peat and clay after the denuding storms of January and February 1974 speaks of their recent emergence from the sand. By 1977-78 there was much more and also a partial covering of the velvety red seaweed, *Rhodochorton rothii*. But, now that the protective sand layer has been depleted it may be only a matter of years before the peat, and possibly also the bones, horns and antlers, will have gone too. The underlying clay, if 60 feet deep here, as it is at Swansea, will survive a lot longer.

Strahan reckoned the uppermost peat bed at Port Talbot to be between one and two feet below O.D., with *Scrobicularia* clay above and below it and a bottom peat layer between 25 and 26 feet below O.D. A discontinuous peat bed at about 8 feet below O.D. found subsequently, falls at about the level of the lower peat in the North docks at Swansea.

A deep core taken in Port Talbot Dock showed a sequence with red deer remains in a narrow belt of peat near the basal gravels, then a great depth of estuarine clay interrupted by two layers of sand, a thinner one of peat, with blown sand at the surface. Eastwards on Aberafan Beach, the layering contains as much sand as clay over the basal glacial gravels—three horizons of each—with a substantial amount of peat deposited prior to the last influx of marine clays.

The story revealed by the sands merely skims the surface of geological happenings in the area, not even reaching down to the material deposited during the Ice Age, but it conjures up a fascinating picture of life as it must have been before the monks of Margam Abbey farmed land later to be inundated by the great sand blows and later still by the sprawling industry of our own time. There is a whimsical reminder yet of those bygone days on this ever changing coast. Glamorgan's only free-roaming herds of deer are now to be found in Margam Forest and the newly created country park on the seaborne sediments at its foot.

2 CRYPTIC CREATURES OF THE BEACHES

Invertebrate life in the sands

GIVEN the opportunity, most people start beachcombing at a very early age and those fortunate enough to retain their youthful curiosity will continue to do so throughout life. There is something inescapably alluring about those sinuous driftlines which snake across the tidal sands as living contour lines. They usually contain a modicum of twentieth century bric-a-brac from far and near and the natural objects will have come together from sources far offshore, from the rocks to east and west and from the sands themselves.

Floating in with the flotsam are the lightweight spheres of whelk eggs, the size of tennis balls, and looking like dehydrated frogspawn. These are produced by common whelks (*Buccinum undatum*), which live well downshore, having no means of conserving their vital body fluids if they wander too far up during the moderate tides of the neaps and get left high and dry by a subsequent low spring tide. The papery white compartments of the egg masses are usually empty by the time they wash ashore, but they may contain developing embryos which failed to escape in time and are reduced to disintegrating yellow blobs sticking to the walls.

Mermaid's purses are also egg cases—inflated horny oblongs containing the single offspring of one of the cartilaginous fishes, initially as an egg and later as an embryo. This method of reproduction is quite unlike that of the bony fishes, where the thousands of tiny eggs in the 'hard roe' are fertilised rather haphazardly in the water by the even more numerous and invisibly small sperms from the 'soft roe'. Mermaid's purses are produced more sparingly, with none of the bony

4. Egg cases of whelk, dogfish and skate

fishes' margin for wastage, but the superior provision for food and protection ensures a better survival rate.

Dark brown purses with a similarly curved prong at each corner are likely to be those of the thornback ray (*Raja clavata*). These are a little over two inches long. Those of the common skate (*Raja batis*) are more than twice as long and other species can be distinguished by their appendages. More slender purses, translucently yellow and with spirally coiled attachment tendrils from the corners, are those of lesser spotted dog-fishes (*Scyliorhynus caniculus*), which are known also as rock hounds and rock salmon. These, too, are usually empty when they wash ashore, the youngsters having broken out and swum away.

Other lightweight debris riding ashore on the little waves which curl in over the sandflats are cellular white fronds of hornwrack (*Flustra foliacea*). These colonies of moss animals or Bryozoans are named after the brown wracks of rocky coasts and there are certain red seaweeds of similar shape and size but none of similar texture, with surfaces symmetrically patterned by many little rectangular boxes glued together. Similar species insufficiently rigid to stand on their own, may spread themselves over the surface of marine weeds. One such, whose white undulant margins advance across the olive-brown fronds of wracks and oarweeds drifted from the Mumbles, is *Membranipora membranacea*.

Wispy strands of other plantlike animal colonies branch upwards from the driftline debris, from purses to pebbles, the little white boxes strung end to end in single file to form branching filaments. These are various kinds of sea firs or Hydroids, which are not related to the sea mats and are usually dead when cast ashore. When active and submerged, fleshy tentacles will protrude into the water from the chalky cells and waft to and fro gathering oxygen and food, although some of the cells of the moss animal colonies are modified to perform other duties.

Heavier objects forming the jetsam rolling landwards along the sea bed are mostly sea shells, and these are abandoned in wide belts across the sands, imparting a haze of pink and yellow and a pearly lustre while wet. Some, like the limpets, periwinkles, dog whelks and mussels, have been dislodged from rockier habitats to the west. Others, the two-shelled Bivalves, smooth or ridged, plain or striped, are the remains of animals which live cryptic, unseen lives beneath the sand, and reveal their beauty only in death. Here are the tellins, cockles, nut clams, oysters and many another.

The ocean drift is spread across the surface for all to see but, like the emergent peat beds, this is but the tip of the iceberg. The apparently empty shore may teem with life, this lapsing into temporary somnolence when the tide withdraws, but busying itself, each kind after its own fashion, as the water returns. The uncountable host of creeping things below sustains a less cryptic host of shorebirds above.

Paddle seawards as the tide floods in over the sun-warmed beach and you will see evidence of the hidden presence. There are ploppings and gurglings in the moistening sands, mini fountains and strings of bubbles, then threads and blobs of pink and white flesh making exploratory incursions into the advancing layer of water, which brings new food particles and stirs up those which had slumped onto the surface at the ebb.

Some animals emerge wholly into the water as their temporary homes become flooded, the burrows collapsing behind them, but it behoves them to dig down again before the tide recedes. Sands which can be readily pushed aside when wet become quite firm and resistant to penetration when dry. Try walking on wet sand and see how the pressure of the foot on the yielding surface squeezes out the water to leave a hard, dry footprint. This would present a problem to something like a worm or a sandhopper, an even bigger one to a heart urchin (*Echinocardium cordatum*) which requires a bigger hole—excavated by the wriggling of short spoon-shaped spines on the undersurface, to depths of as much as eight inches.

This loss of sand mobility under pressure is known as dilatency. Really dry sand becomes mobile again and those holiday cricket matches of the beaches would be hard work on the dunes. Muds are quite different, yielding up their water less readily, and are said to be thixotropic. In fact few beaches are of either pure mud or pure sand, which is quite devoid of food particles and therefore of dependent animal life. Most are a mixture of both. Generally, as the surface becomes less suitable for cricket it becomes more suitable for burrowing animals, but some creatures are geared to life on the cleaner beaches.

A digging session in the sands off Blackpill, where the shelter afforded by the Mumbles allows finer particles of mud and organic matter to settle out, is likely to be much more profitable than excavations in the more exposed and cleaner shore at Margam, where the churning of the sand by waves is a hazard in itself to soft-bodied animals, as well as preventing the lightweight organic food particles from settling. Shells here exist principally as battered fragments.

Feeders on organic deposits are thus commoner at the Blackpill end of Swansea Bay than at the Margam end. The Baltic tellin (*Macoma balthica*) is one such, and the paired pink shells of this are usually the most abundant in the Swansea shell hoards. They can tolerate a lot more mud than there is here, moving their rotund little bodies very little in pursuit of life's necessities.

Thin tellins (*Tellina tenuis*) prefer cleaner sands. They are less portly and are well able to move through the damp matrix from one feeding area to another. After lying low while the tide is out, they begin to function like little vacuum cleaners as it flows in over their hideout, putting a long tube or siphon up to the surface and waving its tip back and forth to sweep up the edible fragments, in the mode of food gathering which characterises the groups of animals known as deposit feeders.

Their fragile pink, white or yellow shells are less common than the more robust ones of the Baltic tellin at Swansea, but more so at Margam. Ligaments connecting the open halves are sufficiently tough to endure the buffetting of the waves, so that the beach seems to be strewn with tiny coloured butterflies among a scattering of severed wings.

Also of rare beauty when the sun shines are the iridescent shell linings of the diminutive nut clams (*Nucula turgida*). Those lying with the inside uppermost give the illusion of a sprinkling of pearl buttons, with a row of tiny triangular teeth beside the hinge. Nut clams can live in gravel, sand or clay, extending from low water mark down to a depth of nearly 500 feet (150 metres). When the shell is open sea water is drawn in across the fleshy foot by an array of minute beating hairs or cilia on the rounded leaf-shaped gills, and this yields up its oxygen to 'blood' which is more often blue than red. A narrow arm or palp sweeps to and fro dragging food particles towards the mouth, so this, too, is a deposit feeder.

More noticeable along Swansea's driftlines by virtue of their size are the ribbed white, brown or grey shells of edible cockles (*Cardium* (or *Cerastoderma*) *edule*). In fact these are *not* edible from this particular site because of urban pollution, and notices have been erected in the carparks to warn would-be-cockle-gatherers of their unfitness. Many of the Margam cockle shells are smaller, as though fewer are able to reach maturity here.

Cockles can live their entire lives beneath the surface because they are able to pull in a constant stream of water when the tide is in—this providing all the food and oxygen they need. They live on plankton—minute plants and animals which get wafted around by the currents and can be filtered off as the water passes over the gills. Such animals are referred to as suspension feeders. When the tide ebbs the siphons are withdrawn and the cockles become inactive. It is the duration of these spells of enforced idleness which dictates how far upshore burrowing animals can live. If they penertrate too high there may be insufficient time to imbibe the necessary food and oxygen.

The possibility of drying out, which is the chief hazard to animals of rocky shores during the period of low tide, scarcely applies to them. Only the surface of the sand dries out or warms up or alters its salinity drastically as a result of rain or evaporation. A few inches down all is snug and damp. If it becomes less so than desirable most animals can retreat to more comfortable depths.

Thick trough shells (*Spisula solida*) get cast up from the downshore sands. They are suspension feeders with short siphons, so must stay only just beneath the sea bed while feeding, but go deeper as the tide withdraws. Their chunky shells, as broad as they are long, mingle at Margam with those of a small *Spisula* species, which is often humbug striped, the black bands occupying concentric zones which indicate each year's growth. Blackening is most marked in shells which have been washed onto the clay banks, where mud sticks to the rough parts and bacteria use up the available oxygen, so that black sulphides are formed in the resulting anaerobic (or air-starved) micro-habitat. These resemble the sulphides which sometimes produce a black layer below the sand surface on muddier shores, where the fine particles exclude air. Oxygen is not one of the commodities in short supply in the churned up sands at Margam, but it is in the sticky, fossilised estuarine clays.

Peppery furrow shells (*Scrobicularia plana*), whose fossil remains are so prevalent in the blue 'plasticine' claybanks here, are unable to live in the Margam of today, as there is no suitably soft mud. Nor are contemporary shells to be found in the driftlines. The worn ones of horse mussels (*Modiolus modiolus*) occur, these being the main mussel species below the tide, where they replace the edible mussel (*Mytilus edulis*) of the shoreline, cutting out up-Channel at about the same place—in the region of Nash Point. There are just a few edible mussels living at Margam, in spite of the dearth of anchoring rocks. These cling with their 'guylines' or byssus threads to the unstable security of pebbles which become lodged in gullies of the clay beds.

Common saddle oysters (*Anomia ephippium*) also hold onto these by calcified or limey threads from the upper side. Their rather shapeless shells have a shimmering transparency outside as well as in. The much bigger shells of common oysters (*Ostrea edulis*) get cast ashore from deeper waters, their nacreous substance often honeycombed by a boring sponge, *Cliona celata*, or a boring worm, *Polydora ciliata*.

Flattened, fan-shaped shells of variegated scallops (*Chlamys varia*) turn up quite often in driftlines from Mumbles to Margam. They come in red, orange or black and have lopsided ends to the straight hinge at the junction of the two shells. Unlike most animals of sandy beaches, they do not burrow, so have to stay below low water mark in order to avoid being snapped up by birds or dried out by summer suns. They are, indeed, remarkable for shelled Molluscs in being able to swim. The sticky byssus threads which anchor most Bivalves in the sand are present only when they are very small. After this the animals lie flat on the sea bed with shells agape when they are relaxed.

If disturbed the sudden closing down of the upper shell causes the animal to shoot backwards, hinge first, but water can also be shot out sideways, so that the escape is directional. During free swimming the motion is different, with water being expelled at each side of the hinge so that the animal progresses in the opposite direction. It moves in a series of jerks, to the rhythmic flapping of the shells, as though the scallop is eating its way through the water with gaping bites. A curtain of flesh dangling from the inside of the upper shell valve directs some of the expelled water downwards, so that the swimmer rises from the bottom and stays suspended so long as the forward propulsion is maintained. The flat streamlining and broad supporting saucer shape are admirable for this flying saucer type locomotion.

Red-patterned pink common necklace shells (*Natica alderi*) can be found as far up channel as Kenfig, although more characteristic of the wave-cleaned sands of West Gower. They are one of very few species of sand-burrowing Gastropods or sea snails. Prey is sought by moving along under the sand surface and the many tellin shells with a neat hole bored through the pointed end, show where they have met with success.

Netted dog whelks (*Nassarius reticulatus*) are also sand burrowers whose shells are to be found at Margam, although possibly living in muddier sands with more rocks than these. With them are thick-lipped dog whelks (*Nassarius incrassatus*), grey tops (*Gibbula cineraria*) and others drifted across the shore from rockier habitats, along with sting winkles or oyster drills (*Ocenebra erinacea*), the latter carnivores distinguished by the ornamental ridges down the length of the shell. A serious pest in commercial oyster beds, they drill through the oyster shells with their radulas and suck out the flesh from within. They live well downshore in fairly muddy sand among rocks, but migrate upshore to spawn.

A spadeful of sand lifted from Margam Beach may reveal the exquisitely fashioned conical tube of a little Polychaete (many-bristled) worm called *Pectinaria koreni*. The tube, 1-2 inches long, is curved or straight and quite fragile. It is a perfectly fitting jigsaw of similar-sized sand grains set in a white 'mortar'. Most of the grains here are of translucent white silica,, decorated with a few of black, orange or red. They include none of the irregular shell fragments which give the untidy look to the bigger more pliable tubes of the sand mason worms (*Lanice conchilega*), which inhabit more sheltered sands from the Gower Peninsula up-channel to St. Donat's Bay. So smooth is *Pectinaria* externally that it can be mistaken at first glance for a tusk shell.

After a few moments on the damp sand a bunch of shimmering golden club-shaped humps will emerge from the broad end of the tube. These bend downwards to get a grip on the surface and drag the tube forward, caddis fashion—finally tipping it up as they shovel their way back into their familiar world of wet sand, assisted by a row of stout golden bristles along each side of the body.

Here they live, obliquely head downwards, excavating a vertical shaft to the surface. Sand containing edible debris trickles down this funnel to the feeding tentacles (those same golden 'clubs') and is imbibed.

After extraction of the desirable fraction, the unwanted sand is passed back to the surface through the hind end of the tube. *Pectinaria* is therefore a sand swallower—employing the fourth and last of the modes of feeding to be found among shore animals—viz. deposit feeders, suspension feeders, sand swallowers and carnivores, preying on the other three. Oxygen is extracted from water entering through the upper (narrower) end of the tube, which can be closed by a leaf-like flap on the animal's tail when there is a danger of it getting clogged by sand.

The other Polychaetes or bristle worms likely to be encountered on the Swansea Bay beaches are carnivores, and hence need to be more active than the rest in order to catch them. Small paddleworms (*Phyllodoce maculata*) can sometimes be seen wriggling their narrow greenish-yellow bodies through displaced spadefuls of sand. They live downshore, often in the sandy pools alongside Margam's vertical walls of blue clay. On a more average type of shore they tend to inhabit sands containing scattered rocks.

Viewed through a hand lens—an essential piece of equipment for anyone who wants to get the best out of their beach combing—these worms are quite striking. 'Maculata' means spotted and there are dark brown spots on each segment of the much segmented body and another in the centre of each of the leaflike paddles which undulate rhythmically along either flank. These paddles enable it to swim in the pools as well as to row through the wet sand, both modes of progression assisted by sinuous wrigglings of the muscular torso. The Swansea Bay paddleworm are 2-4 inches long and quite slender, with a propensity for tying themselves in knots when brought out of their natural element.

They are commoner in summer, but can be unearthed quite near the surface in December.

Broader and altogether more conspicuous are the bright pink ragworms (*Perinereis cultrifera*) glinting green and bronze and excavating burrows for themselves in the blue clays. They can be found by breaking clods of this open with a spade. Like the common ragworm (*Nereis diversicolor*) of softer modern estuarine muds, these have a dorsal blood vessel making a red line down the back and a pair of curved black jaws which they are very willing to extrude when teased. Black 'eyebrows' behind the jaws distinguished them from their commoner relative. They will swim unwillingly in the sandy pools, using the numerous paired tufts of bristle feet as *Phyllodoce* uses its better adapted paddles, and employing the same graceful body movements.

Another of this ilk, the green king ragworm (*Nereis virens*), which reaches a foot or more in length, tackles the Margam peat beds, whose consistency is between that of the glutinous clays and the friable sands. Their stay here may be limited, as the peat overlies the clay and has been wearing away quite quickly since it was exposed by the commercial taking of the protective sand cover. Sedimentologists at Swansea are currently working on the rate of sand replacement, but it seems unlikely that the material so precipitately removed will be replaced by natural means in our lifetime.

The clay beds are shared by common piddocks (*Pholas dactylus*) whose beautifully sculptured white shells can be up to 6 inches long. They are very brittle—an unbroken one on the sand surface is a rare prize—and it is incredible that these can bore into the stiff clay which seems so suitable for the potter's wheel and no doubt furnished many a stout pot for our ancient forebears before their compression under later sediments. The sculptings are roughest at the front end of the elongated shell pair and assist with drilling. Piddocks tackle firm sand or mud, peat or wood and even soft rock east of Dunraven. They are plentiful in the Mediterranean and very near the northern extremity of their geographical range here. With them are the similar textured but less angular white piddocks (*Barnea candida*) which burrow less deeply. Fragmented shells of another boring Bivalve, *Hiatella arctica,* are also to be found.

Margam is one of the poorer hunting grounds for shore animals, yielding few of the riches of more sheltered beaches, yet even here there is a wealth of interest for those who are not too proud to go down to the sea with a spade and pail, as in earlier life. There may be fewer deer antlers and aurochs horns than in the mid-seventies, but a 'times ten' hand lens can open up a whole new world to the inquisitive fossicker.

3 BIRDS OF THE OPEN SANDS AT BLACKPILL

Waders, waterfowl and gulls of the beach: others of the immediate hinterland

THE birds which prey on the many and various food items lying unseen beneath the sand need no lens to appreciate their finer points. Indeed, most will not be hunting by sight at all, as there is little to be seen, except by the scavengers along the driftline. Almost imperceptible movements, bubbles, burrow mouths and worm casts may help in prey location, but many birds will be engaged in what the behaviourists call random search, particularly if feeding at night. This random search can be a vast operation, involving thousands of beaks 'stitching' their way across the shore with sewing machine precision.

Swansea's Royal Institution houses a unique first edition of the oldest Swansea bird list, which was compiled by the Rev. Oldisworth in 1802. In this he wrote 'It is probable that no county in this island nourishes so great a variety and abundance of natural productions as that of Glamorgan'. Without knowing how familiar the author was with the rest of Britain, we can grant this statement a degree of authenticity on the grounds of the vast range of habitats encompassed by the triple county—from mountain crag to lowland wood, bleak moorland to fertile farm, waveswept cliff to tranquil lake and rolling sandhill to spreading mudflat. By 1802 there would have been some industrial sites too. The Swansea he wrote about still supports many thousands of birds: their numbers boosted by the great influx of shore birds to the intertidal sands in winter.

The harder the weather, the greater the number of birds, with big flocks moving west in search of milder conditions, as continental winters reach chilly fingers into Eastern Britain. The various plovers are particularly vulnerable to cold, as their short bills can only reach into surface soil layers, from which invertebrate populations retreat deeper as ice crusts form at the top. Glamorgan thus receives more than the national average of these little birds, and West Glamorgan more than East.

Ringed plovers anticipate the freeze-ups by arriving early and may already have reached the 300 mark on the Blackpill sands by September, with as many as 445 by August in 1978. Only 7,000 of these handsome little birds winter in Britain, and the Bristol Channel offers haven to 1,000 of these. Unfortunately they are under pressure, the site of developments on the Swansea foreshore in the 70s coinciding with a gathering ground of about half this quota. Like the less prolific grey plovers, these are at the northern limit of their continental wintering range, which spreads south along the coast of France and Iberia and through the Mediterranean. 155 grey plovers had assembled at Blackpill by January in 1978.

Golden plover and lapwing or green plover are not strictly shorebirds, preferring a diet of leather-jackets and worms pulled from coastal fields. Of the longer-billed inland waders the biggest 1978 gathering of snipe was on Swansea Airport: 33 in mid February, when woodcock were skulking in the seclusion of the Clyne Valley. The 1962-63 freeze-up brought both into Swansea city, with snipe in the neighbourhood of Sketty Road and woodcock foraging in parks and gardens.

5. Dunlin in Winter

Most abundant of the foreshore waders are dunlin, small birds with long beaks able to reach down to more productive feeding layers than those which supply the plovers. A count of 2,800 at Blackpill in January 1978 was impressive, but there were far more further up the Severn Estuary, with 9,000 assembled at Rhymney Mouth on 6th May in that year; the largest single flock seen in Glamorgan since 1966. These were presumably stoking up for their mass move, away to chillier nesting grounds.

One observed on this date at Blackpill wore a colour ring placed on its leg in North-east Greenland in the Summer of 1974 by Dr. Peter Ferns of Cardiff, so here was an easterly rather than a westerly movement to escape the cold. West from Greenland would bring the dunlin into the influence of the cold Labrador Current flowing down the New England coast. To benefit from the waters warmed off Florida and the Caribbean, they needed to intercept the Gulf Stream on its life-giving passage to the North-east. (Another of the birds ringed in Greenland turned up in Trescoe on the Scilly Isles.) Pure flocks of Greenland dunlin up to 10,000 strong were feeding on the Gwent-Glamorgan border in 1973-74, these representing a quarter of Wales's population of 40,000.

Dunlin are the most abundant waders in Britain as a whole during the colder months—some overwintering and some passing through. They come from different sources. Rocket netting and measurements of birds further up the Severn Estuary by Peter Ferns has shown that three different races visit Glamorgan. The Greenland birds, *Calidris alpina arctica*, will head off north-west in Spring; the northern race, *Calidris alpina alpina*, will be flying east-north-east for the Euro-Asian Arctic shores through to Siberia.

Birds of the southern race, *Calidris alpina schintzii*, will be bound for less distant breeding sites in Iceland, Norway, the Southern Baltic or Britain itself. Here they may nest anywhere on the mountains and moors north from mid Wales, in habitats which they may share with golden plover. It has been suggested that these outlying southern populations became established long ago, when the ice sheets of the last great glacial epoch were withdrawing northwards and these areas supported tundra. Descendants of the early colonists have managed to hang on in the uplands, at altitudes up to and exceeding 3,000 feet, as the ice retreated, followed by the birds which evolved into the two northern races.

Greenland and Iceland dunlin are likely to have wintered well to the South—in Morocco or Mauritania. The South Wales shores are an important refuelling station in April and May, when the three races mingle on their passage north.

They fatten rapidly on invertebrates gleaned from Glamorgan's shores, adding one gramme a day to their body weight. Greenland birds will continue to feed until they have built up 20 grammes of fat, and will then fly direct to Greenland without stopping to refuel in Iceland. This is a prodigious feat for so small a bird and the energy expended must be made good before the serious business of producing a family begins.

Little time is wasted, however. The Arctic summer is short and the main provender fed to the chicks comes from the freshwater pools and lakes in the forms of insects and their larvae, during the brief weeks of the thaw, before they are once again sealed by ice. Days are long, giving plenty of foraging time, and the young grow quickly, to accompany their parents south as the frozen pall of winter overtakes the briefly floriferous and fruitful tundra with its hordes of tasty insects.

Mostly they are in the dull grey of their winter plumage when they arrive, but the black belly feathers and rufous back (which give them their alternative name of red-back sandpiper in North America) may be donned before they leave our shores in early May. It is then, in spring, that we get our biggest flocks.

Females are slightly larger than males and have longer bills. These are flexible, slightly down-tilted and supplied with as many nerve endings as our index finger, making sensitive probing tools. Up channel they eat mainly ragworms and spire-shelled snails: in the sandier Swansea area Baltic tellins and small crustacea are likely to be the main attraction.

Knot are much larger than dunlin but their bills are no longer, and they feed on much the same range of food. They, too, breed in the Arctic, but in a different type of terrain, favouring dry rocky wastes with a sparse lichen cover, mosses, grasses and arctic-alpines rather than marsh and saltings. Here they eat seeds, shoots, roots and spiders as well as aquatic life from the pools—among which mosquito larvae figure large. This brief domestic phase lasts little more than two months before they are on their way south again, some to share the August beaches with holiday makers.

In 1978 there were knot around throughout the year at Blackpill. The maximum here was 214 in December, but elsewhere in Glamorgan flocks reached to 2,200 and 1,480 early in the year. They bunch together more closely than dunlin when feeding and show a barring of the rump when they take off instead of the conspicuous white of the other. The name is said to arise, not from the characteristic knotting up of groups, with youngsters relegated to the inferior feeding positions at the periphery, but from the 'not, not, not' call.

Sanderling are a pretty sight, sprinting through the spindrift as fast as their little legs will carry them—a synchronised ripple just ahead of the tide, with pale feathers catching the sun. Although usually in small flocks, these can build up to almost 400, as in October, 1978. Like the others, they will engage in mass flights under the direction of no detectable leader, but every member lifting, falling and turning with almost electronic synchronisation, yet evanescent as a puff of smoke. The governing factor of such precision exercises remains a mystery.

They breed in much the same stony tundra sites as do knot, favouring the slightly denser plant cover supplied by prostrate willows. When they come south they show a preference for sandier shores, spurning the softer ones that are acceptable to dunlin and knot. They feed on sandhoppers and shrimps as well as snails and bivalves. The maggots of kelp flies, waxing fat in driftlines of seaweed, will tempt all three species away from the tideline. Small though they are, sanderling are among the world's furthest flying migrants, some getting as far as the tips of the southern continents, others stopping short to 'winter' on tropical beaches en route.

Even smaller but a lot darker are the little stints which appear occasionally in September. Much more special was the white-rumped sandpiper seen by D. Chatfield in March 1970, feeding along the edge of the high tide with dunlin, but not flying off with them. Evidently this colonial stranger sought company, but knew it did not belong. This is the second record for Glamorgan, the first being at the same place 13 years before, but in autumn.

Curlew sandpipers are more regular, but are not seen often. Purple sandpipers usually stick to the rockier area at the Mumbles end of the bay, but not so the turnstones, which would be expected to cleave to such stony sites. No less than 268 of these were counted on the sands in March 1978, a year when the largest number ever recorded in Glamorgan, 1,346, collected on Whiteford Point in Gower.

Bar-tailed godwits, tweaking lugworms from the sand with long slender bills, can be quite common and may occur at any season. The 1978 maximum was in February, when 271 were counted, but black-tailed godwits come spasmodically, in ones and twos. Succulent lugworms are a temptation to many, besides bait-seeking fishermen, but none are better equipped to haul them from their U-shaped burrows than the godwits. These use an inbuilt skill instinctively; gulls use cunning to supplement less adequate tools and jab at the tail end of the worm as it surfaces to eject a worm cast of moist sand, from which it has absorbed all the organic titbits.

The slender curving bills of the curlews, flocks of which reached 233 in November 1978, are particularly adept at winkling shore crabs out of their shells. Whimbrel are passage migrants, more likely to be seen in spring than autumn. Their evocative call has given them the local name of 'Severn Whistler'.

An avocet in 1978 caused some excitement, as did one in 1973 which was the fourth record for Glamorgan in this century, though two old records for the Swansea area date back to 1804 and 1827. The wary redshank, 'warden of the marshes', peaked at 268 in October in 1978, but flocks reach to 1,000 on occasion. The spasmodic jerking of the head is a little reminiscent of the more constantly bobbing sandpiper's. A few spotted redshank may pass through in late Summer, still in their breeding plumage.

Oyster-catchers prefer the North Gower Sands, but there are plenty of cockles in Swansea Bay, on which they feed up to 500 at a time. Away from the sands, on the playing fields and lawns, they are more likely to be resting than feeding, although oyster-catchers breeding away from the coast wax satisfactorily fat on worms and other animals hauled from among the grass bases. A couple of white mutants or partial albinos were seen in August and November 1978. Another, pure white except for shoulder patches and tail, was around in January 1964, being treated as perfectly normal by its fellows.

When the Gower Ornithological Society carried out a concerted dawn chorus 'listen' on 28th April, 1968, shorebirds were found to be first in the field, leaving the more familiar garden participants to join in later.

It was not that their broader horizons enabled them to detect the coming of the dawn that much sooner, but that they work on a tidal, not a diurnal rhythm, and had probably been actively feeding for half the night.

One early rising Sketty robin, however, upheld the songbirds' cause by producing an exuberant little melody at 4.29 a.m., well ahead of his rivals, but eight minutes behind the first rippling curlew call and only one minute ahead of the 'cockadoodle' from a barnyard rooster. Whimbrel and herring gull tied for third place two minutes after cock crow.

Next contribution, from a passerine, was the unmusical caw of that forager of the foreshore, the carrion crow, at 4.38 a.m., with only wood pigeon and cock pheasant in the next seventeen minutes. West Cross and Sketty blackbirds, song thrushes and wrens had roused themselves by seven minutes past five.

Summer visitors were less willing than residents to get to grips with the day. Having wintered in more pleasant climes, they seemed less excited by the quality of the fine spring morning than were those which had woken to so many grey ones. A cuckoo headed the posse at five o'clock, with the more staccato twin note of the chiff-chaff two minutes later. Last up of the forty-two species recorded were the diminutive goldcrest with diminutive high-pitched song and the almost equally soft-voiced but heftier bullfinch at 5.54 a.m., while laggard humans still had a couple of hours to go before greeting the day.

Moving back a little in time and place from the leafy April gardens of West Cross and Sketty to the winterbound foreshore, there are still a few white-fronted geese to be seen flying over hospital and university or grazing on the Mumbles playing fields. Other geese are rare. We read of a single bean goose in Swansea Bay in 1910, then no more till three appeared at the Steelworks reservoir to the South-east in 1972. Brent geese are little more regular, but seen in ones and twos if at all. Small flocks of whooper and bewick swans fly past occasionally, but press on to bodies of fresh water without alighting on the sea.

Shelduck, an intermediate group linking geese and ducks, tend to behave more like waders than their nearer relatives. They take unusually small food particles for such large birds, filtering tiny spire-shelled snails and crustaceans from wet, muddy sands, so that they do not compete with other ducks. Their numbers have seriously dwindled during the past half century, but they are still the most numerous of the sea ducks.

Common scoter are next in abundance, the 1978 maximum here being 165 on 28th December. Velvet scoter do not appear every year. Pochard and tufted duck usually resort to salt water only when driven from fresh water by ice or disturbance, and the big exodus from inland in the

15

17

16

18

Plate 4   CRYMLIN BOG—*Author*

15. View seawards across part of Crymlin Bog in
    August 1979, chimneys of Tir John Power
    Station on far right
16. Great fen sedge (*Cladium mariscus*)
17. Flowers of insectivorous bladderwort
    (*Utricularia vulgaris*)
18. Weed-cutting boat on Tennant Canal; South
    margin of Crymlin Bog

19

20

Plate 5   PANT Y SAIS BOG—*Author*

19. Tennant Canal curves through eastern end of the Pant-y-Sais gap, March 1980, view N.E.
20. Bridge over Red Jacket Canal in 1981. Tow-path under left arch; canal with slot for lock gate on right. Tennant Canal at left follows reeds beyond slag of old Cape Copper Works
21. Larvae ripped from reed cigar galls by bird— probably reed bunting or greenfinch
22. View N.W. over Tennant Canal and E. part of Pant-y-Sais
23. Greater spearwort (*Ranunculus lingua*)

21

22

23

6. Iceland gull and little gulls in flight

1962-63 freeze-up was to the less saline mudflats up channel towards Cardiff.

Smew, garganey, pintail and red-breasted merganser are seen only once in a while off Brynmill and Blackpill, and there were 56 wigeon on 2nd October 1978. 11 eider were seen in late March, but these usually stick to the Burry Inlet between Gower and Carmarthen.

Occasional grebes and divers cruise along the coast and there are passing sea-birds; gannets, shearwaters, auks and, of course, the homelier cormorant and shag. Much of the special interest of the Swansea foreshore, however, lies with the gulls—for those bird watchers sufficiently erudite to sort one species from another! With the exception of ruff and reeve, which come but rarely, no group of birds has a more confusing array of seasonal moult sequence and of juvenile to adult plumage phases.

In autumn all feathers are moulted, though not so precipitately as to cause the flightlessness suffered by geese and ducks. The spring moult is partial, involving only the contour feathers of head and body. Gradually the mottled plumage of the young fades to the smoother greys and whites of the adults. Just as the birds' conception of day and night is ahead of ours, so is their conception of Summer and Winter. Black-headed gulls will be donning the chocolate caps of the breeding season through the chilly days of February, and discarding them again in the height of our summer holiday period.

It seems likely that their calendar is geared to light intensity and day length, ours to the tardier build-up of a comfortable warmth. *Homo sapiens* has become partially nocturnal, his late eating habits tiding him over till the morrow is well ripened.

The morning exodus of gulls from the night's roost to the rubbish tips for breakfast is a much more hurried sortie than the leisurely home-coming in smaller groups at night. For smaller birds with smaller food reserves, the need to break the long night's fast becomes particularly crucial during the short days of winter, when few but starlings and the odd wagtail find easy pickings on the tips after these have been combed by the more dominant gulls and crows.

7. Red-breasted merganser and sheldrake

Among the less usual gulls now seen not uncomonly on the Swansea foreshore are Mediterranean gulls, which can turn up any time except midsummer. These breed in South-east Europe and usually winter within the Mediterranean. Little gulls, which breed in North-eastern Europe, are becoming increasingly common in West Glamorgan during winter, and will also linger till May and June, some staying for several months.

The ring-billed gull identified at Blackpill in 1973 was the first British and second European record of this American species, which breeds in the Great Lakes and winters among the sunbathers of the Florida beaches. It is distinguished from the larger herring gull by the black band at the tip of the yellow bill. An adult was present for a fortnight in March, the same or another from 5th December to 31st March in 1974, and a youngster in first summer plumage for the first fortnight of June, 1973.

Another stranger at Blackpill in early June 1973 was an adult glaucous gull, followed by an immature, which stayed from mid-November of that year till mid-February the next, and another for a fortnight in March. These were first records for Swansea of this big gull from the frozen North, which has almost pure white plumage. Similarly pale but smaller Iceland gulls have been turning up at Blackpill since

54

1973 and 1974, both adult and juvenile. These nest in Greenland, seldom in Iceland, where some of them spend the winter.

Common gulls, which move south for the winter, have been increasing, like our home-bred ones, the winter roosts building up to 3,500 at Blackpill and 5,000 at Mumbles by 1973. In this year two, possibly three albinos were seen about from March to May, with one of them back in October to remain until February. Flocks taking to the air on a calm day will adopt a regular V or line formation, but, if it is windy, no attempt is made to maintain position, each bird making the most of the air currents to gain the lift necessary for a long freewheel glide down invisible sky corridors. Herring gulls reached to flock sizes of 2¼ thousand in 1973 and greater black-backs numbered 80 in 1975, but lesser black-backs are irregular.

Skuas, near relatives of the gulls, provide ornithological excitement on occasion. Pomarine skuas recorded well over a century ago at Cardiff, were not seen again in Glamorgan until 1963 (at Kenfig), since when they have paid several visits to Swansea Bay, the first in November 1970. The 1978 sighting was of a light phase bird. The arctic skua of June 1970 was a dark phase one. Great skuas sometimes pass down channel, but well out to sea.

Migratory common and arctic terns gather on their way through in May and September. Strong winds brought 146 to Blackpill, 750 to Jersey Marine and 200 to Kenfig Pool in early September 1974. The two whiskered terns of that May at Blackpill were a first county record, to be followed by another at The Steelworks Reservoir in September of the same year. Black terns and the rare white-winged black terns stick more closely to the fresh water of the reservoir, but little terns and sandwich terns can build up on the sands to groups of 15 or so and small numbers of roseate terns sometimes appear.

Our two most intelligent bird groups have used their native wit to broaden their horizons during recent decades. The Laridae (gulls), from being predominantly shorebirds, have become a familiar sight inland: the Corvidae (crows), from being predominantly inland birds, have been exploiting the culinary offerings of the shoreline with increasing regularity. Both have also adapted well to urban life.

Regular counts of jackdaws and carrion crows on the Blackpill Beach were carried out by members of the Gower Ornithological Society in 1975 and monthly maxima appear in *The Glamorgan Bird Report* for that year. Daws, generally, outnumbered crows, but began to tail off at the beginning of the breeding season in April, with none at all seen in June and numbers not building up again until August. Evidently they feed their broods on non-marine organisms. The September maximum of 175 was the largest, the February maximum of 130 next, with a drop to only 21 in November and January, but 58 in December.

Crows were present throughout the year and rose to their highest figures in the summer months, with 46, 80, 84 and 56 from June to September and November's 21 the lowest count of any. The extra late summer birds were juveniles of the year, which started appearing towards the end of June. On 25th April a grey-backed hooded crow (the 'hoodie' of the North) shared a sand bar with its southern cousins. This and another at Kenfig Hill in October, were the first seen in Glamorgan since 1948—but another two visited in 1976 and one in 1977.

Starlings also resort to the beaches and there was a big hard weather movement of these birds in December 1965. Such a movement to beat all others occurred during an icy spell in December 1967 and continued over two days. Against the backcloth of a black tracery of starlings, continuous streams of fieldfares and redwings passed west over Swansea city, to the milder conditions of Gower and on to Ireland, and with them parties of lapwings, several hundred strong.

1964 was a waxwing winter—an event which occurs about once a decade—but mostly in Eastern Britain. One garden boasted 12 of these beautiful tame finches, which can consume 170 cotoneaster berries in a day. Others crowded in the hawthorns, their favourite rowan berries having long since disappeared. They come to us from the spruce and birch forests of Northern Europe—from Finland to Siberia—not because of a dearth of winter fruits in their home terrain, but because of good feeding in the spring, enabling the breeding population to build up to 'explosion point', at which the best of berry crops could not suffice for all. South Wales can normally expect only a small overflow every few years.

Snow buntings wander to Swansea spasmodically: bramblings are rather commoner. Small numbers of these colourful finches appear irregularly in the winter chaffinch flocks of Singleton Park, sometimes staying from January to April, as in 1966. The icy January of 1963 brought unusually big flocks, at a time when water rails could be seen 3 together round the few stretches of fast flowing stream which remained unfrozen. 150 were recorded then in Singleton alone: there is seldom a year when some do not stray across from Eastern Britain. In that memorable January redwings greatly outnumbered the resident birds at Singleton.

Little flocks of around 20 siskins can sometimes be watched at Clyne in the colder months, with a smattering of redpolls. These smaller finches enjoy the small seeds of streamside alder and birch. The odd intrepid blackcap has been staying on through the winter since the beginning of the 1960s and firecrests will sometimes be around until February. Crossbills are an occasional bonus among the Singleton pines and a twite was spotted in March 1976.

Tree pipits and wood warblers occur with the more widespread songsters of the Clyne Valley in May and June and a group of 5 spotted fly-catchers has been observed enjoying the flies which breed on the Clyne rubbish tip. Rare lesser spotted woodpeckers can be seen summer or winter and have probably bred at West Cross. Grey wagtails haunt Clyne and Singleton waters with dippers and may also breed, although both species are more typical of mountainous regions.

Since the coming of the alien collared dove in the sixties, the native, migrant turtle dove has been much in the minority. In the 1820s the nearest breeding collared doves were in Turkey and the Balkans. By the 1930s the expanding population had reached Hungary: by 1952 representatives were in Eastern England. 1962 saw the first bird at Swansea and 2 years later a flock of 29 was foraging in a Sketty garden, with smaller groups spread through the western Swansea suburbs. From then they have been steadily consolidating their position, the flocks more numerous but no larger, with one of 28 at Brynmill in January 1977 and an unusually big gathering of 40 at Gorseinon in Autumn 1978. Theirs is a success story—like the gulls' and crows'. Not all wildlife is on the wane.

4 SANDS FROM THE SEA

Accreting coastline: Spartina west of Swansea: Advancing sand at Crymlin: Losses and Gains at Witford Point and Baglan Bay

WHEN the stark impact of the Industrial Revolution was an unforeseen phantom of the future, a belt of golden dunes encircled Swansea Bay from Blackpill in the West to Porthcawl in the East and beyond to Ogmore Mouth. Today this dune country is severely diminished and the shelduck and oyster-catchers which formerly nested there are hard put to it to find suitable terrain.

There is a fine stretch, still, at Crymlin Burrows south of Jersey Marine—an accreting dune system inheriting and reincarnating much of the botanical best of a great past. Every effort should be made to conserve this living image of what used to be.

Urban sprawl has almost swallowed up the Swansea dunes and the flowery glory of Baglan is but a fragment of its former self to seaward of the BP Petro-chemical Works. The next five miles of coast around Port Talbot has been covered by housing estates and British Steel, while the Corsican pines planted to stabilise Margam Burrows are being ripped out by commercial sand diggers. But happily, over the county boundary in Mid Glamorgan, much of Kenfig Burrows remains inviolate and its wealth of unusual plants and animals is recognised as a national asset, and admirably managed by the Mid Glamorgan County Council as a local nature reserve.

Around 1805, when Dillwyn botanised around a Swansea of less than ten thousand souls, the beautiful mauve sea stock was quite common as far West as Sketty Lane at Singleton. Then it dwindled and was regarded as extinct for more than a century before turning up again, in abundance, at Baglan and Crymlin in 1964.

Creeping wild asparagus grew at Blackpill when Swansea citizens were jog-trotting along the Mumbles Railway to their rural playground under the limestone cliffs at Oystermouth. This has long since disappeared and now has a tenuous hold in Glamorgan at one tiny site only, on the South Gower dunes.

Conceived in 1804 to carry limestone, coal and iron ore from East Gower and the Clyne Valley to Swansea Dock, the Mumbles Railway became the first in the world to operate a regular passenger service—from the Spring of 1807. So much was it a part of the nineteenth century foreshore that a carriage fitted with a lugsail and provided with a fair following wind could cover the 4½ mile course in less than ¾ hour; but the passengers were hauled across the dunes by horses for the first 70 years, until the introduction of steam traction in 1877. The service ceased in 1960 after 31 years of electrification.

Lyme grass (*Elymus arenarius*), then a feature of the Blackpill dunes, has also disappeared and may persist in Glamorgan only on the sands of North-west Gower, where it is in a healthy state of increase. The peerless flowers of the yellow horned poppy were last recorded at Blackpill in 1957, before the river mouth was made into a pleasure garden, and the accompanying sea holly has retreated to larger dune systems east and west.

Most of these sands are now tamed, grassed or built over and there is a boating pool on the site of a former salt marsh where *Parapholis strigosa* grew. Few of the larger dune plants remain apart from wild mignonette, growing with the related weld and pink soapwort, a garden escape represented here by both single and double-flowered forms.

The narrow ridge of dunes which protects Sketty's lawns and miniature golf course terminates beachwards in an eroding sand cliff 6-12 feet high, partially stablished by plantings of sapling trees and woody veronica. Singleton Park, with University College and Hospital, is sited on old dune and sandflat over hummocky boulder clay and the eastern part by the prison is still known as 'Sandfields'. Sea winds continue to blow sand across the road opposite Singleton Abbey, which was formerly fronted by dunes. The dip in the meadow where water collects is probably an old dune slack: the tumps in the Botany Garden are old sand hills. In the 1930s the playing fields were marshland behind the seaward sand ridge. Big flocks of oyster-catchers and herring gulls still use them regularly and there were grey lag geese here during the 1962-63 freeze-up.

At about this time, in August 1962 and again in August 1964, some special beetles, *Metoecus paradoxus,* were found at West Cross just south of Blackpill. These are rare in Britain and had not been seen before in Glamorgan. The only British representative of their genus, they live a seemingly dangerous youth in the nests of common wasps (*Vespa vulgaris*).

The female beetle lays her eggs, naked and unadorned, on the weathered wood of posts and palings, where wasps come to chew off fragments to masticate into paper for their nests. Newly hatched beetle grubs get aboard and hitch a lift back to the half finished nest. Here they find their way into the cells and live first as internal parasites and then as external ones, on the wasp grubs.

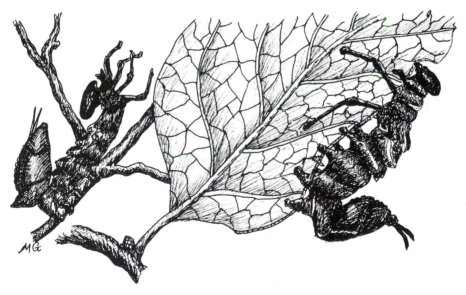

8. Lobster moth caterpillars

These coleopteran 'cuckoos' leave the wasps' nest as adults and start the cycle over again. It is not known whether they mate within the fostering nest before leaving. For so rare an animal there would seem a greater likelihood of finding a partner there than if they delayed until flying free.

Another British rarity here among the beetles is the striking orange and black brush beetle (*Cetonia aurata*), which clashes so blatantly with the purple thyme on which it lives. This is a scarab, related to the commoner bee chafer and rose chafer. *Metoecus* is related to the commoner oil beetle, which spends a comparable youth in the nest of a solitary bee.

One of the rarest as well as the most striking moths of the Swansea area is the lobster (*Stauropus fagi*), which is very local in its centre of distribution in South-east England and much more so in Wales. The angular caterpillar adopts monstrous attitudes when molested, rearing up to wave long wispy legs at its antagonist as though emulating a predacious spider, and menacing it with swollen, pronged tail raised over the body, scorpion fashion. Finally, if these deterrents fail, it squirts a jet of formic acid at the intruder from a gland on the thorax. It belongs to the noble order of the hawk moths.

Another south-easterner reaching west of its normal range in Swansea is the Kentish snail (*Monarcha cantiana*). This flourishes where the old railway line follows round the bay. Of the four British members of the garlic snail genus, the commonest at Swansea is the rarest in the rest of Britain. This is the amber coloured glossy glass snail (*Oxychilus helveticus*). The caruana's slug (*Agriolimax caruanae*) was at one of only four or five British sites when first discovered at Swansea by Quick, but it is gradually spreading in South Wales now. This southerner, from Marseilles, Malta and the Canary Isles, is an aggressive hunter, fleet of foot (by mollusc standards) and stooping to cannibalism. Its remarkable circling courtship activities include a tail licking ritual.

All these live in what is now a fairly stable ecosystem with the friable shoreline backed by the railway embankment and A4067 road. Coastal curvature keeps south-westerly swells at bay, although not eliminating all erosion. Sand build-up is widespread, and a plant both willing and competent, is doing its best to aid the process; but is unwelcome.

Cord grass or rice grass (*Spartina anglica*), an able reclaimer of maritime muds, had become something of a problem on the sands of western Swansea Bay by the 1970s. Here it threatened to take over a golden holiday beach and transform it into a waste of vegetated mud, as it had at Penclawdd in north-east Gower after its introduction to the Burry Inlet in the late 1920s. The Swansea City Parks Department and Glamorgan Naturalists' Trust went into battle against it at Blackpill, to prevent South Wales's so-called 'Bay of Naples' from suffering a similar fate.

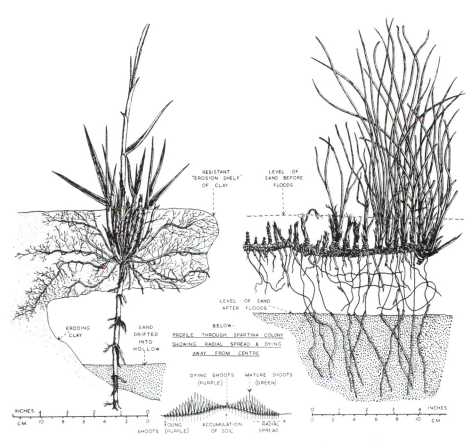

9. Stabilisation of saltmarsh soils by cord grass and sea rush. Left: Roots of *Spartina anglica* holding surface clay against undercutting by waves: Right: Rhizome of *Juncus maritimus* washed out of sand and held only by damaged roots

In muddy places the mat of fibrous breathing roots stays close to the surface to overcome the oxygen deficiency brought about by waterlogging. In less stable sandy soils the far-spreading underground stems or rhizomes anchor it against displacement by rough seas, far more efficiently than with the sea rush, whose horizontal rhizomes may be undermined and the descending roots stripped of their outer layers by storm or flood.

The cord grass probably reached Swansea during the late 1940s and was well established by the late 1960s, with other plants such as sea aster in its shelter. Its success was no doubt helped by the increase of silty mud on the Blackpill foreshore, which was blamed on the dredging of deep channels in Swansea and Port Talbot Docks and the diversion of tidal scour by a developing sand bar. It spread by those insidiously creeping underground stems and wave-dispersed seeds; treatment with herbicides proving quite ineffective in checking it.

Big clumps were dug up by the Parks Department in 1970, but were left lying around, so promptly re-rooted and romped across new acres. By April 1971 there were over five hundred patches advancing on a broad front along half a mile of shore. In September of that year the Park's bulldozers again got busy and the plants were buried this time—above high water mark. A working party of eighty volunteers from the Naturalists' Trust turned out on a chilly February day in 1972 to grovel in the muddy sand for the greater good of Swansea, and after three hours there was scarcely a wisp of *Spartina* to be seen. Several tons of muddy vegetation was carted from the foreshore. The hidden seeds and stem fragments sprouted in the following Spring, as anticipated, but other blitzes have been launched and it seems that constant vigilance may bring victory.

East, beyond the sturdy bastions of Swansea Docks, is a fine stretch of virgin beach, from the BP 'Tank Farm' to the mouth of the River Neath. Clean sand has been drifting in from the sea ever since that last post-glacial drowning of the coastal lowlands. Recent interruptions of the longshore currents by major works like the Port Talbot deep water harbour, have in no way hindered it. The beach is advancing inexorably seawards and behind it the dunes and the sandy plain to which these convert in time.

The rising base level as the sea flooded inland caused the rivers Tawe and Neath to drop their load into 'lagoons' cut off behind dune ridges. More sand blew in from the intertidal flats and modern man clinched the deal by planting a line of factories along the landward side of the A483 and finally sealing any breach that might develop between Crymlin Burrows at today's advancing shoreline and Crymlin Bog, which had built up in an embayment of the post glacial shoreline.

A walk from damp, acidic hollows inland of the road at Jersey Marine, across road, creek and dune ridges to the beach, is a walk back in time. The spatial changes passed en route are the same as the temporal changes that would be found by digging down to past deposits at the starting point.

It is all currently happening. The sea is giving up what it has scraped away from more senescent acres elsewhere, so that we can see the birth of the system as well as the growth to maturity, in a story too long to be followed in one human life span. At the turn of the century the sea lapped to the edge of the coast road, which now runs between ¼ and ½ mile inland, and it was possible to paddle from the road at high tide.

Boys of the 1930s ran 100 yards or so further seaward and over the first dune ridge for their high tide swims. Those who ventured out to the further ridge were likely to be cut off by an awesome expanse of sea on the flood.

An old painting in the new Tower Hotel at Jersey Marine shows the area in 1867 with an arm of the sea encroaching behind the dune ridge which is now occupied by the A483—almost to the foot of the camera obscura tower. The gap in the dunes of 113 years ago is now closed and the old inn reduced to mere footings, but the tower still stands where the Pant-y-Sais Gap breaks free of the bordering hills onto the coastal plain.

While new factories spread along the 'fixed' dunes to landward, 'unfixed' dunes are emerging from the Bristol Channel to seaward. Happily the natural accretion more than compensates for the unnatural encroachment. God giveth and man taketh away, but great is the fulness thereof.

Exciting advances have been made if we go back even half a century, with the Crymlin coast creeping seaward by ¼ mile on a broad front between the printing of the 1941 and 1972 O.S. maps. The mile long inlet parallel to the shore, which now fills with water at high tide to separate the inner dunes from the outer, is only a few yards wide except on the highest springs. In 1940 it marked the main coastline, with almost everything beyond lost to view twice daily beneath the waters.

Tide-washed sands to seaward of the inlet have become drifted over by fine silts and colonised by salt marsh plants, which are gradually being pushed back towards the mouth of the Neath by freshwater species as the marine influence is withdrawn. The sandbar beyond has built up to a high dune ridge and others are forming in front of it, while new sand bars are emerging on the mighty stretch of golden beach outside. Sand bars start building from the West, to grow steadily eastwards toward the river mouth.

Their tips get pushed inland in times of storm and that of the main seaward dune currently bends back up river, in spite of the scouring effect of the river coming out. (In fact the river flows at a lower level, beyond the growing top of the ridge, except at high water, and it is evident that its force then is no match for the great tides—second largest in the world—surging up and down the Bristol Channel.) A branching creek drains the land just behind.

Recent gains on the West bank of the Neath at Crymlin are partially offset by losses on the East bank at Baglan. Crutchley's Proposed Railways Map of 1841 and the O.S. map of 1946 show very different pictures from that now existing. 140 years ago the long coastal spit of Witford Point protected the broad expanse of Baglan Bay opposite the greatly recessed Crymlin coast. Baglan Bay exists now in name only;

Witford Point not at all. This last has disappeared at least once before and re-appeared, only to be washed away again. (See fig. 11.)

In 1840 it extended westwards, but the 1876 map shows no sign of it on a smoothly rounded coastline. By 1897 a short broad headland had re-developed and been pushed slightly upstream, while by 1914 this jutted north-west as a long narrow peninsula. Already an inlet was biting into its base from the South and by 1962 it had vanished without trace. Baglan Bay behind has disappeared largely at the hand of man, being a useful place to deposit surplus industrial waste and the new surfaces so raised being invaluable for wharves, works and warehouses.

It looks as though Witford Point is currently trying to re-form inside the estuary, but comparison of aerial photographs taken in 1946 and 1977 shows a recession along the seaward edge of Baglan dunes. Five or six ridges ran parallel to the shore there in 1946, unaligned with the three curved ridges to riverward of the partly vegetated jumble of sandhills on the main body of the dunes, but these had disappeared by 1977. By that time most of the dune complex was covered by the Petro-chemical works and a shifting series of pools and curvaceous mounds appears on the foreshore within the river mouth. On the ground these make a fascinating sequence, from fully saline hollows downshore to freshwater communities upshore, although the difference in level is negligible.

Dr. Michael Collins and others have established that there is a move-ment of sand into Swansea Bay in an E./E.N.E. direction during about 20% of the year, whenever waves are big enough to stir the sand off the sea bed and set it in motion. The estimated two million tonnes moved annually is not evenly deposited. Some areas get none; in others it comes and goes. The odd storm with waves 10 metres high and 10 seconds apart can move 115,400 tonnes of sand in one tidal cycle: at 8 second intervals twice this amount would be moved.

In such a storm in January 1975 vast quantities of the more easily transportable fine sand, silt and mud were washed into Port Talbot's tidal harbour in a few days, settling as a 5 feet deposit which had to be dredged out in an emergency operation to restore harbour depth to 32½ feet below Ordnance Datum.

During periods of high wave activity the floor of Swansea Bay itself, below the shifting sands, gets scoured away and glacial clay deposits of Flandrian origin turn up in Port Talbot Harbour. Entry of sand into Swansea Bay and its distribution around the coast depends on the interplay of various factors such as sea-bed topography, configuration of the coast, wave action and tidal currents.

Collins and Banner have found an anticlockwise circulation of sediments in the western part, off Swansea, and a clockwise circulation in the eastern part off Kenfig. The load carried in from the South-west

Plate I WADERS OF FIELD AND
SHORE—*Keri Williams*

1. Top: Bar-tailed godwits in flight
2. Left: Curlew in flight
3. Top right: Dunlin wading
4. Bottom right: Golden plover in breeding plumage in April

Plate II   SALTMARSHES OF THE RIVER NEATH—*Author*

5. Top: View upstream across the A48 road bridge at Briton Ferry (The moored boat is at Giant's Grave)
6. Mid left: Saltmarsh scurvy grass
7. Mid right: Greater sea spurrey
8. Bottom left: Glasswort
9. Bottom right: View downstream across Albion Wharf (Briton Ferry dock entrance left, Crymlin Burrows right)

66

divides, to curve along the shore both ways and be deposited or recirculated—westwards and out from Mumbles Point or eastwards and out from Sker Point. The central and eastern part, around Port Talbot lies directly in the path of the south-westerly swells and the direction of coastal transport is less uniform, small variations in the angle at which waves and currents strike the shore deciding which way they shall run along it.

The investigators conclude that for the Port Talbot stretch 'Most longshore transport appears to be to the south-east, but there can be little doubt that most of the mobile sand is ultimately carried by the waves to the berm' (= beach) 'and from thence by aeolian transport' (= wind) 'to the coastal dunes. 'Some may move North to the Neath "Delta" to be recirculated in the bay and some may continue its south-easterly path towards Porthcawl.'

The final leg of the River Neath, which snaked across the sands in the 1840s to the south-west, became confused during the next two decades and the 1859 map shows it occupying several channels and entering the sea by two of these in a south-easterly direction. By 1870 the guiding breakwaters had been built and it flowed in a straight line to the south-west, this channel little modified by 1897 except for a tongue of sand licking seawards beyond the directional embankments on either side.

There is an incredible amount of sand on the move here as the big tides surge to and fro. More and more is being deposited at low water mark where the confined river emerges from its long intertidal haul. The deposits are of sea sand, not river silt, although deltaic in form, as though the river is pushing out what is trying to get in.

The distance across the sand at low water from the head of the Baglan saltmarsh to the sand bars at the river mouth is just over 2½ miles. That from the recessed corner of Witford Point to the river exit is 1¾ miles and that from Witford Point due west to the river channel at mid tide level is ¾ mile. It is the continuation eastwards of this mighty expanse of foreshore which forms the Aberafan Sands—seemingly purpose-built for summer cricket matches—but quite devoid of plant life at the foot of the restricting promenade.

A host of burrowing bivalves lives in the acres off Witford Point where land snails formerly crawled among the marram grass. Practically untrodden by shell collectors, the sands are even more thickly strewn with shells than are those off Blackpill. Tellins are commonest with the cockles there; scallops at Baglan, in great drifts of brick-red, orange, slaty black and fawn. Tellins do occur, in modest numbers, Baltic and common tellins and the similar but more angular *Tellina fabula*.

Common oysters and saddle oysters are frequent, pullet carpet shells (*Venerupis pullastra*), rayed trough shells (*Mactra corallina*) and razor shells (*Ensis* spp.) less so. Any of the sand dwellers, apart from the fleeter-footed swimming scallops, might show the neat hole drilled by a prowling necklace shell, whose remains can also be found. Shells of another pinkish sea snail, *Actaeon tornatilis*, are rarer.

No less than fifteen species of sand worms have been dug out at Baglan—catworms, ragworms, bristle worms, round worms and ribbon worms, including the two with sandy tubes, *Lanice* and *Pectinaria*. Probably most significant, however, are the sand hoppers, the sideways flattened Amphipods, *Haustorius arenarius* and *Bathyporeia* sp., and the woodlouse-like Isopods, *Eurydice pulchra* and *Eurydice affinis*.

On the seaward side of Witford the foredunes are contiguous with the main dunes. On the riverward side they are more fragmentary and stray away over the beach. They protrude only a foot or so above base level, loose, pale and topped by wispy sand couch. At first they are separated by shelly tidal sandflats, then by low 'pans', where a skin of silt overlies the sand and clings to boots to leave lines of sandy footprints across what appears to be mud. Further up the Neath Estuary towards the elevated oil pipeline which conceals the Baglan saltmarsh, the silt layer is coated with a film of green algae and the going becomes treacherous.

On a drear winter day the scrappy sandhills and scattered salt pans look like a defeated dune system in retreat. With a spirit-boosting dose of sunshine lighting up the plant tufts, they more resemble the pioneering community that they actually are. The lost acres are to seaward, not riverward, and of these no recognisable trace remains.

The Open community had advanced 300 yards and more beyond the high tide driftline by the end of the 1979 Summer, disappearing from view under the higher tides and hence containing no marram or other species unable to withstand salt water about its roots. It is surprising how much *is* able to withstand this treatment, not least the little birds' nest fungus, *Cyathus olla*, with buff-coloured 'eggs' or spore packets in single grey cups merging almost invisibly into the ground.

Sand couch forms a monoculture on the foremost dunes until seedlings of blue fleabane and sea orache emerge in May. Evening primrose, rock sea lavender, biting stonecrop and ragwort appear further back with the first of the marram grass.

The silted pans seem undecided whether to be mini-saltmarshes or dune slacks, and there is a subtle change from one to the other in an upshore direction. To seaward they are usually bare, but some are exclusively occupied by annual sea-blite in an open community, with each plant 1-2 yards from the next, giving a 5-10% ground cover. About 10% of these bore dark red foliage in October 1979, a colour expected in conditions of water shortage, real or apparent, due to saltiness, but here it was induced by no habitat factor. The constant proximity of purple-red and yellow-green colour forms showed the difference to be genetic or inborn.

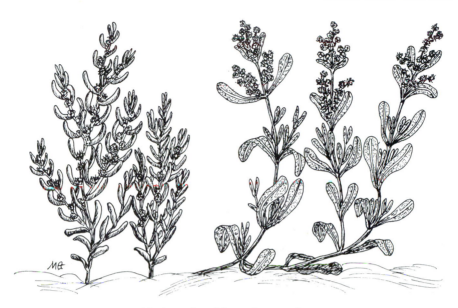

10. Annual sea-blite and sea purslane

Sea purslane and sea aster are the next to appear, both very depauperate, but upshore the scope widens, with salt marsh grass (*Puccinellia maritima*) and sea sedge (*Scirpus maritimus*). One almost fully vegetated slack dominated by fiorin grass (*Agrostis stolonifera*) contained a remarkable mixture of rushes, with sea rush and mud rush from the saltings, toad rush and jointed rush from freshwater marsh and sharp rush from the dunes. By 1980 the sharp rush (a plant of the drier sands) had been drowned out and replaced by pioneering clumps of sea bulrush and great reedmace.

Drifted seaweed shows that all must tolerate inundation by salt water on occasion, although many, like autumnal hawkbit and false fox sedge, would do very well without. Celery-leaved buttercups thrive in these half and half conditions with sea milkwort and scurvy grass. Sea arrow grass and marsh arrow grass grow together, but only the latter shows the splaying of the ripe, disarticulating fruits that must have put the namer in mind of arrows.

Some slacks at this high water level are dominated by velvety, capsule-studded mats of the moss, *Bryum pendulum*, which must be one of very few associated so closely with the sea. Plants with it are necessarily small, to allow it light enough to grow, and include knotted

69

pearlwort, dwarf centaury and the stiff little sea fern-grass (*Catapodium marinum*).

Short-tailed field voles live in the denser cover of the dunes, foraging locally: the far-ranging rodents of the foreshore are long-tailed field mice, which need less cover, as they are around more at night. Almost every artefact lifted in October 1979—board, polythene, plastic or other rubbish—hid a mouse's store of straw-coloured sand-couch grains or, more often, the chaff discarded after the grains had been eaten. The little granaries were from 3-5 inches diameter and, although sufficiently well anchored not to be washed away by the tides, surviving grains would be well salted by the time they came to be eaten, if not, indeed, decayed or germinated through the constant wetting.

May and June 1980 saw a thriving population of rabbits venturing downshore to feed, these nibbling preferentially at the succulent leaves of sea arrow-grass and mud rush, with aster and sea plantain as second choice and the others mostly ignored.

The half vegetated landscape of the tideline provides suitable terrain for ground-hoppers, which enjoy unobstructed hopping space. The rare *Tetrix ceperoi* is here, as well as the commoner *Tetrix undulata*. Multiple heads of buck's-horn plantain, with many subsidiary flower spikes emerging from the base of the main one, are probably induced by the caterpillars of *Palaena*, a Tortrix moth.

One of the commonest of the beach beetles identified by Roy Perry is the Carabid, *Broscus cephalotes*, but the turning over of tidal drift reveals many more, with shimmering wing cases, green, bronze and black. Spring sees the frothy globules of spittle bug larvae (*Philaenus spumarius*) 'forever blowing bubbles'; summer the mature froghoppers spurting out of the gloom to merge perfectly again as they land. Snails and woodlice feed on vegetable detritus, harvestmen and centipedes on vegetable feeders.

The lives of all are fraught with hazard in this changing seascape. Stormy seas banked the sands perceptibly higher to seaward of the salty slacks in the winter of 1979-80, so that a sheet of shining water was ponded back at the ebb in early March. The destiny of many will depend on whether these sandbanks flatten out to allow the trapped water to leave with the tide. Summer 1981 may see this area as saltmarsh or sand flat, embryo dune or freshwater slack.

Fortunes of plants and animals ebb and flow like the tide itself. Calamity for some is bonanza for others. That motto of 'Adapt or perish' was never more apt. Whichever wins this turbulent corner, the land or the sea, in ensuing years, we may be sure that the apparently defeated legions will be lurking somewhere near, ready to repopulate if fortunes should change. Just one storm could be enough.

Part Two

Sediment Filled Valleys of
The Neath Complex

Mayflies, water snails and shrimp

One of the battles we have got to fight is to establish the public right to acquire land for conservation and recreation, if necessary by compulsion.

Sir John Cripps in "The Countryman's Countryman" (Ecos 1(2) 1980).

5 WATERY WILDERNESS OF CRYMLIN BOG

The Story in the Peat and Today's Unique Vegetation

CRYMLIN Bog occupies an ancient inlet of the sea which bit back into the Coalfield for three miles, almost to where Skewen now stands. The great sand blows of the thirteenth and fourteenth centuries blocked its entrance and the silty estuarine clay across which the tide had entered became progressively covered by the remains of marsh plants. The peat mass cradled by the mile wide, ice-scoured basin is now 14-15 feet thick, but still not above the water table, so the whole area remains swampy, composed partly of alkaline fen and partly of acid bog.

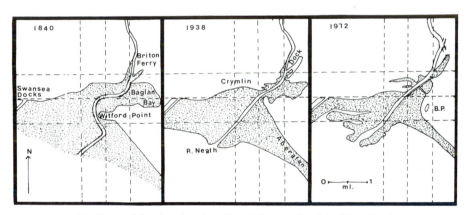

11. Maps of the changing shoreline at the mouth of the River Neath

It is thought that the River Clydach once took this route to the sea. At present this flows into the River Neath at Neath Abbey near Bendles Pond, possibly 'captured' by that larger river which was cutting down more vigorously to a lowered sea level and getting progressively bigger by the capture of others in the now famous 'Waterfall Country' of its upper reaches.

An eastward extension of the bog leads off in the South along another ice-broadened rift towards Llandarcy. This valley was followed by the ancient River Neath—which now reaches the sea a mile further east, around the opposite flank of the 86 ft. high hill.

Professor Anderson has found the rock floor of this old course of the Neath to be cut deeper than that of the later course—to 117 feet

72

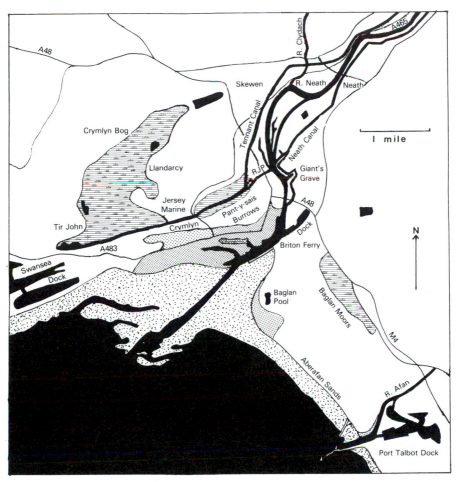

12. Map of waterways, marshes and dunes at the mouth of the River Neath (R.J.P. = Red Jacket Pill)

below Ordnance Datum. The Tennant Canal, after hugging the west bank of the modern river, cuts away through this valley—Pant-y-Sais—and along the southern margin of Crymlin Bog to the docks at Swansea. Like the Bog proper, the Pant-y-Sais Valley remains water-logged, reed-filled and difficult of access.

The two occluded river basins retain no evidence of their marine origins in their vegetation, although salt marsh turf borders the River Neath in the more easterly valley to well beyond their inland limits. They are today occupied by what is probably the biggest reedswamp in South Wales—where the south-easterly based reeds thin out and become more coastal. It has not always been so.

Lightfoot, an eighteenth-century botanist, visited the area in 1773 and found an abundance of white water lily and frogbit, implying that there must have been a greater area of open water then than now. The site was currently known as Cors Crym Llyn, suggesting both bog (cors) and lake (llyn). The bog was also known to Welsh-speaking locals as 'Gwern Fär', which has been translated as the 'Moor of Wrath', but, with Llandarcy Refinery alongside, oil has now come to the troubled waters. Two extremely attractive water plants previously present, but for long regarded as extinct, are lesser water plantain (*Baldellia ranunculoides*), and floating water plantain *(Luronium natans)*, but the former was rediscovered in 1977 during a survey by Andrew Lees.

Species of a raised bog existing in the North in Lightfoot's time and now almost certainly extinct are bog rosemary (*Andromeda polifolia*), the two larger sundews (*Drosera anglica* and *D. intermedia* and the brown and white beak sedges (*Rhynchospora fusca* and *R. alba*). The raised bog persists, but in impoverished form. It is typified now by cotton grass and bog asphodel, with bottle sedge and water horsetail in standing water.

Rainfall may well be too low at present for the active growth of raised bog, but it could be more than coincidence that disappearance of the distinctive species coincided with the rise of the great copper smelting industry in the early part of the nineteenth century. The raised bog, lying above the flushing influence of ground drainage and watered only by rain, would have been more affected by sulphur dioxide fallout from the furnaces than the rest.

With no river to scour away accumulating silt and plant debris, reeds have been able to advance into shallowing areas to swallow the open water quite rapidly. Plots of bulrush or reedmace occur; the common great reedmace in the shallows and the rare lesser reedmace in deeper water. This last is at one of very few sites in South Wales.

More noteworthy still is the great fen sedge (*Cladium mariscus*) which is co-dominant of about 5 hectares east of the central Glan-y-Wern Canal. This is a scarce plant of East Anglia, the Shropshere Meres and the western oceanic fringes of Scotland and Ireland, which is in one of its only two South Wales stations at Crymlin.

Another speciality among the sedges is black bog rush (*Schoenus nigricans*), which is even more characteristic of those spray-washed Gaelic fringes, although present in East Anglia. It, too, is known at only two other places in South Wales. At Crymlin it is locally common among the purple moor grass which clothes areas less soggy and more acid than the reed beds.

Slender cotton grass (*Eriophorum gracile*), found by Andrew Lees in 1979, is a new species for Glamorgan and a second record for Wales, although frequent in Irish bogs. He also turned up two sedges which

13. Four rare sedges found on Crymlin Bog in 1979 by Andrew Lees. From left to right: Slender cotton grass *(Eriophorum gracile)*, mud sedge *(Carex limosa)*, tufted sedge *(Carex elata)* and dioecious sedge *(Carex dioica)*, female above, male below

have not been seen for half a century: the bog sedge (*Carex limosa*) and the dioecious sedge (*Carex dioica*). Tufted sedge (*Carex elata*), which is locally abundant in carr woodland, grows here at the south-western extremity of its geographical range and is a rare plant even in the East Anglian Fens.

There is some question as to whether this invading sedge fen has built up fairly and squarely from the former lake bed or whether it has short circuited the depths and advanced as a floating raft across the water. Certainly parts have that precarious blancmange-like feel underfoot that savours of quaking bog: and, incidentally, support a curious combination of round-leaved sundew from the bog and reed from the fen. The poles of ornithologists' mist nets have a nasty way of suddenly meeting no resistance after being thrust through the twelve inch fibrous surface crust. No doubt some of the mire is afloat and some aground, but it is no place to visit alone.

Probably it never has been. A 14 ft. core of peat taken from the south west by Professor Godwin tells of the sequence of sticky layers that have gone into its making.

The uppermost 3 ft. of peat beneath the living bog consists of the remains of sedge and bog-moss impregnated with pollen from grasses and heathers, so it seems that an open moorland community grew here while this layer was accumulating.

From 3 ft. down to 7 ft. there are increasingly more twigs of birch and alder in the peat. Both are catkin bearers, producing copious wind-borne pollen, but birch pollen is commoner. Birch woods produce a more open canopy than alder woods, permitting better light penetration and the abundance of fern spores (which are as resistant to decay as pollen grains) indicates that this light was utilised by a healthy fern flora.

Below this, to where the peat meets the underlying clay, the ferns fade out and the woody remains give evidence of alder wood with mature oaks and hazels. So we have a compressed thumbnail sketch of a clayey estuary being invaded by a fen woodland of alder as the sea withdrew, this thinning to a ferny birchwood which, in its turn, was overtaken in a worsening climate by bog-moss and sedge.

The top of this peat core (and the present height of the bog above sea level) was 19½ ft. above O.D. The bottom, at 5½ ft. above O.D., is 10 ft. higher than the peat bed below Crymlin Burrows to seaward. Clearly there must have been a subsequent build up of peat after a later invasion by the sea which spread marine clays on top of earlier terrestrial deposits.

Any such upper peat layer deposited to seaward of the present bog must have been destroyed by marine erosion before the protective layer of sand arrived. Today's bog is. only slightly above the level of high spring tides, but is effectively insulated from infiltration of salt water by the growing sands, which have been further stabilised by the A483 coast road, a railway and two mineral lines and a row of factories.

Scrub woodland hides these later developments from the bog except towards Swansea, and merges into an impenetrably wet carr woodland of grey sallow with downy birch, alder and alder buckthorn, this last at the south-western limit of its geographical range. The waterlogged woodland floor of the latter disappears in summer beneath lush ferns including the rare and handsome royal fern (*Osmunda regalis*), giant horsetail, yellow flags and great stools of tussock sedge. Its wetness does not save it, however, from occasional conflagrations, so even-aged stands of young trees push up among the starkly blackened remains of their predecessors in places. After a fire north of the Tennant Canal in 1979, scores of acres became covered with royal fern risen like Phoenix from the ashes. It was growing as prolifically as bracken in 1980, and, like that more cosmopolitan fern, its underground foodstore had saved it from the flames—a shorter, chunkier rhizome in this instance.

Magnificent swards of uncommon blunt-flowered rush (*Juncus subnodulosus*) grow in the soggy ground opposite, with equally uncommon red rattle. Firmer ground followed by the towpath separates this fen carr from the Tennant Canal and the bog beyond. It is little used now and is difficult of access in late summer due to invasion by Japanese knotweed and bramble. European gorse effectively bars all passage towards the west, forcing the walker onto a track behind.

Tips of fly ash from the Tir John power station at this end have become pleasantly clothed with young woodland which bulges eastwards into the bog and facilitates botanical exploration into an otherwise difficult area. Removal of ash is scheduled for the 1980s. Reeds to the south encroach across the canal at times, but the channel is kept open by periodic clearing as it supplies water for industrial purposes.

The power station is now closed and one of the two mineral tramways serving it, the 'up hump' and the 'down hump' lines, lying between the main railway and the canal, was closed in 1964. Nine years later goat sallow and grey sallow had grown 6-7 ft. high along the disused track in parts, gorse and broom to similar heights in others. Downy birch was up to 5 ft. with Japanese knotweed overtopping it in summer.

Ground invaders include relic dune plants from pre-factory days— rest harrow and hare's-foot clover, with sand sedge and sharp rush spilling down onto the towpath. The dusty brown sand and industrial clinker are not sufficiently acid for a reciprocal invasion of heather from below; supporting instead 'middle-of-the-road' species like yellow parsnip, golden rod and perforate, elegant and creeping St. John's worts.

The line alongside, when still in use in 1973, had blackened growths of broom surviving against the rails, although badly damaged by passing trains and splaying out each side like toppled brushwood fences. Birch and sallow saplings endured similar punishment and acorns collecting against the rails germinated to produce oak seedlings which were summarily beheaded when they reached to 7 inches.

The Glan-y-Wern Canal, which crosses the bog obliquely, was constructed in 1790-91 and is credited with being the second oldest of the industrial waterways of the era, the first being a 'cut' at Aberdulais in 1740-51. Oldisworth, writing in 1802, states 'It was found necessary to take the canal for nearly 2 miles through the midst of Crymlin or Crumlin bog or morass, the soft spongy ground of which rising up repeatedly after the surface was cut away seemed to present an insuperable obstacle to the completion of the undertaking.' He goes on to comment admiringly on the tenacity of the 'navvies' or 'navigation men' who wallowed in the filth to produce a cheaper method of getting the highly prized bituminous coal to the sea.

This was mined at Glan-y-Wern Colliery on the Kilvey side of Crymlin Bog, and Rhys Phillips, writing in 1925, tells us that it formerly went by 'a tedious and expensive land carriage' for shipment in the Tawe River at Foxhole. Now it followed the eastward curve of the Glan-y-Wern or Crymlin and Red Jacket Canal to emerge onto the River Neath opposite Briton Ferry.

Cargo was transferred into bigger river barges in a broad canal basin just below a double-arched stone bridge, both of which have survived into the 1980s, at the foot of the hill south-east of Pant-y-Sais where the old Copper works stood. Lock gates which controlled the ingress of tidal water from Red Jacket Pill disintegrated in the 1950s. River barges left Red Jacket Canal for Red Jacket Pill at high tide and debouched onto the River Neath at Trowman's Hole, where the flat-bottomed barges of 40-80 tons burden known as trows were moored.

The Tennant Canal absorbed part of the Glan-y-Wern in 1817 and was fully opened in 1824. It remains today as the most continuous area of open water and contains most of the aquatic plant species which have been swallowed up elsewhere by the advancing reeds.

Mare's-tail (*Hippuris vulgaris*) is one of the most striking, its leafy stems undulating gracefully beneath the surface like their namesakes in full flight, but thrusting sturdy, tight-leaved flower spikes above. This varies in amount from year to year and was particularly abundant in 1979 when weed cutting operations by a paddle boat with V-shaped scissor mowers mounted on the bow produced a flotilla of severed fragments to drift upstream with the wind and take root, extending a once quite discrete colony at the junction of the two canals.

Canadian pondweed formed dense stands in that year, but did not throw up any of the rarely seen, long-stalked white flowers as it did so profusely in the more crowded growths of shallower water in the Glamorgan Canal at Pontypridd. Lesser marshwort (*Apium inundatum*) produces masses of feathery leaves below water and crisper ones accompanying lacy flower umbels above.

The bladder-bearing filigrees of insectivorous greater bladderwort (*Utricularia vulgaris*) are much more difficult to spot unless topped by yellow, pea-like flowers. This is a plant of neutral, eutrophic water, but the rarer and more acid-loving lesser bladderwort (*Utricularia minor*) also occurs at Crymlin, mostly on the raised bog of the North.

Sunken rafts of ivy-leaved duckweed are permeated by fronds of narrow-leaved pondweed (*Potamogeton berchtoldii*) and the pea green fronds of various-leaved water starwort (*Callitriche platycarpa*) acts as a foil to the dark water moss (*Fontinalis antipyretica*). There are still a few white water lilies, but most of the floating leaves are those of broad pondweed.

The canal banks are a joy in late summer with red marsh cinquefoil trailing into the water and occasional stands of elegant flowering rush (*Butomus umbellatus*) with pink umbels six inches across. Upstanding

10

11

12

Plate III PLANTS OF CRYMLIN BOG—*Author*

10. Left: Hairy sedge
11. Top right: Marsh forget-me-not
12. Mid right: Bog asphodel
13. Bottom: Bog pimpernel

13

Plate IV   AT THE MOUTH OF THE RIVER NEATH—*Author*

   14.   Top left: Royal fern on vertical rock face alongside the Neath Canal at Briton Ferry

   15.   Top right: Water plantain leaves in a sward of water crowfoot

   16.   Mid left: Cattle on Crymlin saltmarsh. View across river mouth to Baglan pipeline

   17.   Bottom left: Part of the anchoring root system of sea holly

   18.   Bottom right: Prickly saltwort

bog myrtle (*Myrica gale*) with bluish, aromatic leaves, dwarfs the creeping willow (*Salix repens*) at its feet. It is known in Glamorgan at only one other site apart from Gower, and has its own small species of aphid, *Myzocallis myricae*.

Bogbean (*Menyanthes trifoliata*) lines the canal where it borders the eastern extension of the reedswamp through Pant-y-Sais and it is here that the rare greater spearwort (*Ranunculus lingua*) reaches its zenith as a belt of midsummer gold—succeeding the marsh marigolds behind a fringe of lesser reedmace.

Young flower spikes of great pond sedge, another of the waterside dominants with reed sweet-grass, may have the stamens ripped out in early spring, roughly as though by a bird's beak. Specialities turned up here in 1979 by Lees are whorled water milfoil (*Myriophyllum verticillatum*), at what is probably its only site in Wales, and least bur-reed (*Sparganium minimum*), which is a north-westerner, present at only 4 other Welsh sites, and 3 of these in the North.

In spite of a good coverage of lime-demanding blunt-flowered rush, there is an area of raised bog on Pant-y-Sais typified by acid-loving mosses such as *Sphagnum fimbriatum, S. papillosum* and *Polytrichum commune.* The smaller *P. piliferum* of the bordering towpath forms crimson patches in March and April, when the frilly saucers of the male heads are massed together, and Roy Perry has found rusty-coloured clumps of the liverwort, *Solenostoma crenulatum,* covered with black 'drumstick' heads of spores at this season.

Crymlin Brook dissecting the bog at right angles is kept open for drainage purposes, the displaced material banked alongside making it possible to walk between flowing stream and stagnant reedswamp until the brook itself diffuses out among the reeds and is lost. Blue skullcap is unusually common along the banks, with yellow and purple loosestrifes, marsh woundwort, gipsywort and greater willow herb.

Common and intermediate starwort (*Callitriche stagnalis* and *C. intermedia*) thrive in newly cleared sections beneath the surface, where they are immune from any polluting influence of floating oil films escaping from the Llandarcy Oil Refinery, or impurities in drainage waters from old mine workings. In fact little oil escapes except into the pools immediately below the works, where plants and animals are few. That which does is filtered out among the reed bases and spreads scarcely at all, so that oil pollution poses no more threat at present than airborne soot from the Carbon Black Works in the South-west.

Dr. Jenny Baker has found that the reeds are able to remain quite healthy with as much as 32.2% of oil in the top 4 inches of soil water, oxygen diffusing down through the shoots to supply the creeping stems below. With higher oil levels the reeds sicken and die.

Blue-green algae are tolerant of more vicissitudes than any other group and one of these, *Oscillatoria,* is the only genus able to survive in

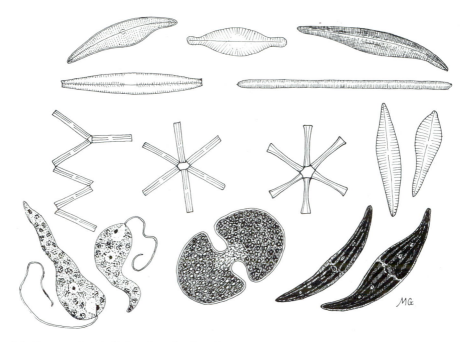

14. Genera of unicellular algae in Crymlin Bog. Top: Diatoms; *Cymbella, Navicula* and *Gyrostigma*. Upper middle: Diatoms; *Fragillaria* and *Synedra*. Lower middle: Diatoms; *Tabellaria* (two ways of cell attachment), *Asterionella* and two forms of *Gomphonema*. Bottom: Euglenoids and green algae, *Cosmarium* and two forms of *Closterium*

oil films near the three refinery effluents. The more familiar green *Spirogyra* and *Vaucheria* and a member of the Chrysophyta, *Tribonema,* float only in cleaner water. Figure 14 shows examples of eight genera of diatoms present in the brook, two characteristically shaped green algae (*Cosmarium* and *Closterium*) and some of the motile green Euglenoids.

Mostly the brook is crystal clear, with greater water plantain, iris and unbranched bur-reed (*Sparganium emersum*) in addition to the usual branched bur-reed. More noteworthy is the big colony of least bur-reed (*Sparganium minimum*) which was spared extinction by a lucky accident. It occupies a single pool lying in the direct path of a proposed pipeline. Only the impracticability of getting earth-moving machinery onto the treacherous floating bog around the pool caused the ensuing embankment to veer away to one side and leave its habitat intact.

Cattle stay out of the wetter reedbeds, feeding mainly among the soft rush and purple moor grass, where yellow ants build their anthills well up among the grass stools above winter water level. Unlike the reed-beds, which are often a monoculture, forty or so subordinate plants can be found in the rushy pastures of the north and west.

The abundant ferns, both here and by the brook, are predominantly lemon scented mountain ferns (*Thelypteris oreopteris*) with marginal spore packets, although so close to sea level. Narrow buckler fern (*Dryopteris carthusiana*) has been found by Dr. Quentin Kay to be quite common in the north of the bog, although rare in South Wales. Maps of 1610-57 show the eastern margin of the bog to be dotted with trees—an outlying part of 'Coed Ffranc', the 'Norman Wood'.

The tree-crowned banks of old hedge lines penetrating the west side of the bog are a legacy of more extensive farming at times when attempts were made to drain the area. Drainage schemes, such as one in the early part of the nineteenth century, have been only moderately successful. A sodden area as close to sea level as this needs pumps to rid it of sufficient surplus water to make agriculture the viable undertaking that it is on the Somserset Levels across the Channel. As it is, the high water table keeps disturbance to a minimum, allowing mammals like water voles and stoats, which are not averse to getting their feet wet, to pursue their lives uninterrupted by the industrial bustle which surges about their ancestral haven.

Only one harvest is coveted—and practicable—that of 'Norfolk' reeds for thatching. These are in great demand for what is now a lucrative luxury trade. Cereals have been bred for shorter straw to minimise lodging in rainstorms and what straw there is gets mangled in modern combine harvesters and is usually burned. A tentative proposal is to cut 25 acres here and 25 acres on Oxwich, Gower, every other year.

Caterpillar tractors, as used in Holland and the English Fens, could take mowers onto much of the Crymlin reedbeds after a dry summer, but it is likely that cutting would be done in winter, when only reed buntings and wrens are among the reeds in any numbers. The present reed stands would need to be burned first to get rid of the trash and start with a clean growth of parallel stems.

Carried out at the right season, to avoid disturbance to breeding birds and invertebrates, this would do no harm to the vegetation, and is practised on Nature Reserves such as Radipole in Dorset. The seasonal access of light gives subordinate species a chance to multiply and alleviate the tedium of the reed monocultures, as alongside the open water glades at present. Naturally some of the 'monoculture' would need to be left for reed warblers and other specialists.

In fact islands of green vegetation are invariably by-passed by a fire, these acting as reservoirs of plants and animals for recolonisation. Light fires at Crymlin leave the peat still damp, with green shoots pushing through a week after the flames subside. After a bad burn, only plants with buried rhizomes, such as the reeds themselves, will sprout immediately—others take longer. The solid rootstocks of ferns, sedges and purple moor grass can take a lot of punishment by fire with no permanent ill effects, and did on Crymlin in the drought summer of 1976. Most vulnerable are the lichens on the burned sallow twigs, recolonisation being a slow process.

The initial pre-harvest burn, however, might prove an insurmountable obstacle with all that petroleum spirit and crude oil crowded against the eastern margin of the bog. Agricultural fires have posed a threat at times in the past, with all available manpower called out to form a 'thin red line' of defenders around the refinery.

What must be avoided at all costs is further infilling by rubble and rubbish, but this is a very real threat at present. Tir John's pulverised fuel ash tips have been absorbed quite acceptably by woodland, but only at the expense of some rich fen areas. The Nature Conservancy Council does not schedule areas as Grade I sites of exceptional biological importance lightly, and this is such a site. During recent years both Crymlin Bog and Pant-y-Sais have been under threat from tipping, for which no valid planning permission exists, and quantities of rubble have actually been dumped on the latter. Bitter battles have been fought by local residents and conservation bodies, both county and national, and prospects are much brighter in 1980.

Swansea has spread in the west, Baglan and Port Talbot in the east, Neath and its neighbours in the north. The Crymlin complex is all that remains of what was once so biologically rich—a lung for the people and a refuge for other forms of life. May the wisdom of planners see that it remains so, and that our children will not find themselves blaming us for the loss of an irreplaceable asset, the negation of a miracle of survival through all the vicissitudes of the industrial revolution.

6 ANIMALS OF CRYMLIN BOG

Sanctuary for Rare Birds and Reservoir of Little-known Invertebrates

CHOICE water plants and rare sedges are only a part of what Crymlin Bog has to offer. Many naturalists regard the area as one of the most important ornithological sites in South Wales, while specialists in any of the lesser groups invariably emerge with some interesting and unusual records.

Where else in Glamorgan except in North Gower, could the winter bird watcher sit snugly in a car and watch a hen harrier quartering low over the mire with languid flapping flight; gliding, not as a gull glides in horizontal plane, but the wings uptilted in a shallow V?

Marsh harriers were resident on Crymlin Bog in 1882, in spite of extreme rarity at that time: then they disappeared. Now, since the 1950s, they seem to be trying to stage a come-back, and Crymlin Bog, along with the Steel Company's nearby reservoir of Eglwys Nunydd, is among the places where they have been sighted in recent years.

Merlins bred along the Glamorgan coast during the latter part of the nineteenth century, but abandoned all their sites there with the increasing tourist pressure of the early part of the twentieth. Crymlin Bog is not threatened by tourists and merlins have been spotted here in the 1970s. Who knows, they may yet breed again here, in defiance of all the pressures round about.

Day-hunting short-eared owls course purposefully to and fro, peering into the vegetation for voles, and barn owls adopt a similar technique at dusk, staying closer to the ground, like ghostly will-o'-the-wisps, where only the foolhardy would risk venturing in to disturb their quest. Little owls keep sentinel watch on battered fence posts and tawny owls hoot warnings to potential prey animals from the older established carr woodlands.

More diminutive, but no less exciting than the birds of prey, are the bearded tits or reedlings which turn up here in 'eruption years' such as 1975, when there is a population explosion in their native terrain of East Anglia or West Europe. South Walians who formerly trekked to Cley and Blakeney or down to the Camargue to see these handsome blue, russet and pied birds, have been increasingly able to do so on home ground during the 1970s.

Think of bearded tits and one automatically thinks of bitterns and the eerie booming emanating from hidden depths among the reeds. Bitterns are said to have bred at Crymlin a century and a half ago, before the general contraction of the population back to East Anglia. Then, after a long silence, one was seen again in November 1961. Visits by ornithologists are too sparse for us to know if they are breeding again yet, but there is always a chance, now that the first major steps have been taken.

This is part of a general reappearance of bitterns and bearded tits shared by the reedbeds of Oxwich, Margam and Kenfig. The concept of a 'Broadland' here in the South West, is not so outlandish as it may at first seem. Nature will do her bit in supplying the species if man will co-operate in protecting the habitat.

Reedbeds of these dimensions without reed warblers are unthinkable, even this far west, and reed warblers are here in droves during the nesting season, each cock vigorously declaring territory, but the population as a whole is quite uncountable in that trackless maze. It is known, however, that there are two main colonies.

The scratchy songs of some 300 breeding pairs of sedge warblers add to the general pandemonium in early summer and whitethroats throw in more discordant notes. Walkers on the canal towpath catch tantalizingly short glimpses of many little brown birds flitting through the reed tops, which harbour plenty of caterpillars, flies and aphids to attract them.

Some of these may be grasshopper warblers, birds which we have come to associate in Glamorgan with the young forestry plantations, but which find an equally suitable environment here among sapling-sized saw-sedge and reedmace. There are willows in plenty for the willow warblers and these had a bonanza in 1979, feeding on the little yellow beetles, *Galerucella lineola,* that decimated their shelter trees, a feast which they shared with tits and chaffinches.

Chiff-chaffs are marginal, but reed buntings very much in evidence, handsomely marked males selecting song posts through a much wider range of habitats than just the reeds. Redstarts can be flushed from the line of sallows along Crymlin Brook and redpolls from the birch carrs, these having been seen with young in July.

Willow tit, stonechat, pied and grey wagtail, although sometimes seen, are not known to breed, but yellow wagtails do, along with skylarks and wrens. There is no shortage of foster parents for cuckoos, nor of food for insect hawking swifts and hirundines, which may gather in the reeds preparatory to migrating south.

Snipe sit very tight, but a splashy passage through tussocky purple moor grass will usually flush at least one, to go zig-zagging off on a flight calculated to make things difficult for marsh cowboys with guns. Jack snipe visit in winter, along with other waders. It is then that the occasional wigeon can be spotted on the canal and 20-30 teal are usually somewhere around.

Water rails almost certainly breed, but are elusive and more often heard than seen, finding all they need without ever breaking cover. The rare spotted crake was a regular summer visitor at the end of the last century and bred, but has not been seen since. Moorhens are still an integral part of the canal scene and coot drop in from larger bodies of open water, common sandpipers from more rugged mountain wetlands.

A small heronry with at least four nesting pairs has been discovered recently, one of few in these parts, and possibly a partial replacement for the diminishing colony at Margam Country Park to the east. Kingfishers appear regularly in the non-breeding season and green

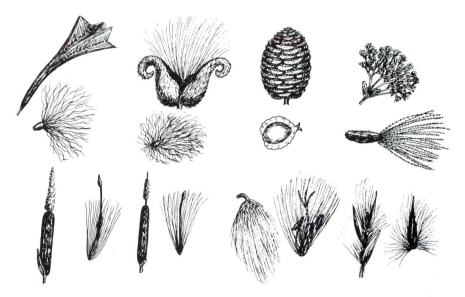

15. Wind-dispersed seeds and fruits of water plants. Top, from left to right: Willow herb, fruit capsule and seeds; sallow, ditto; alder, fruiting catkin (or cone) and seed; hemp agrimony, fruiting head and single-seeded fruit. Bottom: Great reedmace, head of male and female flowers and single-seeded fruit; lesser reedmace, ditto; cotton grass, fruiting head and single fruit; reed, part of fruiting head and single grain

woodpeckers, magpies and wood pigeons forage over the bog from the marginal woodlands. Prior to 1973 sand martins nested in a cliff of fly ash at Tir John Power Station.

Flocks can build up to vast numbers over these unfrequented acres in autumn. September 1977 yielded 1,000 swallows on the 14th, 1,500 jackdaws and no less than 5,000 starlings on the 17th. Herring gulls gather here between feeding forays and 500 were counted in August 1977.

Gulls go regularly to clean pools within the refinery to bathe and preen, but also disport themselves on the fouler pools at the edge of the bog below, apparently taking no harm. A greater black-back ringed in Tenby was found here starved to death because of nylon fishing line around its neck which prevented it from feeding. Another possible hazard to the birds here is lead poisoning from lead shot picked up, particularly by young birds, as grit for the gizzard, the bog being used as a rough shoot by the locals. They are the top predators of this complex ecosystem. There are many links in the food chain below the birds they shoot, some aquatic and some terrestrial.

The gulls make sorties into the urban hinterland to feed, but most of the birds' needs are supplied by the bog. Seeds remain edible long after

87

ripening and some of the most sought after are the nutlets of pondweed and water milfoil which are produced at the water surface, bur-reed, bulrush, dock and water pepper at its margins and the lightweight ones of birch, alder and sallow which waft down from above. Guelder rose elder and hawthorn supply fruit eaters in season. Insects, spiders and freshwater molluscs produce a generous spread for the animal eaters, but the brilliant coloration of some sounds a warning for the over eager.

Spherical scarlet water mites more than ¼″ across weave among the submerged pondweed like animated lentils. The tiny water boatmen (*Plea leachi*) which compete with the bladderwort in preying on water fleas, are dwarfed by these brighter associates as they pop to the surface for air.

Andrew Lees' survey revealed one of the two British species of raft spider, *Dolomedes fimbriatus*. This is one of the wolf spiders, which carry its egg sac around with it. A female will produce 3 per season, sometimes 4, bearing each for 2-3 weeks, the first holding possibly 750 eggs, the others progressively fewer.

Her 'raft' is the surface film of the water, which she employs as web spiders employ their silken strands. She rests her front feet on it in order to sense the vibrations which trigger off a quick dart in pursuit of prey, followed by a return along the anchoring thread which she spun as she went. When threatened herself, she will scurry down a plant stem, immersed in a silvery air bubble. This generally southern species is uncommon in Britain, with only one other known site in Wales, this on the border in North-east Flint.

Lees also found the water spider, *Argyroneta aquatica,* which is somewhat commoner, but of special interest because of its underwater existence. Like *Dolomedes,* it carries air below the surface, mostly trapped between legs and body, and strokes the bubbles off so that they float up into a web spun between plants, and bulge this upwards to produce a diving bell. Here it lives, in splendid isolation, depositing egg sacs in the upper part of the summer residence and constructing another near the pond bed for overwintering. Oxygen diffuses in and carbon-dioxide out, so the transported atmosphere is self-sustaining.

Small black flatworms (*Polycelis nigra* and *P. tenuis*) change shape constantly as they progress and the even more contractile leeches include *Hemiclepsis marginata* and *Theromyzon tessulatum*. Peter Dance has found a dozen kinds of Molluscs in the bordering canal. Ramshorn snails, like neatly coiled ropes, are represented by the white, white-lipped and keeled ramshorns (*Planorbis albus, P. leucostoma* and *P. carinatus*) and the flat ramshorn (*Segmentina complanata*).

Moss bladder snails (*Aplecta hypnorum*), also here, are rare and local in Wales. Not so the wandering snails (*Lymnaea peregra*), which speckle the silty canal bed, and those lovers of hard waters, *Bithynia tentaculata,* largest of the spouted water snails. Tawny glass snails (*Euconulus fulvus*) tuck their translucent shells into damp hiding places by day and come out to feed by night, or, like the abundant and similarly translucent marsh slug (*Agriolimax laevis*), during showers.

Iridescent pea mussels (*Pisidium pulchellum*) are commonest of the freshwater bivalves. Others skulking in the mud are quadrangular pea mussels (*Pisidium milium*) and horny orb mussels (*Sphaerium corneum*).

Also found here are great diving beetles (*Dytiscus marginalis*) and alder flies (*Sialis*), phantom midges (*Chaoborus*) and water crickets (*Velia* and *Microvelia*), water measurers (*Hydrometra stagnorum*) and water scorpions (*Nepa cinerea*), two back-swimmers (*Notonecta glauca* and *N. viridis*) and the lesser water boatman (*Hesperocorixa sahlbergii*). The bug *Hebrus ruficeps,* hides in patches of Sphagnum moss.

Roger Parsons has studied the aquatic fauna in Crymlin Brook and found this to be healthily diverse among the submerged growths of water starwort. Animals most tolerant of oil pollution near the effluents are the larvae of mosquitoes and hover-flies, both of which can break through the surface films to breathe the air above, so are in no danger of asphyxiation.

Water beetles, water bugs and fresh water cockles are the most sensitive to pollution. Cockles are filter feeders and suffer particularly where fine mineral particles are suspended in the water, because they get silted up internally when trying to sift out something more edible.

Of the crustaceans water hog lice survive better than freshwater shrimps. Of the water bugs, pond skaters and water crickets are quite immune so long as the tension of the surface film remains sufficient to support their featherweight flittings in search of drowning flies and other prey. The same goes for the scudding whirligig beetles. Brook water varies from slightly acid where most fouled to fairly alkaline (pH 6.6 to pH 7.8).

Dr. A. E. Stubbs recorded no less than a dozen species of damsel and dragonflies on Crymlin Bog in July 1979: as diverse an assemblage as might be expected anywhere. One of the damselflies, *Ischnura pumilio,* figures in the 'red data list' of very rare species, making this an important site on grounds other than diversity. Another rare Welsh damselfly is *Coenagrion pulchellum.*

Both of these have better known relatives on the bog, the common ischnura (*Ischnura elegans*) with penultimate blue stripe, and the common coenagrion (*Coenagrion puella*) with more blue than black. Large red damselflies (*Pyrrhosoma nymphula*) emerge from the water in late May and are around until early August. Green lestes damselflies (*Lestes sponsa*) are later, being on the wing from July to September.

Most abundant of the dragonflies are common sympetrums (*Sympetrum striolatum*), scarlet males and khaki females flitting along brook and canal and far from open water in considerable numbers. These are later still, appearing at the end of June and being around until late October. Black sympetrums (*S. scoticum*), smallest of the true dragonflies, are here too, emerging a fortnight or so later and persisting almost into November.

Other more solid darter dragonflies include the much earlier broad-bodied and four-spotted libellulids (*Libellula depressa* and *L. quadrimaculata*), both of which are migrants. Another, the blue-bodied *Orthetrum coerulescens,* is of very restricted distribution in Wales.

The superb emperor dragonfly (*Anax imperator*) is another of the bog's Welsh rarities. With a wing span of up to 4 inches and body length up to 3½ inches, this is Britain's largest hawker dragonfly, able to include smaller dragonflies on its bill of fare—fast though these can be in eluding capture. This is very much a south-easterly species in Britain with few Welsh records, these including one for the Glamorgan Canal just north of Cardiff and others at Kenfig Pool.

There are 291 species of craneflies in Britain and Dr. Stubbs identified six of special interest at Crymlin in 1979. *Phalacrocera replicata,* whose larvae live among wet moss, is possibly the first Welsh record of a species which is rare anywhere in Britain. *Limonia ventralis* has been found before in Wales only at Kenfig Pool and seldom appears in England.

Helius pallirostris is another of Britain's rarest craneflies and the only other Welsh record of *Limnophila abdominalis* is from Borth Bog, which like Crymlin, is one of the principality's more valuable wetlands. *Erioptera neilseni*, although usually common where it occurs, is very local and recorded seldom, in either England or Wales, where it has been found only in Angelsey and the Lleyn Peninsula. The equally rare *Ptychoptera minuta* is centred along the mid-west coast of Wales.

Oxycera pulchella is a small black and yellow striped soldier fly aping the hover flies which ape wasps in the hope of deterring predators, and no doubt usually passes for a hover fly. It is on the wing only in July in a few localities, and these always southerly.

Chrysops viduatus is one of those horseflies with big iridescent green eyes which look so splendid under a hand lens that it is worth risking a bite to look at them closely. Only the females suck mammalian blood: the better natured males feed on nectar. There is an old 1908 record of the fly *Hybomitra mühlfeldi* for Crymlin, another for Hereford and another for the Norfolk Broads; that being Britain's sum total to date.

Dr. Stubbs has identified three rare local snail-killing flies of the family Sciomyzidae. Most live in wetlands and they were formerly known as marsh flies, but they are now usually referred to as snail flies because a few frequent dry downland. It is the larvae which prey on snails.

The black narrow-bodied *Sepedon sphegea* lives among the taller growths and can be seen sitting around on iris leaves and the like at any time from late March to late October. Records are sparse and are all south of Shropshire and Brecon. *Dictya umbrarum* is a northern species, few having been found in Great Britain outside Scotland, and there are very few British records of *Antichaeta analis*.

The hover fly, *Parhelophilus versicolor,* is scattered through southern England but is very thin on the ground in Wales. An extremely local form of the hover fly *Anasimyia 'transfuga* form B' has been found and another hover fly, *Tropidia scita,* which is a local fenland species.

Treacherous though the going is, cattle venture out along the edge of the brook, leaving cow pats which are pounced on by yellow dung flies while still warm. As many as 30 copulating couples and a few uneasy trios will gather on a single offering and speckle the surface with new-laid eggs.

They are an important part of the rich web of life at Crymlin, supplying sustenance for the yellow wagtails, which are among the more attractive summer residents. During the winter months when few other insects are about, they can be life savers for other insect-eating birds, but many do not survive that long. Fungal spores may invade through their breathing spiracles, permeate the internal tissues and kill them. Dead flies stuck to reed and rush in autumn are covered with emergent fungal threads bearing more spores to infect more flies. The damp summer of 1979 was a particularly propitious year for the fungal parasite. Not only the common dung fly, *Scathophaga stercoraria*, is here, but Britain's largest dung fly, *Scathophaga scybalaria*, which is rare in Britain and known otherwise in Wales only at the north end of Cardigan Bay.

Grey sallows alongside the brook suffered badly in 1979 from attack by veritable hosts of silky yellow willow leaf beetles (*Galerucella lineola*). Here, as north through the Coalfield and south to the Somerset Levels, almost the entire foliage of every bush had been reduced by July to tattered brown epidermal layers held together by the leaf veins. By August some twigs were sprouting a few pathetic green leaves at the tips, but the annual growth rings for this year must have been small or non-existent.

Alder leaves, like great water dock and many others in this year of few ladybirds, were badly affected by aphids in 1979, their edges inrolled and their surfaces sticky with excreted honeydew. Chrysomelid beetles nibble holes in them and tortricid moth caterpillars leave behind silken webs and a frasse of processed leaf material. *Wachtliella persicariae* midges produce scarlet roll galls on persicaria leaves and *Lipara lucens* chloropid flies cause cigar galls in reed stems.

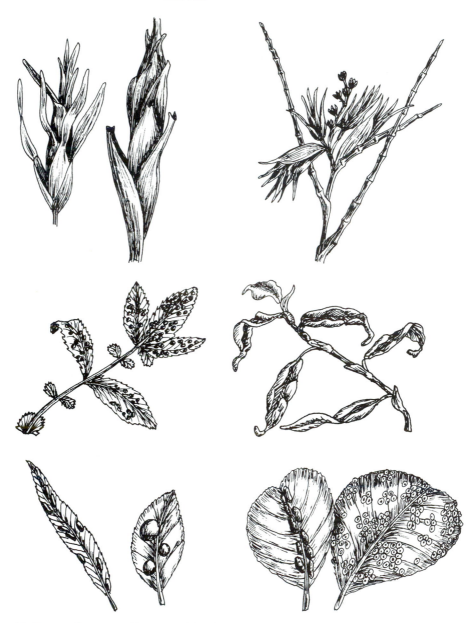

16. Insect galls on water plants. Top left: Cigar galls of reed, gall fly *Lipara lucens*. Right: Tassel galls of jointed rush, plant louse, *Livia juncorum*. Middle left: Scarlet galls of meadowsweet, gall midge, *Dasyneura ulmariae*. Right: Scarlet galls of water bistort, gall midge, *Wachtliella persicariae*. Bottom left: Bean gall of (left) willow sawfly, *Pontania proxima* and (right) sallow sawfly, *Pontania viminalis*. Right: Galls on alder, pouch gall (left), gall mite, *Eriophyes axillare*, and pimple gall (right), gall mite, *Eriophyes laevis-inangulis*

92

It is almost impossible to open a mature cigar gall without a sharp tool, but birds can manage it. Thousands of specimens in a very heavy infestation on Pant-y-Sais in March 1980 were found to have been rifled. The operation had not been easy, to judge by the shaggy mass of reed fibres ripped loose and splaying upwards from each chamber robbed of its developing fly.

Reed buntings are the most likely candidates, or perhaps there was a major visitation of greenfinches. Both feed principally on seeds, but collect insects in summer. This new source of insect food was so well wrapped as to need a seed-eater's technique to get at it. Great tits are another possibility, but the havoc was not discovered until few whole galls were left to tempt more takers, and no birds were seen in the act.

Lipara galls occur throughout Glamorgan, but have never been observed in such profusion, nor to have been exploited in this way. One wonders what motivated the first bird to experiment. Nature has her own devices for dealing with plagues. The learning of new skills is part of evolution.

1979 and 1980 were good years for migrating butterflies, painted ladies being particularly in evidence, resting in wan sunshine with rapidly shivering wings. Hemp agrimony and devil's bit scabious are prolific nectar providers and attracted numbers of peacocks, small tortoiseshells, red admirals and meadow browns. Common blues and small coppers preferred bird's foot trefoil and heather. By late August generous second broods of green-veined whites and small whites were abroad.

Commonest of the day flying moths in August, apart from the inevitable *Crambus* grass moths, are six-spot burnets, whose caterpillars were feeding on Iris leaves during July and protecting themselves from predators by exuding droplets of liquid containing cyanide.

The Pant-y-Sais corner of the bog has yielded two unexpected rare moths: the southern wainscot moth (*Leucania straminea*) and the silver hook moth (*Eustrotia uncula*). The white-striped, orange-tinted wainscot caterpillars feed on the leaves of reed and reed grass from October to May and the rather drab moths are on the wing in July and August. Silver hook caterpillars are sedge feeders, but utilise reeds as well. They also are striped, but on a green ground, and are around only in July and August. Like the other, this is a southerly species, but its British headquarters is further north, in the East Anglian Fens.

Bees of many kinds sip the heady nectar of water mint and wasps share angelica and hogweed with hover flies, drone flies and green bottles. Grasshoppers and froghoppers spurt everywhere: wolf spiders make light of their load of eggs and web-building spiders knot their egg cocoons into silk-festooned water plantain heads. No doubt, if sufficient specialists were available, all these, the beetles, bugs and others, would yield as many rare and interesting specimens as have the flies.

This little corner, fortunately spared despoliation, has ample capacity to diversify yet further the rich flora and fauna of a county of many facets. Meanwhile small boys fishing with worms catch perch and eels in the canal and Crymlin Brook is teeming with sticklebacks. With so much still water, this is a paradise for frogs, which figure in the diet of moorhen and heron. No naturalist need go away without food for thought.

7   NATURAL FEATURES OF THE NEATH ESTUARY: A REMARKABLE SURVIVAL

Industrial Encroachment and the Case for Conservation: Geology: Plants and Animals of the Western Saltmarsh

THE Neath Valley is as rich in industrial history as any part of Glamorgan and it is one of the miracles of our time that so much of its estuarine landscape has survived the centuries of human endeavour. A sizeable fragment of the vast wilderness of windswept sandhills and waterlogged alluvium that once encircled Swansea Bay is with us still, in the growing dunes of Crymlin Burrows and the long tongue of saltings licking six miles up river to Aberdulais beyond Neath.

As far back as the middle of the thirteenth century coal and iron were being worked around Neath, but the real beginning of industrial development here came with the smelting of copper towards the end of the sixteenth, leading to the rise of Neath as the premier Welsh producer of refined copper and lead.

This enterprise owed its existence to the forested hills of the hinterland. When the copper and tin industries of North Devon and Cornwall ran short of fuel, the charcoal potential of the South Wales forests was at once recognised and it was deemed more profitable to bring the ores to the charcoal than to take the charcoal to the ores.

River Tawe is more navigable than the Neath and, with the building of the Swansea Canal in 1799 and the change to coal for fuelling the smelting furnaces in the nineteenth century, Swansea overtook Neath and became the world's primary metallurgical centre. Iron and coal figured significantly in the Neath Valley too, giving rise to a ship building industry whose century of activity ceased with the closing of the Neath Abbey Ironworks in 1874.

Wharves have risen and crumbled; moorings have been dredged and silted up and a half-built floating dock was swept away by a storm in 1885, causing the project to be abandoned and leaving the Neath Harbour Commissioners with an unpayable debt.

Whole lifetimes of commendable enterprise and back-breaking labour are but small events in the history of the vastly tolerant and time-worn landscape of Swansea Bay, and leave only temporary scars. Artefacts come and go, while the sands of time continue their inexorable build-up to the west of the river mouth. The vegetation marches steadily across the accreting and abandoned acres and the wintering flocks of waders come, as they have always come, to ever-changing mudbanks teeming with unseen life.

So far so good. There has always been a remnant of countryside to provide the reconquering legions. Twentieth-century technology is more destructive than any we have known. The Neath Estuary is today's reservoir of wild plants and animals, the scars of the industrial revolution having cut more deeply around the mouth of the River Afan at Port Talbot and the River Tawe at Swansea, than they have here.

Destroy the healing elements and there will be no curing of tomorrow's industrial maladies—just a perennation of the degraded dereliction with which we are all too familiar in this part of the country. There is an indisputable conservation case for keeping at least the western flank of the estuary free from further development and concentrating this on the man-made acres that are being constantly filched from the tidal flats of the east.

Geologically, scenically and biologically the Neath is an outstanding river, from precipitous headwaters to spacious mouth. Its estuary is the centre of that stretch of coastland from Swansea to Port Talbot which was deemed around the turn of last century to be one of the most picturesque in the land, attracting travellers and writers, awheel, ahorse and afoot. Elis Jenkins, in his excellent symposium 'Neath and District', reminds us that practically every British artist of note and many from abroad painted here in the sixty years between 1770 and 1830. Thomas Hornor alone, left us some two hundred or so paintings of the lower course of the Neath as it then was.

Down among the muddy dilapidation and discarded mattresses of Briton Ferry Docks, it is only too obvious that the artists' vision of the Baglan Bay that was is gone for ever. But climb to the top of the suspected Iron Age Fort on Warren Hill and look seawards across the western dunes or hillwards across the northern saltings on a crisp winter day of azure skies and scudding cumulus, and it is equally obvious that the resilience of the wildscape is enormous, given a sporting chance. May we long enjoy such panoramas, and know that the complex web of lesser life is still able to contribute to an ecological whole fit to live in.

This heritage that is our trust is no accident. The scenic mixture of rocky crags and riverine flats is dependent on the proximity of the Coalfield to the sea—that same factor which boosted the industrial revolution. Fracturing of the rocks by the complex faulting associated with the Neath Valley Disturbance, gave access to the ice and water which carved those attractive hills, now wooded or heather-clad, but still too precipitous to encourage developers.

The flatter land has survived because of its intractability, even to agriculture, a fact appreciated by Leland as long ago as 1536-39. Sandy parts are too mobile, their surface here today and somewhere else tomorrow. The wetlands are too wet and too close to sea level to drain easily. The estuarine complex proper is subject to tidal inundation. But tides can be excluded by sea defences, and have been in many instances, where industrial concerns encroach marginally; whilst tipping is a constant threat.

But about 600 acres of saltmarsh remain, with a further 1500 acres of foreshore at low water. Add to this some 300 acres of sand dune and 750 acres of freshwater marsh, together with woods, fields and open water, and the extent of our conservation responsibilities becomes clearer. The Nature Conservancy Council has estimated that 1362 of the 3548 hectares of the Neath Complex have been lost to development projects—35,000 acres or nearly two fifths of the whole.

The alignment of the Neath Valley was determined initially by the major geological fault which directs it on its way south-west across the Coalfield. It is more spacious than any other in Glamorgan, as a result of deep scouring by ice to give a classic glaciated U-shaped trough.

The moving mass of ice dug softer or damaged rocks deeper, gouging out three great basins in the lower course of the river. When it melted it left terminal moraines along the rock barriers delimiting the seaward ends of the upper two. One of these is at Clyne, 4 miles upstream from Neath town; the other connects Tonna and Aberdulais 2 miles further down. The lowermost of the rock barriers passes between Jersey Marine and Briton Ferry, about 3 miles downstream from Neath, and supported no moraine, although hollows in its surface became clogged with ice-gouged debris.

The floor of this lower basin above Briton Ferry, where the A48 road bridge crosses the river, is more than 130 feet below present Ordance Datum, a rock core taken by Professor Anderson failing to reach bedrock at that depth.

Melt-water would have ponded back in the ice-scooped basins as post-glacial lakes, but eventually broke through a drift-plugged dip in

96

17. Reed warbler and flowering rush

the rock barrier and started cutting down into the sandstone ridge beneath. Two narrow rock channels, one 80 feet below Ordnance Datum and the other 117 feet below, lead seaward from between Briton Ferry and Llandarcy. The shallower and more easterly follows the course of the present river; the other leads south-west through the Pant-y-Sais swamp to the seaward end of Crymlin Bog and carries no river at present—only the Tennant Canal.

Both channels are buried under millions of tons of debris, some ice-borne or river-borne from the hills and some sea-borne from the Bristol Channel. A rock profile in the basin between Briton Ferry and Neath descended from 15 feet above O.D. to Coal Measure rock 137 feet lower. Most of the core consisted of clay, with 17 feet of gravel at the beginning of the upper half, suggesting more turbulent conditions of deposition, and two narrow peat beds indicative of swamp vegetation higher up, although still 20 ft. below today's soil level.

At the coast the old river channel is more than 100 feet below the present one—cut down to a lower sea level when much of the water now in the sea was piled over the polar land masses as ice. Around that time coastal forests spread far into the Bristol Channel. Later the leafy valleys were inundated, first by water and then by debris.

Curvature of the modern river's final meander decrees that the deeper water—and hence the wharves and docks—shall be along the eastern side. Without their sea defences the river would scour more deeply into

97

the unstable land behind (as it did when Baglan Bay was formed) sharpening the bend.

The slacker current on the inside of the curve to westward allows sand and silt to settle out as a gently shelving shoreline leading back to accreting saltings. Behind these is the settled dune grassland which houses the golf course.

River sediments get sandier towards the mouth, but retain sufficient organic detritus to nurture a good population of invertebrates and their attendant avian predators. The estuary holds up to five thousand waders in winter, with shelduck on the lower marshes and herons in the shallows.

Lapwings breed on the saltings, their numbers building up to sizeable flocks there in winter, leaving the barer shoreline to grey plover, redshank, curlew and common gulls down from the north. At this season fieldfare and redwing, brambling and redpoll spill over the marshes from neighbouring hedgerows.

Ringed plover bring off lively chicks most years and strident calls of nesting oyster catchers cut across the melodious trilling of skylarks. Turnstones come only rarely to this somewhat unstony habitat: golden plover, knot, dunlin, sanderling and bar-tailed godwit are passage migrants en route for other wintering haunts.

A broad belt of salt marsh borders the sandy hummocks of the golf course on the Swansea side, where pied wagtails feed over the greens and meadow pipits on the 'rough'. Below it are the muddier flats of the foreshore where lugworms supply incentive for desultorily prodding gulls.

The veriest novice in natural history matters will appreciate how much insect life teems on the flowery dunes, but it may take a visit with someone as knowledgeable as Roy Perry of the National Museum of Wales to show how true this also is of the salt marsh and riverside rubble dumps.

At the back end of summer, after a season of multiplication, the unpromising looking sand and mudbanks are hopping with life—and the marks of probing beaks show that there is more for the taking underneath. Sea aster covers the main marsh with yellow balls of flowers and the flamboyant white of sea mayweed brightens the spoil banks. Both emanate an aura of plenty, giving off a heady scent associated with sugars manufactured during summer suns and secreted in the fall to tempt pollinating insects. Flies, bees, wasps and butterflies flock to sip the nectar.

Others lead more cryptic lives, skulking under flotsam and jetsam or wherever the necessary humidity can be maintained. These clear up Nature's rubbish, or eat each other in passing. Some sally forth only at night and must be sought in obscure corners by day. Every log upturned

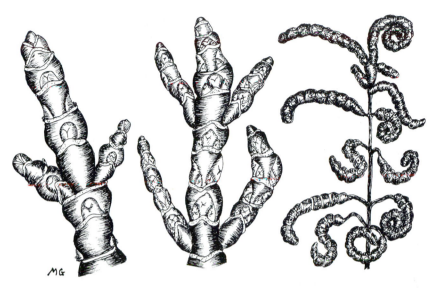

18. Two kinds of glasswort, *Salicornia pusilla* and *Salicornia ramosissima*

reveals some new organism, but logs not replaced spell death to those which found haven there. Roy Perry, with sweep net and pooter, brought many little known species to light in September 1979.

The lowermost plant community is dominated by glassworts—robust, bushy *Salicornia ramosissima* and more spindly *Salicornia pusilla*. The first bears three flowers at each joint of its succulent stems, the central one larger than the others and forming the apex of a sunken triangle. By October the flesh has withered from the branch bases, leaving a naked woody axis, and the branches themselves below the Baglan Bay Works on the opposite shore are coiled like fat green caterpillars.

Salicornia pusilla bears its flowers singly and is referred to as fragile glasswort, because the stem segments disarticulate at fruiting time. The species occurs on both the Crymlin and Baglan sides of the Neath but the only other Welsh record seems to be for Aberthaw—others coming from South and South-east England.

Even so far downshore as this, tiny black flies of the family Ephydriidae occur in multitudes in autumn, but the habitat is too specialised to show any great diversity of species. These triangular Dipterons crawl among the glasswort bases, flying scarcely at all, and climb the stems as the tide seeps higher through their little world. What then? One can only assume that they float up with the water as their mini-forest gets submerged, as certain salt marsh aphids do. They can weigh no more than these or the blue tinted *Lipura maritima* insects

99

which form rafts on rock pools, and they have a more splayed surface than either with their wings half spread when at rest. Gentle water movement in marginal slacks would achieve an effective distribution without enough turbulence to risk drowning.

A broken fringe of cord grass (*Spartina anglica*) mingles with the upper glasswort and has increased during the current decade, but not yet to the exclusion of the annual sea-blite, which grows vigorously at this level. *Spartina* is also invading salt pans higher up, but upshore zones bared by the passage of heavy vehicles become colonised by sea-blite and glasswort well above their usual zoning.

It is fairly certain that freedom from competition with established perennials is more important to these annuals, which must start afresh each year, than is periodic inundation by the tide. Seeds drifted across the surface will germinate wherever they can find space: the salt water once regarded as a necessity in itself, probably serving more in excluding rivals.

The two succulents also thrive on upshore rubble where boats are drawn up near the A48 road bridge, but show that they miss the downshore moisture content here by growing three times as tall where evaporation is curtailed in the shade of boats which remain land-bound for long.

Pure cord grass stands are usually regarded as unsuitable for insects, but the mixed *Spartina/Salicornia/Suaeda* belt of the Neath yielded a number of species in the autumn of 1979. Most interesting of the beetles was an unusual relative of the familiar soldier beetles— *Anthocomus rufus,* whose scarlet wing cases cause it to resemble a small cardinal.

As unexpected as any were the abundant caddis flies (*Limnephilus affinis*) with hairy bronzed wings arched over their backs and reprehensible prongs on their legs: unexpected because caddis larvae normally live in fresh water and the nearest fresh water is a long way off.

There were plenty of true flies about, some of the Syrphid hover flies well below the zone of nectar-bearing flowers which usually attracts them. Picture-winged flies, *Urophora cardui*, which cause the juicy green stem galls of thistles, occur here well below the tolerance range of their usual plant hosts. St. Mark's flies blunder through the lower air, with hairy legs adangle, and the wasps include ichneumons and chalcids.

A 1-3 ft. clifflet bounds the upper side of this western cord grass fringe and sea purslane (*Halimione portulacoides*) dominates the edge of the saltings above. In the early 1970s this species occupied almost the whole: now the drainage has deteriorated and it is being pushed back towards the edge of the little cliff, where it is in a position to trap river silt and build up the level to the point where red fescue can grow. The water-logged sward behind is now covered with salt marsh grass and sea aster.

Plate 6   MOUTH OF THE RIVER NEATH—*25 Jack Evans, rest Author*

24. View upstream across W. saltmarsh to A48 bridge over River Neath. Ferry Boat Inn Quarry left, Briton Ferry right. November 1979
25. Mating grasshoppers
26. Sea milkwort or black saltwort
27. Mounded sea-purslane on Baglan Saltmarsh looking east to the Petro-chemical works. November 1979
28. Winter sunset at the mouth of the Neath with the limestone humps of the Mumbles in the distance

101

29

3

31

Plate 7 CRYMLIN BURROWS: EARLY PLANT COLONISTS—*Author*

29. 'Salt spray rose' (*Rosa rugosa*) (with tide-borne debris at its base)
30. Sea stock (*Matthiola sinuata*) first year rosette and small second year flower spike
31. Flower spikes of hoary mullein
32. Earth nut pea or tuberous pea (*Lathyrus tuberosus*)
33. Spreading growth habit of hoary mullein (*Verbascum pulverulentum*)

32

3

102

Before construction of the marina near the A48 bridge, purslane occupied freely draining rubble banks there with sea plantain. The general upheaval has altered both the type and stage of the plant succession.

Many shore crabs (*Carcinus maenus*) live in this *Halimione* marsh, those which can find drifted polythene or boards to shelter under being spared the bother of constructing burrows. Opaque Jenkins's spire shells (*Potamopyrgus jenkinsi*) wash down from freshwater sites to strand on the saltmarsh, but indigenous molluscs have to be dug for.

Black Staphylinid or 'cock tail' beetles wriggle their narrow bodies through the plant bases—a possible food source for omnivorous crabs, whose grubby coating of mud offers admirable concealment.

Far and away the most abundant of the September fauna were the little moth caterpillars which drag their silken cases around with them, caddis fashion. These are *Coleophora* moths, one of two species which feed exclusively on sea purslane.

Tubes of the *Coleophora* rush moths of Upland Glamorgan are familiar to hill walkers, but those have only a spattering of ginger frass from the rush capsules on their tubular white cases and are extremely sluggish, seldom sticking their heads out to look around. Cases of the purslane moths pick up a coating of silt grains and appear granular, the occasional longitudinal strips where the silk shows through depending on a later enlargement in the diameter of the tube as the caterpillar grows.

The off-white larvae are very active, bringing all three pairs of walking legs out of hiding to move around, scrabbling mainly along the edges of the fleshy leaves where they can get a better grip. Holes nibbled through the thickness of the water-storing leaf cells usually leave a brown skin of epidermis at one end holding things together. Openings nibbled into the triangular purslane fruits allow entry of other than these.

Very few of the inert pupae which succeed the mobile larvae are about in early September, the numbers increasing through October. Legion they may be, but there is purslane in plenty to supply them, on both sides of the river, and able to sprout from the tops and bottoms of shoots which have been damaged by local oil spills.

At high spring tides the plants are submerged and one is tempted to wonder if the case-bound caterpillars are synchronised on a fortnightly rhythm to be on the wing before being overtaken by the waters. It seems unlikely. The period of inundation is short and the silk cases long enough for them to retreat within and still leave room for a store of air. Clamped onto the leaf in the semi-erect position, there would be little space for leakage. They are not unique among moth caterpillars in surviving under water. Those of china mark moths do this regularly in our freshwater ponds.

The elongated pale green leaf hoppers which eluded capture are probably, like most of their ilk, host specific, feeding only on purslane. A more spectacular leaf hopper has a pale blue underside to the abdomen and spreading wings of golden filigree.

More numerous than either in September are speckled brown bugs only ⅛″ long. Adult bugs are capable of prodigious hops for their size, leaping everywhere from the thin cover of dark silt which overlies the firm sand. Nymphs, which are about the same size, remain earthbound, their undeveloped wing stubs incapable of such gymnastics. These, too, might have a problem during high spring tides, unless they can develop through to adults in the intervening fortnight.

The main saltings are of salt marsh grass, with *Puccinellia distans* as well as the usual *Puccinellia maritima*. Only about 5% of the sea aster heads which overtop these seasonally have purple 'michaelmas daisy' ray florets and these are on the same plants as the tight yellow heads, invalidating attempts to divide the two into different varieties.

Tumps are occupied by sea rush, sea arrow grass and red fescue, hollows by sea plantain and sea blite. Pinks and mauves appear in season with the flowering of thrift, sea milkwort, two sea spurreys and two sea lavenders. Most remarkable, however, is the golden samphire (*Inula crithmoides*). At Southerndown and in Gower and East Dorset this is a plant of spray-drenched limestone cliffs. In the Channel Islands and at Chesil in West Dorset it grows on pebble beaches, but it is extremely unusual to find it on saltmarsh and there are no nearby sea cliffs or pebble banks here from which it could have strayed.

Rock samphire and rock sea lavender also give a hint of clifflands. Sea mugwort (*Artemisia maritima*) and the sea hard grasses (*Parapholis strigosa* and *P. incurva*) are more true to habitat.

The flowering of the sea aster brings hosts of flying insects to the marsh. Even the insensitive human nose can detect the sharp honey tang of the aroma arising from the yellow heads, only a little less sickly sweet than that of winter heliotrope, another composite beloved by nectar feeders. It seems that those purple petals can well be discarded as a visual attractant to insect pollinators with no ill effect to the next generation.

Honey bees, small red-tailed bumble bees and large white-tailed bumble bees home in on the aster, taking nectar for themselves and pollen for their grubs. The long sucking prosboces of the tortoiseshell and peacock butterflies are for nectar only—pollen grains would stick in the tube. No British butterfly is known to have mastered the trick of the American Heliconias, which can dissolve the pollen externally in a brew of nectar and then imbibe its proteinaceous contents in solution.

Common drone flies (*Eristalis tenax*), whose adult tastes are more salubrious than those of their detritus-feeding maggots, are very much in evidence. A smaller species, *Eristalis arbustorum,* is here too, along with hordes of *Syrphus ribesii* hover flies. Other flies abound, and the odd seven spot ladybird on the lookout for pickings.

The driftline at the top of the marsh is always a happy hunting ground for entomologists and that of the Neath is no exception. Riverborne logs and seaborne planks accumulate along the fringing sandy beach with dried seaweed and get grown over with hare's foot clover, sea sandwort (*Honkenya*), sea beet and sea orache.,

Only where the debris becomes comfortably bedded in the sand is humidity high enough to sustain much life. Such timber may be riddled with fungi, upturned pieces showing white encrustations of such as *Poria schweinitzii,* with long open pores and dendritic white strands of fungal threads.

Talitrus and *Orchestia* sand hoppers belong strictly to the maritime community and extend down across the marsh, spurting from all uplifted artefacts. These are sideways flattened Amphipods. The wood lice of the upper zones are vertically flattened Isopods, *Porcellio scaber* the commonest.

Earwigs (*Forficula auricularia*) habitually use this sort of cover, along with many different spiders and harvestmen (the familiar, unwinged, daddy-long-legs). Snails and slugs also abound, particularly the little flat coils of *Helicella.* Small black bugs occur on some of the driftwood, but beetles are the most characteristic insects.

One of the prettiest is a little tortoise beetle (*Cassida rubiginosa*) which has two bright green arcs on the gingery wing cases. The head is tucked away under the armour plated thorax—hence the likening to a tortoise. This kind is slimmer than the commoner all-green species.

Carabid or ground beetles come in a number of guises. There are big black ones, smaller ones resembling the common *Pterostichus madidus* of more inland habitats and others, with red legs, thorax and abdomen and black wing cases. Staphylinid or rove beetles, like slender devil's coach horses, are frequent, but notoriously difficult to identify.

From this driftline it is but a short step to the mature dune grassland of the golf course with its centaury, thyme, storksbill and bird's foot trefoil: common blue, grayling, meadow brown and skipper butterflies and from there to the rich dune complex of Crymlin Burrows proper.

8 LESS VIRGIN ASPECTS OF THE NEATH ESTUARY

Ancient River Crossing: Upper Saltings and Canals: from "Lagoon" to Marina: Briton Ferry Dockland

THE long curve of the A48 road bridge was opened in October 1955 on a site which has been of strategic importance since the dawn of history. Completion was set back a year when the builders had to probe 90 feet deeper than anticipated to find bedrock for vital support. Changing sea levels, long past, can still pose problems for structural engineers.

There was no problem just east of the river, where the 9½ acres of Warren Hill rises fair and square above the water, its lower crags stained a rusty brown by weathering and its upper contours apparently moulded by men of the first Iron Age into concentric circles.

Warren Hill owes its existence to two faults. Ferry Fault, followed by the river, separates it from the Earlswood shore to the west, and Giants Grave Fault, cradling the docks, cuts it off from Darren Wen behind Briton Ferry. The drowning of the old coastline to a depth of 80 feet was spread through the Mesolithic and Bronze Ages, so, by the Iron Age, Warren Hill would command a landing place for sea-going vessels, as did the promontory forts of Glamorgan's Heritage Coast, except that the inlet here was on a grander scale. West of Warren Hill is the river crossing: east of it the lofty bridge spans roads and houses in the valley bottom, the head of Briton Ferry Docks and a huddle of railway lines.

The Roman trunk road, *Via Julia Maritima,* precursor of the A48, came to Briton Ferry on its way from Caerleon to Carmarthen, but turned upstream to cross by a ford near Neath.

More sophisticated crossings since have been by boat, hence the names of Briton Ferry and the Ferry Boat Inn on the opposite shore. Thomas Hornor's water colour of the rowing boat drawn up at the delectably rural quay, which attracted travellers and artists for 150 years, is reproduced in Elis Jenkins's "Neath and District—a Symposium".

One of man's early manipulations of the riverine landscape upstream can be seen in the hand-dug channel more than a mile long, which cuts off the river's westward loop and allows seagoing vessels of 2000 tons and more to reach Neath Docks.

The Neath Canal, opened between 1793 and 1795 further east on the broad flood plain, was extended in 1799 to carry coal to the wharves at

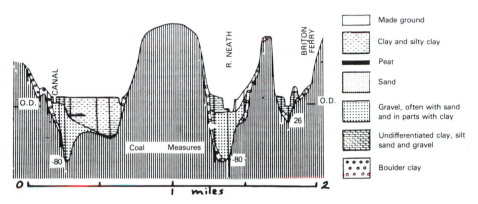

19. Profile diagram through old and new mouths of the River Neath (after Anderson)

Giant's Grave above the bridge, and the site of a shipbreaking concern, still active now, after 75 years. A later extension brought it on south, curving round the rocky foot of Shelone Wood Hill where royal ferns (*Osmunda*) sprout from vertical rocks above the water, and so on to the Baglan Bay Works' pumping station just below the bridge. It ends here, flowing into neither dock nor river except for the slight overspill in times of plenty.

Clanking industry separates much of the lower stretch from the river but kingfishers still dive for young trout and roach where water milfoil and water starwort sway gently in the minimal current, taking refuge among the oaks of the brackenny hill or the bur-reed of the Briton Ferry Canal basin. Nearer to Neath greater spearwort, arrowhead and sea sedge figure among its more notable plants, purple and yellow loosestrife among its more colourful ones.

The Crymlin and Red Jacket Canal (or Neath and Swansea Canal) was opened in 1799 along the western side of the flood plain and improved and extended by Tennant in 1824, to be named after him. The canals are kept open to supply water for industry and offer a first rate habitat for aquatic plants and animals, the Tennant rather richer than the Neath.

Leaving aside the only slightly brackish marsh below Aberdulais, the saltings can be divided into those of the Inner Estuary from Neath to Briton Ferry, and those of the Outer Estuary from Briton Ferry to the sea. The first are close-grazed by cattle and ponies, so that many of the more palatable plants like scurvy grass (an old-time sailors' anti-scorbutic) are pushed back to the creeksides, but aster manages to persist in the turf of salt marsh grasses and thrift.

Steep slopes of soft, glistening mud are exposed by the falling tide under the new Neath Bridge, 5 miles from the river mouth, and the bottom deposits are too well stirred to support other than microscopic plants. Not only is the roothold too insecure for larger ones, but the dense suspension of particles in the water prevents the necessary penetration of light, and pollution is still a problem.

Plants alongside are subject to occasional flooding and are mostly quite salt tolerant, with sea beet, sea mayweed, wild celery and common reed predominating. It is probable, however, that the upper water layers which bathe their roots are not particularly salty. Fresh water floats on the heavier salt water driving in up the estuary floor and much of the twice daily rise of level is accounted for anyway by river water being backed up by the tide rather than displaced by it.

The western towpath downstream from Neath Bridge past the fine ruins of Neath Abbey is between the Tennant Canal and the riverine flats. Reed canary grass, branching bur reed and freshwater sedges border the canal with water milfoil and curled and broad pondweeds in the water; clumps of flowering rush beside. The saltmarsh ditches are bordered by sea couch, red fescue and sea orache, with reed, sea aster and sea sedge in the water.

Moorhens and wagtails foraging on the canal are joined in winter by dippers: cormorants and black-headed gulls on the river by ducks and waders. It is not unusual to see cormorants in dipper territory, as these big sea birds will fly up river to fish in the mountain reservoirs; but it is rare to see dippers in the tidal reaches of cormorant territory.

These sprites of the mountain streams are not sent seawards only by the icy grip of winter in the Uplands, but appear by the canal on mild, moist days, bobbing and curtseying on concrete buttresses, flying through short lengths of culvert and disappearing into urban privet bushes alongside. The slow-flowing, poorly oxygenated and silt-charged waters of the canal seem highly unsuited to birds of the lively crystal waters of mountain brooks, and it is likely that the dippers move to the tumbling tributaries to feed.

Modern developments usually obscure natural features of the landscape, but sometimes they reveal them. Excavation of the roundabout cutting at the west end of the A48 river bridge has exposed a cross section through an unusually wide range of sedimentary features in the Upper Coal Measures just inland of the Rhondda No. 1 Coal Seam, with coarse grits, sandstone, shale bands and coal. This has been designated as a geological "Site of Special Scientific Interest"; the "Earlswood-Lonlas Road Section".

The heathery crag of Pennant Sandstone to riverward of the roundabout is a "Site of Local Interest", the Ferry Boat Inn Quarry here (now used as a dry boat park) having uncovered a fossil river channel. Coalfield and sea meet here and the crag overlooks the new marina on the line of the Wernddu or Rhondda No. 2 Coal Seam, which is displaced to either side by faults leading into the great Neath Disturbance (this veering away along the abandoned course of the river through Pant-y-Sais and extending on up the Neath and right through to the further end of the Brecon Beacons National Park). Rocks scattered over Warren Hill are highly fossiliferous, with *Calamites* commonest, *Lepidodendron* less so, and some contain ironstone nodules.

Until the latter part of the 1970s the wind played through a rustling reedbed in the brackish offshoot of the river where now it rattles in the rigging of moored yachts. Yesterday's pool was shallower than today's harbour and inundated only by the highest tides. A stream from the adjacent alder wood kept it partially filled throughout the year, so that it could grow freshwater plants as well as salt lovers.

Inside a protective causeway was a placid stand of bur-reed and yellow flag with pink water-speedwell (*Veronica catenata*)—the haunt of moorhen and sedge warbler. The main part was subjected to tidal influence and it was the permanently submerged centre which held the stand of reeds whose blue-green leaves were seldom still beneath silky purple plumes. The bluish hub was circled by yellow-green sea sedge flecked with brown, above the algal-matted ramification of close-set rhizomes. The fresh water released by the alder spinney seldom flooded high enough to dilute the residual sea salt in this zone as the tide ebbed.

The driest soils of the circumference were dominated by buff-brown sea rush with richer chestnut mud rush, straggly sea milkwort and parsley water dropwort. The bank to riverward lay above ordinary high water mark but was subject to the same air-borne salt that 'scorched' the sycamore leaves behind. It was clothed with thrift, rock sea lavender and long-bracted sedge (*Carex extensa*), suggesting that the higher, drier soils hereabouts were also the saltiest ones.

By 1979 no traces of this 'inside out zonation' were left; just steep rubble banks carrying a profusion of arable weeds and only a hint of sea purslane and sea sedge at river level. All was not lost, however: a new community of plant eaters and predators had followed close behind the invading flowers. Scallop, oyster and cockle shells in the new ground towering 15 feet above both alder spinney and saltmarsh, showed that it was marine in origin, but no detectable salt remained.

"Weeds" ranged from scarlet pimpernel to great mullein, with already a spattering of oak and buddleja seedlings to augment the planted alders. There was sea milkwort from the saltings, hemp agrimony from the marsh and sand sedge from the dunes. Fruiting weld took on a new lease of life after falling, leafless, to the ground; the stem tips growing on, empty, for a spell, then turning upwards and producing a September crop of flowers. June 1980 saw a pleasant scatter of wild celery (*Apium graveolens*) and tubular water dropwort (*Oenanthe fistulosa*).

Although there was little provender to attract them in 1979, rabbits were exploring over the rubble and nibbling the sweet young grasses. One of the earliest of the more permanent animal colonists is the common ground hopper (*Tetrix undulata*). This is very much at home where there is a lot of soil still uncovered by higher plants, for it subsists on mosses and terrestrial algae. It produces none of the audible chirruping of its larger brethren, the grasshoppers, and also differs in passing the winter as nymph or adult instead of egg.

Field grasshoppers (*Chorthippus brunneus*) and mottled grasshoppers (*Myrmeleotettix maculatus*) were skipping over the new ground in 1979. Both are tolerant of drought, preferring wasteland, dune sand and open rock to lush greensward. Most of the field grasshoppers were buff coloured, and difficult to see against the pale background, but there were a few green ones. The orange-red of abdomen and hind legs is a perquisite of males at courting time, when the females sport yellow undersides to advertise that they are sexually mature and willing to accept advances.

Mottled grasshoppers differ in the clubbed antennae and may appear in as many as a dozen colour varieties. Those seen by the marina were all speckled in light and dark brown, with both sexes stridulating.

Notiophilus biguttatus is a sheeny bronzed beetle which scurries contentedly over the almost bare soil, as in other "new" habitats nearer Cardiff: one of the vanguard of a host of beetles to come. A tiny Carabid already arrived in the early years wore a pair of spots on its shiny carapace. A few slender rove beetles and seven spot ladybirds had moved in, although the latter were nowhere common at this period.

Small orange *Tortrix* moths flutter over ground level chickweed and sandwort flowers; the black plant bugs, *Anthocoris nemorum,* favour mayweed heads. Indeed, most of the insects present in autumn favour the mayweed with its generous nectar supply. A selection has been identified by Roy Perry.

The larger hoverflies are represented by *Scaeva pyrastri* as well as the commoner dronefly (*Eristalis tenax*), *Scaeva* being recognisable by the yellow half moons along the flatted black body. *Syritta pipiens* has the thighs of the hind legs thickened out of all proportion to the slender stripy body, like those of a glossy flower beetle. *Syrphus ribesii* is too common and widespread to miss so popular a banquet, but the unidentified species, with handsome red and black striping is more notable. This is longer and narrower than the Syrphid hover flies and probably feeds on aphids.

Mesembrina meridiana is a relative of the stable flies with distinctive orange wing bases. Like them, it lays its eggs in dung, but the flies range widely in adulthood. *Andrena* mining bees are attracted by the ease of digging tunnels in the newly dumped soil and play host to parasitic

110

black and yellow wasps. Other narrow ichneumon wasps, with slow flight and trailing ovipositors, are too numerous for easy identification. Not so the willow sawflies, *Pteronius salicis,* whose transparent wings do little to conceal the startling orange abdomen.

A plan of the river mouth drawn in 1800, when coal, limestone and metals were being exported from the wharves at Giant's Grave, shows Baglan Bay on the opposite shore to dip well inland, with another easterly inlet upstream. Between them, these occupied the entire dock area and that of the Albion and Whitford Works. Briton Ferry dock came into being concurrently with the railways in 1861. As with today's reclamation schemes (when we 'claim' rather than 'reclaim' land from the sea) they were not excavated so much as delimited by sea walls and the space behind filled with rubble and industrial waste, the docks deepened as necessary.

The partnership of rail freight and cargo vessel boosted an already healthy trade, but for a limited span. Briton Ferry Dock was closed between the two world wars. The beautiful curved stonework stands firm, but the wooden piles have mouldered and rolling banks of shining silt clog the former shipping lanes of inner dock and outer harbour.

In the heyday of trade, ships entering in ballast were loaded with rock and rubble which was tipped out before taking on cargo, and with it the seeds of exotic plants. These germinated and multiplied around the nineteenth century wharves. Some have persisted, others have not. Among those which failed are two yellow cresses—gold of pleasure (*Camelina sativa*) from Eastern Europe and Western Asia, and *Bunias erucago* from southern Europe. The first is usually a weed of flax crops: the shoots and roots of the other are eaten in Greece. Five other cresses survived, along with the riotous yellow melilot.

Wallflower cabbage (*Rhynchosinapis cheiranthos*) spread outwards from the dock and is now one of the principal species on Baglan dunes and across the river at Crymlin. By November 1977 the carpark at the Baglan end of the Aberafan seafront was infested with it, dwarfed and beaten groundwards by biting sea winds, but with a profusion of flowers out of character with the humble habit. By 1979 it had been beaten into submission, but probably not for long.

This species is centred around the West Glamorgan coast in Britain, extending down channel to old Carmarthenshire and up to Gloucester, with one record on the Cardiganshire coast but all others to the south. A pre-1930 population extending as far north as Northumberland is now extinct.

Another of this prolific cress family which supplies so many invasive weeds is the large-flowered perennial wall rocket (*Diplotaxis tenuifolia*). Individual pods can contain a hundred seeds and a well grown plant has been estimated to produce over half a million. It flowers on late into the autumn, too, supplying more colour to the docks flora in November than any other and cropping up in every type of community except the saltiest. Once introduced, there is no knowing how far so fecund a plant may spread.

The Mediterranean hoary mustard (*Hirschfeldia incana*) is another of Briton Ferry Docks' acquisitions. Like a hairy version of black mustard, it produces seeds less copiously and has spread little from its few sites as a casual in Southern England. Indeed, it does not appear at all in that botanists' 'Bible', "Atlas of British Plants", although now growing in several places in Glamorgan.

Hoary pepperwort (*Cardaria draba*) from the Mediterranean and Western Asia, has romped away in Britain. Not for nothing did it earn the name 'Scourge of Kent', soon after its arrival at Ramsgate in 1809. It is said to have come in the straw palliasses on which fever stricken soldiers were carried home from the island of Walcheren. The hay, disposed of to an Isle of Thanet farmer and ploughed in for manure, soon earned the newcomer another name of 'Thanet cress'. It reached Glamorgan in 1830, its success due to its ability to spread by root buds as well as seeds—which were formerly ground for pepper (hence a further name of 'poor man's pepper').

Yet another of the world's conquering cresses which has spread from the scrap of saltmarsh outside the sea wall of the east bank to the Crymlin marshes opposite is dittander (*Lepidium latifolium*). This striking, white-flowered plant was also grown as a condiment in the past. It is essentially one of South-east England and was rare in South Wales, but has waxed abundant along tidal reaches of the River Taff and in Cardiff and Barry Docks during the 1970s. Nevertheless, Crymlin is probably one of its most westerly sites.

A more aristocratic species coloured the eastern wharves with its subtle yellow-green pea flowers throughout the summer of 1980. This was wild liquorice or milk vetch (*Astragalus glycyphyllos*), which is a newcomer here, although a British native. It aspires to the stature of a semi-shrub, each clump a yard across, and *'glycyphyllos'* refers to the sweet leaves—formerly used medicinally and still giving the distinctive flavour to liquorice allsorts. The long succession of flowers keeps the bumble bees busy from the end of May and by mid June the prolific pods are already beginning to ripen, like little hands of bananas.

The most settled of the docks communities by the end of the 1970s were the stone walled quays separating the inner and outer basins. Lush red fescue grass lapped around the old bollards, unhindered by grazing animals, and liberally sprinkled with burnet moth cocoons. Bird's-foot trefoil, clovers, creeping cinquefoil and liquorice added colour.

Rubbly tops of the outer harbour walls are less stable and character-ised by biting stonecrop, Oxford ragwort and ephemerals such as

112

20. Common ground hoppers and thyme-leaved sandwort

thyme-leaved sandwort and early hair grass. In May and June superb but scentless flowers of wild mignonette rise in profusion, with a soupçon of the related weld or dyer's greenweed and low tumps of kidney vetch. Towards the river mouth, where wide stretches are moss-covered, thrift, sea milkwort and buck's horn plantain appear.

Sloping faces of walls everywhere are dominated by sea purslane, with rock samphire and rock sea lavender above, along with the widespread beet and mayweed. The estuarine wrack, *Fucus ceranoides,* with an upper fringe of channelled wrack (*Pelvetia*) clothes the lower faces and spreads across scattered rocks on the mud below.

Denizens of this mud start attracting waders as soon as the ebbing tide withdraws. Redshank, usually limited to twenty or thirty, numbered a hundred or so in mid November, 1979, and dominated the period of low water with their evocative calls and flashing black and white wings. The accompanying oyster-catchers and ringed plovers were silent, and only an odd ripple of sound came from the curlew.

Common gulls fly in from the north after the breeding season and can build up to about three hundred. Six herons, probably from nearby heronries, were flushed from the sea wall in early October 1979—an occasion when snipe were feeding on the eastern saltmarsh and linnets were about in flocks of thirty to forty.

Wildfowl are never numerous, but small flocks of mallard, wigeon and teal may congregate during the colder months. Sometimes a few common scoter peel away from offshore groups to explore up the estuary, while juvenile sheldock appear some years, showing that the species must be breeding in the vicinity. The virtual desertion of Margam Moors by the white-fronted geese coincided approximately with the disappearance of the Morfa Pools, but the chill January of

113

1963 brought fifty-five to Neath and another thirty-one came in March 1966.

The mouldering rock-filled timber pier to seaward of the harbour entrance carries its own little saltmarsh of sea purslane, a seeming anachronism in so well drained a site, fifteen feet above river level on the falling tide. But the accompanying red fescue is combed flat by the current and the pier is actually no higher than the purslane flats of the opposite shore. It is the river bed which is so much lower this side.

Sandwiched between the new riverside Albion Wharf, opened in 1973, and the excruciating chaos of the busy scrap metal yard, is the most mature of the wasteland vegetation. Bracken and oak trees are well established among the more easily distributed shrubs like sallow, privet, buddleja and Japanese knotweed. With them are great mullein and evening primrose, mignonette and weld, wild carrot and yellow parsnip.

Mauve creeping toadflax and common yellow toadflax flower on through the early frosts and hybridise to give a half way form with purple-veined yellow flowers—a rather bilious compromise like that achieved by crosses between sickle medick and lucerne in Cardiff Docks.

White campion is common, bladder campion and sea campion less so, as on the eastern side, the two last producing an albino form which lacks the red veining on the inflated calyx. They do not often occur together, but do so again near the junction of the Tennant Canal and Red Jacket Pill to the north-west, where they, too, produce a hybrid. No red campion (usually the commonest of the four) has been found in the dock, and plants with pale rose flowers are probably a coloured form of the white rather than the better known hybrid between the two.

There is progressive infilling in a seaward direction behind the wall which keeps the river within bounds, so the plant succession gets younger towards the coast. It is most diverse where sand is incorporated with the slag, nurturing hare's foot clover, rest harrow, storksbill and carline thistle: least diverse on the deep new deposits where ploughman's spikenard, sticky groundsel and hairy sedge are among the most interesting.

This infill drops abruptly to an extensive saltmarsh, which is hidden until one is almost upon it. The near view is screened by the dock area to the north and the petro-chemical works to the east; that from the opposite shore by the sea wall against the deep channel and that from the sea by the pipeline bringing oil from Llandarcy Refinery under the river to be lifted high above the water on ¼ mile or so of stilts en route to BP Chemicals and British Steel.

Sea purslane, again the commonest marsh plant on the freely draining sands, grows radially in a billowing sequence of silver-grey

114

21. *Coleophora* case caterpillars on sea purslane

mounds which catch the slanting rays of winter sunlight to give the effect of movement. Sea-blite separates this loose softness from the broad belt of sand (or water) behind the outer sea wall and a big area around the eastern drainage creeks carries a pure glasswort community. *Spartina,* rather unexpectedly, occupies an upshore position near the inner sea wall, where sea slaters (*Ligia oceanica*) of all sizes scuttle among the rocks and lurk under any available artefact on the level, with sand hoppers and shore crabs.

Seawards, towards the pipeline, the marsh becomes more diverse on its landward fringe, with salt marsh grass and aster predominating; but riverwards the fluffy-textured sands continue more or less unvegetated to the long gash of the pipeline pier.

The pier base gives harbourage to the two wracks of the dock and these shelter acorn barnacles and rough periwinkles, orange and black. At the pier's end this little community marches on at right angles across the sands, following the scarcely visible line of the eastern breakwater. At high tide this disappears: at low tide it is no more than a negligible sanded ridge of stones, topped by depleted ranks of sea-worn timber stakes.

Their gaunt skeletons, protruding from hundreds of acres of empty sand, seem almost defeated, but aerial photographs show how they still guide the deep river channel in a straight line across the swirling flats. Thrown into stark relief by the blaze of a winter sunset behind the triple hump of the Mumbles, they highlight the herculean efforts of early industrial man to bend the elements to his will.

115

Part Three

The West Glamorgan
Dunes and Moors

Short-eared owls

*The recreational use of the coastline has been increasing for decades.
Beaches and dunes are resources: they must be assessed, managed,
conserved and exploited on a sustained yield basis, within a framework
of balanced priorities and regional demands.*

Iwan Richards in "Heritage Coasts, Planning and Management" (Ecos 1(2), 1980).

9 CRYMLIN BURROWS: A GOD-GIVEN SANDSCAPE

Prehistoric peat bog to modern sandy grassland: lime-rich dune to acid heath: saline creeks to freshwater slacks: unusual plants: common invertebrates and birds

COMMUTERS on the A483 between Briton Ferry and Swansea Docks see only a tawny expanse of grass-grown sand to seaward—sometimes partially flooded in the east and latterly partially shrub-grown in the west. Those who avail themselves of the parking spaces at the Jersey Marine roundabout or by the Tourist Information Centre nearer Swansea and stroll across those flowery sandhills, will see that there is a great deal more to it than that. Even so, they can view only part of the story.

In geological terms, these dunes are a very recent addition to the Glamorgan landscape, as we saw in Chapter 4, but their beginnings belong to pre-history. These manifest themselves as a bed of peat only one foot below Ordnance Datum, with the innermost sandy ridge piled to 35 feet on top.

This dark chocolate-coloured layer is mostly about 4 feet thick, increasing to 9 feet where it fills an old channel. It tells us that an acid peat mire once existed here, the well rotted remains being of heather and *Sphagnum* moss, with reeds and bog myrtle in parts.

Professor Godwin, who has studied these ancient plant remains, thinks there is little doubt that the peat bed under the dunes is contiguous with the lower of two peat beds under Crymlin Bog, a little further inland. It may correspond with a greater thickness of peat on the bog because the weight of sand on top would have compressed it.

Had the vegetation forming the old peat bed been significantly affected by salty waters from the estuary or drainage waters from the land, the component plants would have been different. Although based on estuarine clay, they must have grown well above the sea drainage levels and been watered only by rain containing negligible amounts of minerals. The result was a raised bog, such as we see today in the rainier Welsh uplands.

With the great sand blows of the Middle Ages, everything changed and the changes are still going on. Early sand deposits were impregnated with salt and contained a lot of pulverisd shell fragments. The salt would have washed out as soon as the level built up above the tides, but the lime content of seashells is more durable. This dissolves slowly,

Plate 8   CRYMLIN BURROWS:
            LATER PLANT COLONISTS—*Author*

34. The rare yellow bartsia, showing sticky glands (*Parentucellia viscosa*)
35. Dutch rush (a horsetail) (*Equisetum hyemale*) with bird's-foot trefoil
36. Dutch rush with rest harrow
37. Heather hill and wooded valley at Jersey Marine. Vegetation creeps across the old A483 by level crossing—the main road from Cardiff to Swansea via Neath until the opening of the A48 road bridge in 1955.

119

Plate 9   MARGAM BEACH AND BURROWS—*Author*

38. Old saltmarsh creeks exposed by shifting sand on Margam Beach
39. Great mullein among toppled Corsican pines
40. Viper's bugloss on dune grassland
41. Evening primrose alleviates man-made desolation of gravel digging and steel waste tipping
42. Mats of wild thyme pierced by kidney vetch and dewberry
43. Hairy rock-cress (*Arabis hirsuta*)

120

becoming available to the plants, which pass some on to the animals, particularly the snails, which need a generous helping to fabricate shells of their own.

Eventually the free calcium carbonate is used up or washed out by rain, and the remains of the plants which it has helped to nurture accumulate as an acidifying layer of humus. This is the stage reached now on the oldest, innermost, dune pastures, where lime-living plants have been superseded by acid-loving ones. Between the tended turf of the golf course greens heather is growing again, as it did on the peat beds far below in ages past.

The whole geographical sequence is to be seen at Crymlin, from the pristine yellow sand thrown out of the tidal treadmill onto the embryo dunes, back through marram-clad sandhills, fescue-clad sandflats and heather-clad heaths to the verge of the great bog itself (if one can override the intervening row of factories). Not for nothing were classes of university students from Aberystwyth brought this far south for botanical field studies in the forties and fifties.

Only part of the Crymlin succession is as straightforward as this: the River Neath along the eastern flank introduces a new dimension by infiltrating behind the maturing ridges to bring salty waters lapping at the back as well as the front.

This means that a walk from the Swansea end of the dunes east towards the river is just as much a walk back in time as is a walk towards the sea in less complex situations. In the course of both, the plant communities get progressively younger—from mature freshwater marsh or wooded swamp with higher dune grassland and heath—out to newly initiated saltmarshes and embryo sand dunes. It is logical to study the development of these on the return walk.

By July 1980 the most seaward dune ridge had advanced several hundred yards eastward after leaving the shore where this dips inland. Its growth was stimulated by slight deflection of the longshore current by a recently placed boulder bank outside the oil storage tanks near Swansea Docks. Viewed from the Neath side it ran far out to sea, but when standing athwart its mobile crest, it was apparent that it was heading in a direct line across the embayment to meet the coast again as this curved out towards the deltaic sands at the river mouth.

The sea is always trying to iron out the creases, chopping off the headlands and filling in the bays. Here it is taking a short cut across the bay mouth, to isolate a sandy lagoon behind. It is impossible to estimate when the spit will reach the land again to form a tombola, but the resemblance to the more impressive eastward growth of Dorset's Chesil Beach to join the outcrop of Portland Bill and enclose the lagoon of the Fleet behind, cannot be denied.

Most is occupied by pioneering growths of sand couch with outliers of prickly saltwort and sea rocket. On the crest the blue-grey of couch changes to the yellow-green of marram, which peters out in a string of hillocks towards the tip. Scattered over the tidal sands beyond are more clumps of couch, some of just a few shoots, but all with a tail of sand building up to leeward. A spell of calm weather and these mounds will grow, to coalesce: a single storm and they may be swept away.

Incredibly, where sea holly is the only flowering plant to have arrived, there are frequent toadstools, buff above and sooty brown below, like field mushrooms past their prime. These, *Psathyrella ammophila,* are inundated at spring tides, yet persist above ground for at least nine months of the year. They seem to sprout from bare sand, but careful digging may reveal the underground threads clamped onto a couch root, possibly in a mycorrhizal association of benefit to both.

Even more incredibly, mid-July 1980 saw a ringed plover incubating three eggs in the middle of the tide-rippled sand flats behind the spit. Put up from her nest of shell fragments in heavy rain, she was back almost at once, running in, piping, across the pebble-strewn sand and disappearing at each stop, in spite of the distinctively patterned head. It would be lucky, indeed, if the clutch hatched before the next spring tides washed it away. Once out of the eggs all should be well, as the nimble chicks can scamper over the beach from the word go. The lateness of the brood suggests a re-lay after a disaster such as that now impending. Those pebbles, too, were a surprise, on so many miles of smooth sand. From whence had they come to mingle their smooth roundness with the angular sea shells?

A jumble of embryo dunes has grown up around the sand couch on the inner flank of the new lagoon. Babington's and frosted oraches (*Atriplex glabriuscula* and *A. laciniata*), both with mealy white foliage, may turn up here, but are annuals, of unpredictable occurrence and never plentiful. The low, regular ridge behind, which stretches all the way to the Neath, was clad with sand couch at the beginning of the 1970s, but with marram by the beginning of the 1980s, although still only a third to half the height of the main dune ridge which backs it.

Eastwards this double ridge forms the shoreline; westwards it passes into the corner of the 'Tank Farm', with a considerable spread of dunes to seaward, but its line is unbroken. The plant succession has advanced little further at the inland end than at the seaward, suggesting that sand deposition in front has been quite rapid.

Sea holly is much the commonest species with the marram, particularly in the west, where it is heavily parasitised by broomrape, which belies its name of *Orobanche minor* by elevating livid flower spikes to 18 inches, with another 18 inches below the sand. These are fleshy, an inch across and covered with scale leaves right to the ginger, claw-like roots which clasp the far-reaching side roots of sea holly only a quarter as wide. When they shrivel in winter their bases remain broad.

122

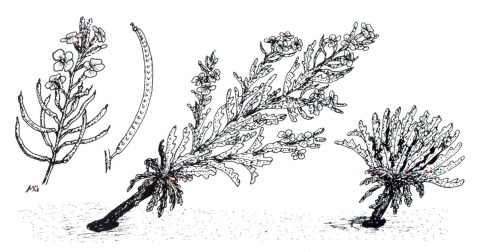

22. The sea stock that returned from supposed extinction

At the end of May, as rolled sea holly leaves emerge from the sand like vellum scrolls, the scaly new generation of broomrape is pushing up like a surfacing fleet of brown zeppelins. Where sea holly peters out away from the coast, the broomrape has to make do with less bountiful hosts, such as cat's ear, and seldom reaches more than 8 inches high. Nevertheless, sea holly is an unusual host, although known to play this role in the Isle of Wight.

Plenty of sand remains bare in this pioneering community and it was here that the attractive mauve sea stock (*Matthiola sinuata*) turned up in 1964. Only in the mid-seventies did it spread inland: now it can be encountered almost anywhere on the Burrows. Lightfoot had recorded it at Baglan 200 years before in 1773: "A quarter of a mile before you come to Breton Ferry on a sandy bank on the right hand by the road from Bridge End"—i.e. the inland side. (He was probably travelling on the old Roman road, *Via Julia Maritima,* because close by, between Briton Ferry and Baglan, is the site of one of 2 Roman miliaries or milestones, the *Victorinus* of the third century.)

The stock is very distinctive, with its first year rosette of scallop-edged, velvety grey leaves and second year sprays of flowers spreading to 2 feet and more. A stem snapped off will cause a circle of new ones to sprout in the third year and the sturdy roots plumb prodigious depths and hold the plant against sand-blow. Seeds produced in the long pods germinate in crowds, but not before some have been wafted off to conquer new fields.

Quoted as abundant by early nineteenth-century botanists, the species disappeared between 1850 and 1964, when it was rediscovered by Gareth Jones at Witford Point, Baglan. The following year Jeffery Bates found it at Crymlin Burrows, where it had romped away by 1968. It had become very scarce in Britain as a whole by then, being known at only four other sites and artificially introduced at two of these. But a colony at Aberdovey in West Wales made a similar comeback in the 1960s.

Were they descendants of the originals or immigrants from elsewhere? There are no known colonies from which they might have drifted with the newly deposited sand—but there is no shortage of shipping...... It is not beyond the capacity of certain seeds to retain their viability for 110 years: those of Indian lotus flowers have germinated after 400 years, although the supposed growth of cereals from Pharoahs' tombs was a hoax! Bird's-foot trefoil and clover, two of the stock's associates, have seeds which can survive for 80 and 90 years respectively and the related charlock is notorious for appearing in newly ploughed grassland as a survivor from an arable phase of some 30-40 years before.

In Glamorgan the sea stock has since turned up at Kenfig and even in West Gower, but no more is known of its local spread than of its initial return. To ensure its survival, seed was scattered behind the iron palings of the 'tank farm' at Crymlin soon after its reappearance. The danger to so attractive a flower is from the picking public rather than polluting petrol; but the conservationists need not have worried; it has survived both and prospered.

The main colour is provided in this zone by wallflower cabbage (*Rhynchosinapis cheiranthos*) and three species of evening primrose, mostly the large-flowered *Oenothera erythrosepala*. There is also hoary mustard (*Hirschfeldia incana*), Oxford ragwort and cat's ear, which often shows swollen stem galls containing as many as 50 chambers housing young gall wasps, *Phanacis hypochaeridis*.

Dewberry is another which nurtures parasitic wasps while sustaining no harm itself. *Diastrophus rubi* galls take the form of woody contortions of the stem and are most often seen in winter when the surrounding herbs die back and the galls are perforated with holes where the wasps have emerged.

Marram, too, may be parasitised, but by layer upon layer of a gilled bracket fungus resembling an outsize 'oyster-of-the-woods' (*Pleurotus*). The flanges radiate from the grass base, their tops drying to the consistency of biltong, while little black *Oxypoda* beetles consume their moist undersides. These are "cock-tails" of the devil's coach-horse fraternity and extraordinarily wrigglesome when disturbed. The fungus has so far defied identification and is one of many special features which Crymlin Burrows has to offer.

The next dune ridge lies within a strip of rough dune grassland in the west and broader, more level saltings in the east. Progressive infilling has pushed the sea water back into the river at all states of tide except the highest, and the sward of sea plantain and others is quite firm to the tread. It curves up-river, around the fragmented end of the ridge, to expand again on its inner side.

The ridge itself retains most of the foredune plants but diversity has increased. There are yellow drifts of sea pansies and kidney vetch and pink ones of sea bindweed and rest harrow. But still there is room for some of the tiny dune annuals; including three cresses, rock hutchinsia, spring whitlow grass and hairy rock cress, and three grasses, sand Timothy, dune fescue and sea fern grass.

As the hummocks level out westwards, the sward thickens to a shaggy limestone grassland, typified by yellow rattle, red clover and a surprising, pink-flowered kidney vetch. Isolated bushes of tamarisk and sea buckthorn appear among the several kinds of willow. The lemon yellow of sea radish and yellow-wort form a colour harmony with the pink of marjoram and basil thyme, which is elegantly tall compared with the squat form of the Gower cliffs. Snowy white centaury and the scarcer lesser centaury (*Centaurium pulchellum*) grow with the commoner pink kind.

Two storksbill occur side by side: the usual *Erodium cicutarium* with paler flowers and laxer growth than the special dune variety (*E.c.* var. *dunense*), spangled with sand sticking to the hairy, glandular leaves. Bugloss (*Lycopsis arvensis*) and gromwell (*Lithospermum officinale*) occur alongside the showier viper's-bugloss and bladder campion stands in for the usually more maritime sea campion. Blue

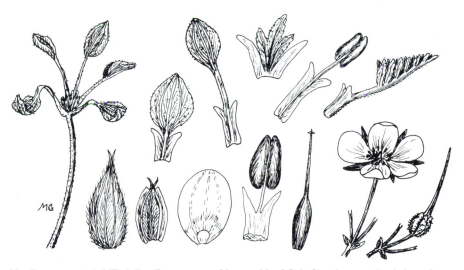

23. Common storksbill; foliar flowers caused by sand burial. Left and upper: Buried specimen; whole flower, two types of sepal, foliar petal, normal stamen and foliar carpel. Bottom: Equivalent parts of normal flower. Right: Undehisced fruit (see page 140-1)

fleabane, purple vetch, red bartsia, scarlet pimpernel, pink soapwort—the number is almost endless. The botanist with pencil and notebook can easily list a hundred kinds of flower on a summer afternoon. If he has a camera he will not get that far....... Yet the wet areas are richer still, ranging not only from shifting to stable soils, but also from salty to fresh ones.

The next dune ridge inland is more or less continuous except for a breach opposite the Jersey Marine roundabout. About a mile of its seaward flank is followed by the main saltwater creek which marked the position of the coast in the 1940s. This fills with sea water at every tide and never dries right out, so that the crossing to what is now the main part of the Burrows is a damp business for all but the pony trekkers. It is also a slippery one, as the gentle flood has deposited generous layers of Bristol Channel silt over the sand, these deepening to glistening mudbanks as the river is approached.

All the usual saltmarsh species are present—even glasswort and sea-blite a good half mile from the open shore—but it is rock sea lavender and not the salt marsh species which dapples the flats with mauve in July. *Spartina* has arrived, inevitably, but it has not taken over and is cohabiting quite amicably with the indigenous flora. When J. A. Steers wrote his "New Naturalist" book, "The Sea Coast", he distinguished Britain's East and West coast saltmarshes by referring to "the local development of *Spartina* in the East." Thirty years later the distinction no longer holds. *Spartina* has come west to stay.

The riverward end of the depression is still dominated by glasswort and sea-blite in summer and is bright green in winter when *Enteromorpha* wraps itself round their starkly bare stems. Next in is a fairly pure community of sea purslane (*Halimione*), grading up to sea plantain with scurvy grass and sea aster. Gradually the salt-marsh grass (*Puccinellia*) takes over with the two sea spurreys and sea hard grass.

There is no stream here to dilute the sea-water flowing in, but rain ensures a steady reduction in salinity. Mud-rush and red fescue become dominant; marsh arrow grass rubs shoulders with sea arrow grass and knotted pearlwort finds a roothold in the sea milkwort swards. Long-bracted sedge and buck's-horn plantain lead up to fearsome tumps of sharp rush. In the narrowing waters of the creek sea-sedge and sea bulrush yield to common reed, which continues as dominant all the way west to the Tourist Office, but with generous helpings of yellow flag, common spike-rush and water mint.

The fen peat flora in the west is superb in summer, like the best of the county's dune slacks—but with a difference. The sea-milkwort or black saltwort (*Glaux*) persists, after all the other salt-lovers have been squeezed out, and forms a veritable carpet across the soggy mosses, pierced by spore-bearing spikes of adder's-tongue fern and moonwort, and plentiful growths of red rattle or marsh lousewort, which is usually uncommon. Last of the brackish water species to linger on are parsley water dropwort and brookweed.

Showy southern marsh orchids reach their prime in June, blushing white marsh helleborine in July. Pale spotted orchids and twayblade, pyramidal and bee orchids grace the humps; the greenish fen orchid (*Liparis loeselii*), unknown here until the 1930s, inhabits damp hollows. This last is very rare in Britain, with its stronghold here in West Glamorgan, on Whiteford and Kenfig Burrows. It is elusive on Crymlin, more so in 1980 than 1979, but is there for those who search long and diligently.

Among the minutiae where there is nothing higher than a moss sward to smother them is the rare chaffweed (*Anagallis minima*) and the two bristle sedges. At the other extreme, where sallow and alder meet overhead, are rumbustious thickets of hemlock water-dropwort and hemp agrimony, greater willow herb and water horsetail, ferns and grasses. Blue skullcap and white gipsywort snuggle in among creeping willows and these into the skirts of the grey sallows.

Here the tidal silts of the east have become the neutral fen peats of the west. Nowhere has there been enough time for nutrients to leach away and give a semblance of the acid peats which occupy the next of the east to west valleys, where silky plumes of cotton grass fluff out as the kingcup petals fall.

This earlier creek has partially disappeared under the coast road in the west but is well away from it in the east. The road margin there curves away up-river along yet another line of dunes which has progressed to the successional phase of scrub woodland. Its seaward face is occupied by tall gorse which is still, unexpectedly, subject to tidal inundation. All low branches are dead and an agglomeration of polythene and other tide-borne bric-a-brac floors the entire belt.

Of particular interest here is *Rosa rugosa,* probably brought by birds from bushes planted outside the Aluminium Cable Works. It thrives in just this type of salt regime on the other side of the Atlantic, where it is known as the salt-spray rose, and its magenta flowers, twice the size of those of a briar, and squat, round hips colour many hundred miles of coastline in New England. A consignment for a Boston nurseryman was wrecked off Cape Cod in 1845 and the plants drifted ashore and took root, none the worse. Since then, their beauty has ensured them a helping hand from man. This scrubby dune is scarcely the sort of place where the rose would have been planted (as it is around Eglwys Nunydd Reservoir) and seed (from bird dung or a crop pellet?) probably drifted ashore, as did the mature stocks in America.

The creek bordering its site curves back into the golf links a few hundred yards after leaving the River Neath, and shows a fine example

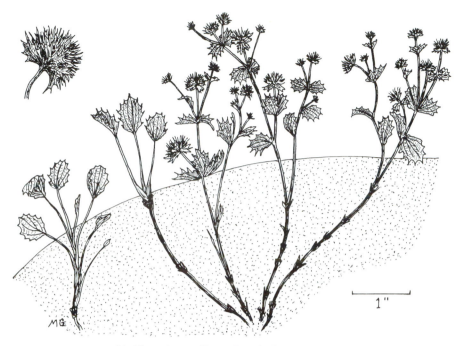

24. Flowering seedlings of sea holly (see page 141)

of "fenceline ecology". On the seaward side of the fence sleek cattle fatten on the sea-washed turf, and plants are fighting a losing battle on the deeply hoof-pocked mud. To landward the little tidal basin fills with succulent arrow-grass and aster in summer, grading back through sea sedge and a little reed to a soft sward of mud-rush and long-bracted sedge. Above is a sandy beach at the foot of a low earth cliff—a beach which follows right up the west side of the river between saltmarsh and golf course. The strip of sand is kept open by pony trekkers and characterised by sea sandwort (*Honkenya*) and a selection of foredune plants strangely far from the sea.

For a quarter to a third of a mile the creek is broad and stagnant—filled with almost pure sea rush, which gets progressively more moribund with increasing distance from the sea. This is an upshore species, normally tolerating only a few hours of tidal submergence per fortnight: here it is constantly waterlogged, and by fresh water instead of salt. The resulting oxygen deficiency is taking its toll and plants flower only along the upper rim of the sad brown sward.

Towards the Jersey Marine roundabout plants more suited to a freshwater regime take over and peaty slacks are dotted with sallows. After nestling unseen in the mossy ground-cover all winter, pea-sized

128

winter buds of butterwort burgeon forth each spring into glandular, insect-trapping leaf rosettes of a bilious yellow, topped with flowers like sickly violets. The delicate pink of bog pimpernel peeps from beneath, with robust flowers of marsh helleborine dangling above. An odd mixture, is this, for Glamorgan, where butterwort belongs to the mountain bogs and helleborine to the coastal sands.

These splendid slacks contain the white bells of round-leaved winter-green, mats of bobble-fruited strawberry clover and one of the rarer yellow sedges, *Carex serotina*. The uncommon variegated horsetail is present, as on all other West Glamorgan dunes, but here, in addition, is the striking Dutch rush (*Equisetum hyemale*), which persists throughout the winter. It grows in spreading swards of several acres, stems blatantly banded, at first with black, then black and white, then not at all as the leaf sheaths peel away. Devoid of branches, the shoots resemble rushes more than the horsetails which they are—until the yellowing, spore-flecked cones appear in July.

Dutch rush is quite rare in Britain, more at home in the North, like red rattle, and extremely rare in Wales and Southern England, yet it grows at Crymlin in profusion. North of the roundabout it has climbed out of the willow slacks onto the roadside bank and tough little shoots were pushing out through the uncompromising tarmac in 1980. Rare it may be, but not delicate!

The purple fodder vetch or villous vetch (*Vicia villosa*), winding its way through low twigs of the alder-sallow spinneys, is rarer still. Less so, but unusual here in the West and savouring more of foreign parts, is the hedgerow or mountain cranesbill (*Geranium pyrenaicum*).

In drier areas is another, the field southernwood, field or Breckland wormwood (*Artemisia campestris* ssp. *campestris*), which has been known here for many years, but only as a casual, not often recorded. Although perennial, it tends to lie low for long spells, then, after a good season, seedlings can be found germinating in April and May and these will produce flowers by September.

1980 was a bumper year for it and spreading cushions a few feet across and a few inches high, were everywhere in its area. The rich green of the finely dissected leaves caused it to simulate massive clumps of mossy saxifrage, a northerner only, in Glamorgan, but the long, bobble-fruited heads lingering from 1979 gave it away for what it was. Southernwood is very local and regarded as a native only on the Breckland heaths at the meeting of Norfolk, Suffolk and Cambridge. There are 4 other sites for it as a casual in Western Britain, 2 of these near Cardiff.

Another easterner, native only in Norfolk and Suffolk, is the hoary mullein (*Verbascum pulverulentum*) which romps away behind the factories to make a spectacle of colour with the colonies of viper's bugloss. Flower-decked branches splay up side by side in July to give 2 feet inflorescences 4-6 feet above the centaury-starred turf. Stamens are soft with silky hairs and the whole plant covered with a mealy whiteness which rubs off to collect in the lower leaf axils, like the fluffy frasse chewed off the common great mullein by mullein shark moth caterpillars.

In more mature dune grassland is yet another of Crymlin's specialities, yellow bartsia (*Parentucellia viscosa*). Its flowers appear at the same time and are the same shade of primrose yellow, their overarching hoods softly downy, their stems and leaves sticky with glandular hairs. This is a south-westerly species, occurring mostly in Cornwall, and nearest neighbours of the Crymlin colony are probably those of Braunton Burrows across the Channel. The only other Welsh plants are at a few sites in Dyfed. Like the related 'rattles', louseworts and eyebrights, they are semi-parasites.

Bartsia is native, Canadian fleabane (*Erigeron canadensis*) is not, but is well established in some of the more disturbed areas, its tufted white florets visited by crowds of short-tongued insects. Sickle medick (*Medicago falcata*) is another in the more unsettled parts and is parallelled by populations in Barry and Cardiff Docks, although not often seen here in the West. Like southernwood and hoary mullein it is regarded as native only in the East Anglian Breckland.

There seems no end to these special plants on Crymlin Burrows, and probably the gayest is the earth-nut pea (*Lathyrus tuberosus*) which spreads its crimson flowers through the western scrub every summer. They are brighter by far than those of the only other known Glamorgan population—in Barry Dock—and their name derives from the tubers on the roots. This again hails from Eastern England, but is not native, having first appeared at Fyfield in Essex around 1880; and it is still rare and scattered in Britain.

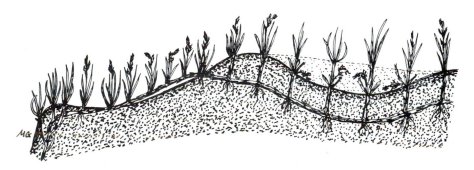

25. Sand sedge; growth forms in relation to erosion and sand burial. Newly accumulated sand depicted by paler stippling. Rhizome follows ground contours except where eroded free (mid left) when young, in which case leaf rosette is not stalked. Burial (right) promotes growth of axis and new leaf rosette on the raised surface (see page 144)

The blowing sands at Crymlin have not stayed on the coastal plain, but have piled themselves against the flank of the steep hill separating the ancient and modern courses of the River Neath. They trickle down towards the estuary road in slow-moving yellow cascades, contrasting sharply with the dark heather, bilberry and *Cladonia* on the Coal Measures alongside.

A single chapter cannot deal adequately with both animals and plants in so dynamic an ecological situation as this, but each reflects the state of flux and development. The seaward fringe is one of the few parts of Glamorgan where the beach fossicker can find the rare strand beetle (*Nebria* (or *Eurynebria*) *complanata*). It is one of the largest to be turned up from the driftline debris under which it spends the daylight hours between night time hunting forays. Beetles much in evidence by day are seven-spot and two-spot ladybirds, which penetrate right to the furthest sand couch of the beaches where there are no aphids to sustain them.

Scuttling myriads of ground beetles live in the short-grazed saltings turf which is largely avoided by shore crabs, although plenty of their shed skins appear in the flotsam trails. The ubiquitous crabs favour permanently submerged creeks, depression pans which crack down to moister soil layers as the surface mud dries, and taller swards where humidity is high at ground level. Sandhoppers leap ecstatically on plant mats which can be moistened by the tide only once or twice in a fortnight and gobies penetrate well up the tidal channels.

The 7 week drought of April and May 1980 proved disastrous for some of the toad tadpoles which became concentrated in wriggling black phalanxes in residual pools at the inner end of the main creek, with hordes floundering helplessly, or already dead, on the damp moss alongside. By the third week of July, this strange 'summer' had been declared the wettest on record since 1907, and the surviving amphibians, greatly appreciative, were spurting everywhere, 'making hay before the sun shone'. Sand-coloured hares had to make longer leaps to clear the channels and rabbits retreated from the drenching drips of the longer grass to the sweet new growths of clearings formerly parched as yellow as the sand beneath.

Theridion and Lycosid spiders, which had been scuttling throughout during the drought, became less active, and the webs of funnel spiders had to be fabricated strongly enough to carry a full load of raindrops. Rare days of sunshine brought out the hunting spiders (*Pisaura mirabilis*) to race back and forth. These are dedicated vagrants, building neither home nor snare, and have to catch their prey by chasing and surprising it.

Slugs appreciated the exceptional wetness in a usually arid habitat and large black, hedgehog, marsh and netted slugs were abroad.

Garden snails were afoot all day instead of only at night, liberally spangled with wet sand grains, and banded and wrinkled snails were almost as common as the brown-lipped and white-lipped hedge snails.

There were shiny glass snails, tawny glass snails and pellucid glass snails, crystal snails and moss snails. The hairy snail with bristly shell was to be found with the related strawberry snail, slippery snail and Pfeiffer's amber snail.

Small heath butterflies, common blues, orange tips and wall browns were on the wing before the advent of the wet midsummer. Meadow brown, small tortoiseshells, small skippers and whites appeared as the sun eventually broke through again. Brown silver lines moths (*Lithina chlorosata*) were flying in May and June, cinnabars, burnets and July high fliers in June and July.

Ponderous, shaggy caterpillars of the unfortunately named northern oak eggar moth (*Lasiocampa quercus*), which feeds on a variety of plants but never oak, have spun themselves cocoons like those of silk moths by June and the lackey caterpillars are growing too big for their communal webs on the willows and wandering off on their own.

24th July, 1980, 5 days after the breaking of the longest wet spell, saw the first swarming of the ants and the convergence of their predators. Song thrushes were particularly assiduous in gathering up the hordes—leaving no visible survivors of the colonies on which they concentrated. Each would swallow six to a dozen of the winged but still earthbound creatures on arrival, then pick up more in quick succession, until there was a tangle of wings, legs and bodies the size of a small walnut protruding from their beak. They seemed unable to leave the fortuitous goodies, proceeding, with little sub-voce pipings of excitement, and dropping much of the booty in their efforts to pick up more than they could carry. Every sortie was punctuated by one brief bob for purposes of relieving themselves.

Blackcaps seemed to have finished with their family chores, swallowing all they picked up and leaping out to catch many in the air. Young robins joining in, flopped repeatedly earthwards with wings and tails spread, to imbibe the unaccustomed solace of warm sun rays between snacks. Minute, sooty black pellets fell occasionally from the sky onto the pale spread of sand—the droppings of high-flying, insect-eating hirundines, perhaps.

By June flocks of screaming swifts have arrived to exploit the aerial plankton, and be parodied by clumsier cohorts of chacking jackdaws. During the late 1970s one of the daws made a nuisance of itself on the golf course by collecting balls still in play, disillusioning though the expected egg flavour must have been!

Already now, in midsummer, crowds of starlings are gathering on the muddy sand of the central creek. Mournful calls of redshank float in

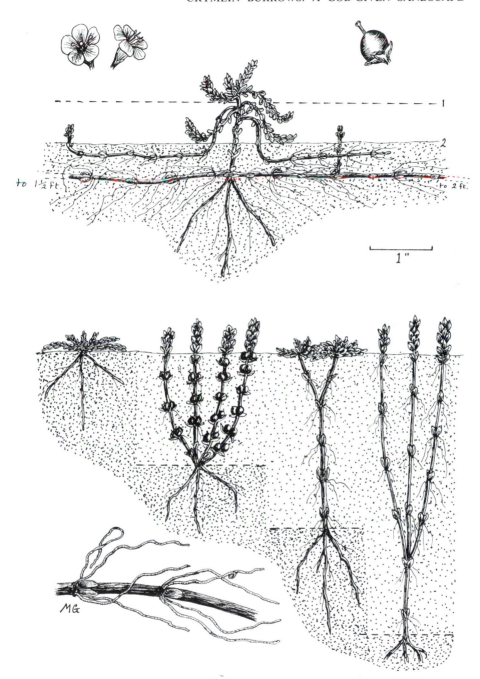

26. Sea milkwort; growth response to moving sand. Top: Bending back and reburial of shoots after loss of sand. Bottom: Normal prostrate plant and three growths forms stimulated by burial with progressively deeper layers of sand. In the first, burial occurred after fruit formation (see page 146)

from the outer sands and well over 100 oyster-catchers were wheeling over the tidal lake between the dune ridges during the high spring tides of 1st June 1977.

By August twittering flocks of linnets are homing in on the seed crops and starling numbers are swelling as the families fledge one by one in their secret holes and come out to join the rowdy mob of adolescents. The wader flocks are beginning to assemble as a prelude to winter, with curlew, oyster-catcher and dunlin to be counted in hundreds, and sanderling bowling along the water's edge like self-propelled tennis balls. Ringed plover prefer to forage on the upper beach, and October 1970 saw a rare Kentish plover here. Many black-headed gulls have donned winter plumage by August, when the first of the common terns are dropping in to feed and rest.

December and January bring the really big flocks of waders and the odd rarity too. Jack snipe and water rail may turn up and peregrines are not unknown. 1975 brought a red-necked phalarope, 1976 a snow bunting—an Arctic species which sometimes arrives in small flocks.

Any habitat which attracts such rarities is a habitat to be cherished. Providentially, this fine new stretch of coastal land has been given into our keeping. The accreting sands are building up to seaward at a time when our planning authorities are becoming, of necessity, acutely conservation conscious. Most of the rest has gone, from Mumbles to the Neath and beyond, swallowed up by industrial development to serve our creature comforts and affluent way of life.

The planning pressure on such land is immense, but we have to get our priorities right. Hundreds of acres of derelict land left over from the industrial revolution have been given a face-lift in the Swansea Valley Rehabilitation Scheme and many more such acres could be used to accommodate the expanding industry of our time.

At Crymlin we have a lung for the vast urban population of the Neath and Swansea Valleys and the great steel conurbation to the east, as well as a refuge for wildlife surviving from a more expansive past. Gower has already served the recreational needs of the West Glamorgan hosts, but is now being called on to serve those of M4 commuters as well. More and more frequently the notices are going up on the Gower approach roads: "All carparks full".

To squander the God-given answer to the pressing wildlife-amenity-recreation problem by shutting off the last remaining length of natural coastline for private development would be inexcusable. May this growing asset be used wisely and not replaced by factories or miles of sterile promenade and housing estates, as along so much of West Glamorgan's erstwhile lovely coast.

19

Plate V OLD DOCKS AT BRITON FERRY—*Author*

19. Top: View from Warren Hill across the two dock basins at Briton Ferry to Baglan Petrochemical works in 1980

20. Middle: Pale lemon flowers of wild liquorice

21. Bottom: Erect pods of wild liquorice

20

21

135

Plate VI FLOWERS OF RESIDUAL DUNES AT BAGLAN—*Author*

22. Top left: Woolly head of kidney vetch
23. Top right: Pair of yellow dune pansies
24. Middle: Spread of dune pansies on open sand
25. Bottom: Pair of sea bindweed flower trumpets

10 SHIFTING SANDS AT BAGLAN

*Diminishing dunescape: specialised communities of mobile sand:
growth responses of plants to burial and undermining*

EAST of the spacious mouth of the River Neath the sandy coast swings
south to face the prevailing south-westerlies. Even the 1½ miles of
promenade, which the official literature tells us has transformed "a
wilderness of duneland" into "Wales's newest seaside resort" with
"developments staggering in their scale and imagination", have not
managed to hold the wind-blown sands. These swirl across the beach to
pile against that bleak stretch of flowerless wall, spill under the stark
railings at its top and bank up along the barriers delimiting plots of
wasteland between the vast housing estate and the sometimes
magnificent fury of sea and sand.

A little of the subdued flowery wilderness survives to westward of the
ill-named "Baglan Bay Village", sand eddying from its seaward flank
and settling out to riverward. British Petroleum's Chemical Works
occupies most of this corner, but the residual dune community outside
can be a riot of colour still. Those who stroll north-west from
Aberavon's most westerly carpark need suffer little disappointment.
Those who go south-east may still find a few dune flowers, game to the
last, competing with town weeds where sand drifting across the rubble
infill is whisked together into little banks.

Seeds of couch, marram and sand sedge arrive almost as soon as the
sand, to sprout from tiny dunes piled 2-3 feet above the hard core.
Underground stems of common horsetail come to bind the heaps
below: surface runners of ground ivy hold them above. Superb orange-
yellow mats of bird's-foot trefoil appear in an abbreviated amalgam of
dune and wasteland plants—dove's foot cranesbill, yarrow, orache,
scorpion grass and plantains. These shallow piles are soon depleted of
their lime and able to support such as sheep's sorrel.

Isolation in a concrete jungle does not spare these plants attack by
parasites. Fungal spores are in those eddying gusts, as well as sand
grains. Orange cups of a rust fungus, *Puccinia poarum,* appear on
leaves of coltsfoot, and fawn blisters of another, *Coleosporium
senecionis,* on those of Oxford ragwort.

The surviving dunes at Baglan have an extended foredune system by
the river mouth, with prickly saltwort, a little sea rocket and orache
venturing well downshore. These are annuals, and likely to be swept
away by the first autumnal gales, but their seeds will swirl to and fro all
winter, sufficient surviving to restart the cycle in spring.

Seedlings burst from disarticulated sand couch spikes to give perennial plants, able to make a more significant contribution to sand stability. They begin to anchor a disordered jumble of sandhills some 300 yards across, like a cauldron petrified in full bubble, and contrasting sharply with the orderly ridge fixed by couch along the Crymlin foreshore and passed by 1980 to the marram phase. There is an aura of impermanence about them, as though, come the morrow, they may have moved somewhere else.

The sand couch is attacked by gall wasps, which produce cigar galls like those formed by Chloropid flies on common reeds. Sometimes the hard 'cigar' of swollen leaf-sheaths sprouts to a 5-6 inch long torpedo shape, with leaf blades still undeveloped, before the adult wasps emerge in mid-April.

Sand wasps (*Ammophila sabulosa*) may colonise sand even as far forward as this. They dig vertical burrows opening into a flask-shaped cavity 1½-2 inches down, which would cave in if dug in very loose sand. Clumps of sea holly and marram grass help to provide the necessary firmness, and divert the trampling feet that would obliterate the landmarks enabling the wasp to re-find her newly-dug hole.

Having made a burrow, using spiny legs as digging tools, the female wasp tucks the displaced sand under her chin and flies off with it, plugging the hole with tiny pebbles and removing the heap which might betray its whereabouts to enemies. So invisible is it, even without disturbance, that she herself has to circle over the spot to get her bearings, in order to return with the caterpillar, which she provides as food for her young. This she locates by smell rather than sight, walking round palpating the sand with chemo-sensory organs on her antennae. Once found, the hapless caterpillar is paralysed, so that it stays inertly alive, as a mummified source of fresh food. It is often bigger than its captor, so cannot be air-lifted, and may have to be dragged a considerable distance to the prepared repository.

It would seem that the spider hunting wasps (Pompiloidea) have a better idea, in catching the food first and digging the burrow after. But this method is open to another danger—that of a parasitoid wasp nipping in while her back is turned, to lay its own egg in the prey. Even its own caterpillar may suffer this added indignity while her attention is momentarily diverted to reopen the burrow, before hauling it down and laying her own egg. It is necessary for the success of the species that the egg of the parasitoid should hatch first and thus take over the provender.

Burrow density is not apparent until the young wasps emerge to leave the sand pitted with open tunnels in areas several feet across, often, at Baglan, under the skeletonised leaves of drying sea holly. These newly emerged wasps fly on into October; possibly as long as there are flowers

27. Buck's horn plantain; response to burial by sand. Dotted lines represent levels at which sand has remained static for long enough for a normal leaf rosette to be formed. Plant at lower centre has produced four leaf rosettes at 1½ inch intervals on a 6 inch long stem, which is normally not produced at all (see page 146)

139

to supply them with nectar and long after the aphids have stopped supplying them with honeydew. Most of the caterpillars around then are "woolly bears", which are unsuitable for growing wasps, although their bristles sometimes tickle the low-flying adults, which stay well down among the plant bases to avoid the autumn gales.

Spiders and harvestmen make less subtle attacks on their prey. Grasshoppers disappear with the first frosts, but the scavenging ground and rove beetles live on, sheltering in the detritus which provides their food.

Food and shelter are most closely linked for the fly maggots which recycle the old rabbit carcases to wriggling, then buzzing life. Drone flies zoom into early winter, their larvae nurtured among the moist debris of the foreshore and may be on the wing again by early March. Butterflies still around in October include meadow browns and wall browns, common blues and graylings.

Psathyrella ammophila toadstools grow in the upper intidal-zone as at Crymlin. The ginger ones further back among the marram are *Conocybe dunensis,* a little-known species described for the first time quite recently. These were collected and identified by Roy Perry.

On a grey day the autumnal sandscape seems to represent no more than the decaying remnants of a fecund summer. It is actually much more: a changing house of recycling energy, with lowly plants and animals too small for human viewing, busily at work on the year's leftovers; creating new life from old for another triumphant emergence in spring. No amount of industrial activity can completely mask this annual resurrection.

Already there are greenswards of young seedlings clothing the sun-bleached sands of summer: thyme-leaved and slender sandwort, chickweed and soapwort. Their relative, the sea sandwort, is endowed with a wealth of water-holding tissue and is still producing swollen fruits like capers after summer's end. Fairy flax, like the common blue butterflies, may produce a second generation in September if rain comes to moisten the sun-warmed sands.

A surfeit of rain at this time and the seeds of the diminutive sand Timothy grass will begin to grow while still in the head, like corn sprouting in the stock. This they invariably do if the strawey stems get sanded over while still erect, or topple to bring the unshed grains in contact with damp sand. Spikes should break up at maturity, but rain at the time of ripening will hinder this. Seeds are generally prevented from germinating before dispersal by an inhibiting substance within the fruit, but this disappears at maturity, whether dispersal occurs or not.

Common storksbill flowers on through November, but burial of the flower buds by damp sand can produce the interesting anomaly of 'foliar flowers' in the second half of that month. In these only the stamens conform to standard pattern, and these already possess paired

140

organs at the base which are equivalent to the stipules of ordinary foliage leaves. In the freak flowers all the floral organs have these. The simple leaf blade of the intended sepal becomes elevated on half an inch of stalk, that of the petals is lobed and that of the would-be fruit has as many as six pairs of leaflets. Parts are pale green with white veins, whereas in plants exposed to the light, even the green sepals are tinged purple. Figure 23 compares normal and abnormal flowers. A later burial, between the time of flowering and fruiting, results in distortion of the central fruit axis from which the name of 'storksbill' comes.

Another Baglan anomaly, found towards the end of 1976, was the widespread flowering of sea holly seedlings. Harsher and pricklier than any of its family, sea holly is so distinctive that these soft-leaved infants producing balls of lilac flowers no bigger than those of sheep's bit scabious, and almost at ground level, presented a problem of identification. Only the odd leaves with marginal spines gave the game away. The flowering seedlings were pushing through the sand in groups of fifteen or twenty, where old fruit heads had been covered over before seed dispersal—about two months after the peak of parental flowering. (See Figure 24.)

Peculiar things happen to dune plants when they are buried or undermined by shifting sands, but this precocious maturity in so gentle a version of a ferociously spiny adult is one of the strangest. A rapid cycle of germination, flowering and fruiting is to be expected of annuals which face life on the open sand, unbuffered against heat, cold and drought, but sea holly is a perennial.

Rue-leaved saxifrage may not aspire to more than an inch before producing tiny flowers and fruits, although well able to reach 4-5 inches in the higher rainfall area of the limestone north of the Coalfield. The small size, which is a response to drought, may be accompanied by a reddening of the leaves, a feature seen also in groundsel, where leathery-leaved dark red plants will flower and fruit when no bigger than new seedlings.

The related ragwort may be similarly toughened, reddened and dwarfed by a combination of drought and high light intensity, possibly coupled with a poor nitrogen supply in the sand. These three factors favour the accumulation of sugars in the plant and excessive sugar leads to the formation of a red pigment, anthocyanin. Evening primrose, rosebay willow herb, Portland spurge, herb Robert and dewberry are others which flush crimson on warm dry sand.

Evening primrose is one which flowers through to December and sometimes terminates its growth with a button rosette of leaves at the stem tip, as foxgloves will in more acid sites. Its nectar is a summer-long source of food for hover flies and bees, while the long fruit capsules open gradually over the months with a steady supply of nutty brown seeds for goldfinch and linnet.

The massed yellows of sea pansy, kidney vetch and wallflower cabbage last from spring to fall and are as striking here as anywhere in the county. Biting stonecrop, yellow rattle, silverweed and creeping cinquefoil start later, but dandelion, cat's ear, Oxford ragwort and various hawkbits can be relied on the summer through. Gorgeous golden clumps of bird's foot trefoil thrive even better on scattered dumps of limey rubble than on the sand itself, producing the deep orange flowers sometimes found on Gower's limestone cliffs.

Red, white and alsike clovers, lesser, yellow and hop trefoils, do well on these heaps, capturing their own atmospheric nitrogen, as few but legumes can, to balance the deficiencies of their artificial substrate. Another, the pink rest harrow, its slightly sticky leaves spangled with sand grains, can live even on spillages of road tarmac. Sea holly pioneered a corner of the Baglan Works enclosure in 1973 where sand had drifted over the ballast floor. By 1979 sea spurge was the chief invader on the seaward side, with sand sedge, ox-eye daisies, hairy sedge and vagrant montbretia.

Most of the plants recorded "Upon the Breton Sands" by Lightfoot in 1773 survived the two succeeding centuries, among them the rare rat's tail fescue. The rather similar grey hair grass (*Corynephorus canescens*) has succumbed, but is a scarce plant in Britain anyway. A worthy gain is the sea stock, holding its own into 1980 but not thriving, as across the river at Crymlin.

In considering Crymlin and Baglan in Chapter 4 we were observing major sand movements over the centuries and the part which these have played in shaping the coastline: but there are smaller movements, from week to week, which can profoundly affect the growth of individual plants. On the forward dunes, where sand is constantly on the move, bowled along by the wind or sliding down unvegetated slopes, life can be precarious. Seedlings get dislodged before their roots gain hold, low plants get buried, tall ones toppled from collapsing sand cliffs and all may be undermined and ripped from their moorings.

For the average plant this spells death. Only those which are specially adapted can live on the more mobile sands. Hence the particular fascination of dunes with their distinctive assemblage of dune plants. Those best adapted are successful to the point of forming a monoculture where few others can survive, yet they scarcely appear elsewhere. Such a one is the marram, which can be measured by the acre in Glamorgan, yet was hailed as a new county record for the 1970s in the neighbouring, duneless county of Gwent.

Plants which can anchor themselves adequately are equally effective in anchoring the medium. In time they come to anchor it so well that a whole lot of other plants will find it to their liking and the tenacious pioneers that have prepared the way will be squeezed out. Their

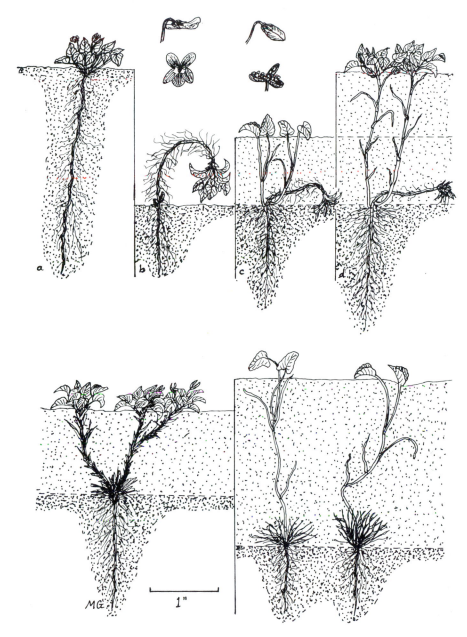

28. Dog violets in eroding and accreting sand. Top: Loss of sand resulting in collapse of old shoots and production of new ones from buds on the roots. Bottom: Response to burial without previous erosion (see page 147)

efficiency has spelled their own doom. This is the essence of plant succession—of the dynamism of Nature, where things are never static.

Just as major changes of coastline are most easily followed on sandy shores, so are smaller scale changes of vegetation cover, and changes in the life form of individual plants. Man can hasten the process by planting more stabilisers, just as he can alter the course of sand accretion by building groynes. Marram is the species most often planted to heal scars and halt the enlargement of blow-outs: on Margam Burrows pine trees were chosen.

Only when it is being constantly sanded over can marram thrive, trapping the sand with erect, wiry leaves and binding it with the mat of creeping stems, which are revealed to depths of twenty feet and more by major sand blows. As the surface stabilises, marram ceases to flower, becomes moribund and gives way to smaller competitors—not large ones, as in most cases of competitive succession. Unburied seeds, which germinate prolifically in November, produce leaves directly: buried ones send up a stem, with leaves expanding only when these reach the light.

A second important sand binder, sand sedge (*Carex arenaria*), is less efficient, but copes better than most. Its horizontal and sparingly branched rhizomes march through the sand, throwing up straight rows of widely-spaced shoots which produce green leaves only when they surface. Sand loss bringing the rhizomes themselves to the surface, eliminates the need for a shoot below the leaf tuft, but slows the growth in length of the rhizome, so that leaves are produced at shorter intervals. If sand level drops lower still, all the rhizome tips grow vertically downwards (as when encountering a sand cliff) and the shoots turn back alongside at 180°. If, on the other hand, sand accumulates again, a stem will grow vertically from each leaf tuft to produce a second tuft at the new surface. (See Figure 25.)

Normally the underground rhizomes follow the surface contours, so sand deposition over a growing tip will cause this to slope upwards to maintain constant depth. Sand build-up over older parts which cannot reorientate, results in a buckling of the leafy shoots struggling up to the light and a failure of some of them to make it.

Red runners of silverweed creep along the sand surface, but are able to send erect shoots to the top if buried and bleached, due to lack of light. The converse happens with depauperate reeds of damp hollows. Here creeping stems are usually pale and buried, but erosion of sand or evaporation of water slows their growth, so that the upright shoots are borne closer together on reddened stems. In rushes so exposed, even the roots turn red. With creeping grasses, like red fescue and fiorin, burial simply means that stems cease ramifying horizontally and turn up to produce leafy tips with new horizontals budded off just below the new sand level.

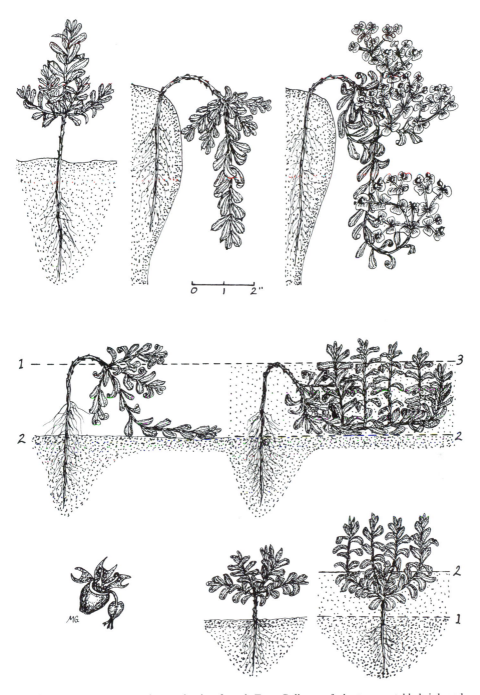

29. Sea spurge; response to loss and gain of sand. Top: Collapse of plant on unstable brink and bending of new shoots to erect position. Middle: Ditto, but new shoots buried. Bottom: Ditto, without initial collapse (see page 147)

145

The lower half of Figure 26 shows how sea milkwort responds to burial, by upward growth of branching stems with widely spaced leaves, and by producing new rosettes at the heightened surface. The upper half illustrates a double response to loss of sand—the downward bending of existing shoots to the lowered ground surface and an enhanced growth of anchoring stems below, which put up new shoots better geared to the new surface.

The buck's horn plantain depicted in Figure 27 produces no horizontal stems and, normally, no vertical ones except to bear the flower spikes. Sand burial shows, however, that it retains the potential to grow long leafy shoots when called upon to 'surface' or 'float' on new sand. As many as three stems may come from a single rosette. Any prolonged halt in the rise of sand level will induce production of a new leaf rosette, which may later become buried in its turn. If time permits, there may be flowers and fruits as well.

With a small increase in level only the leaves of the plantain respond, with basal growth, a familiar phenomenon in grasses but seen in few dicotyledons. The new white leaf bases so produced go red, not green if later exposed to the light. Removal of sand causes a strong reflexing of the leaves, which are pressed tightly against the ground to retain moisture and hold the space won against competitors. So great is this pressure in plants from moisture-deficent areas, that leaves will fold immediately down against the root if a plant is pulled up.

Storksbill behaves similarly, leaf rosettes of both often holding little mounds of sand on a generally denuded surface. On burial, storksbill leaves can push up through 4-5 inches of sand, by growth of the leaf stalk only (a part which is indistinguishable in the narrow-leaved plantain). These elongate with sufficient force for little clods of wet sand as much as 1″ x 2″ x 3″ to be pushed aside. On surfacing, the leaf tips spread, opening a narrow funnel down to the heart of the old rosette. Leaf stalks stop growing only when the whole leaf blade can spread flat on the new surface.

Mature storksbill plants, like bird's-foot trefoil and lady's bedstraw, form radiating surface runners capable of growing obliquely up if buried, to form a circle of new plants around the 'lost' centre. Underground sections bear tiny scale leaves, which are trefoil shaped instead of simple, as with most scale leaves, but which lack the normally large stipules.

Thyme can surface after burial to about an inch and will continue to do so with slow sand accumulation when there is time for a few leaves to form. This ability makes it a first class coloniser of anthills, which are thrown up at a rate well within its growth capabilities, but it prefers the less mobile parts of the dune system.

The little sand dandelion (*Taraxacum erythrospermum*) and other yellow composites 'float' equally successfully. Figure 28 shows the same sort of growth in the dog violet. Severe sand loss causes wilting and death here of the original shoot, which is replaced by more tenuous young ones if reburial occurs. Loss of sand from around sea pansies leads to production of leafy branches from exposed roots, these lacking the usual leaf scar below. Responses of sea spurge, shown in Figure 29 depend largely on the growth of laterals turning up to the light after collapse of the main axis, with or without sand burial.

It would be tedious to list others, but scrabbling with the fingers around the bases of quite ordinary looking plants may reveal quite extraordinary developments beneath the surface, and this can never be tedious. The sequence of past storms unravels itself like a detective story told in living plant tissues, and can be approximately dated with reference to the growth stage of the responding plants. Such activities indulged in on the windy corner at Baglan, can compensate in no small measure for the loss of wilderness to necessary industry.

11 PINEWOOD AND POOLS ON MARGAM BURROWS

Advance of industry: Corsican pinewood: Pools formed by gravel diggers: Forward dune ridge and Inland dune slacks.

ALONG the five mile stretch of coast south of Crymlin and Baglan the dunescape of yesteryear has been swallowed up by modern developments. A few sandy humps remain at the mouth of the River Afan and a grimy ridge to seaward of the Steelworks, but the rest has gone. The last half mile disappeared under new coke ovens as recently as 1976, along with the remarkable towered farmhouse by the beach access road past Margam Crematorium.

The surviving part of Margam Burrows stretches for a mile, from the access road to the Kenfig River along the county boundary with Mid Glamorgan. Much of this is still as rich in plant and animal life as Crymlin and Kenfig, but much is a bleak waste of scraped ground where commercial sand and gravel diggers have been at work. Given time, this man-made desert would revegetate, but it may not be given time. Already the towering black waste tip of The British Steel Corporation has crossed the road and built up along the coast to within a little of the River Kenfig, leaving but a tiny gap for the use of gravel lorries and public access to the beach.

Margam Estate retains ownership and mineral rights of a two hundred metre buffer zone along the seaward dunes, so walkers on the beach are scarcely aware of the devastation behind, but freedom of movement is restricted and there is no longer any view of the sea from the hinterland. Hundreds of acres of firm beach sand with their backing dunes are being withheld from the leisure-seeking public, cut in two by the spewings of the steel mills, while tourist pressure increases beyond acceptable levels on the sands to west and east.

To wildlife, with its essentially practical approach to environment, this is just so many acres lost. To man, with his greater aesthetic perception, it is much more than that. One wonders why the eye-sore has to be a ribbon and not a block and why that ribbon has to be strung along the precious coastal strip and not further inland along the railway, where it would merely broaden an existing intrusion and spare the seascape. Perhaps there are good reasons.

The gravel workings have a less disastrous impact, the hollows filling with water to form new pools and the heaps of discarded sand being readily colonised by indigenous species. Before their coming was envisaged, the sandhills around the access road were planted with trees, which reached maturity before being killed in a fire, but continued to hold the nests of kestrel, crow and woodpecker in their leafless boughs until forced to give way to the works extensions.

Many of the lowlier Corsican pines (*Pinus nigra* var. *maritima*) to the south have persisted into the 1980s. Some have been damaged by fire or pollution fallout, others are being grubbed up by mechanical diggers moving ahead of the waste dumpers or are toppling into sand craters. Nevertheless, this is an unusual type of community worthy of study, whether it is to live on or pass into the annals of history.

Most of the alien conifers planted in Britain are shallow-rooted, their penetration restricted by meagre soil depth or water-logging. Many fall when winds reach gale force. Not so the Corsican pine, which has a gigantic root system, well fitted to plumb and bind the yielding sands.

The bushy top of close set branches is but the tip of the iceberg. Wind-rounded trees, nine to ten feet in breadth and height will be surrounded by a spread of roots radiating thirty feet in all directions. These, thick as a man's arm, hug the surface, protruding as contorted ridges through the carpet of pine needles where sand has blown away from above, the woody trellis which stays the course of erosion. Such

148

30. The mighty root system of a wind-stunted Corsican pine

roots, encountering the brink of a sand crater, can be seen to arch downwards for another 3-4 yards before re-entering the sand as a branched filigree, to terminate in a fuzz of fine absorptive rootlets.

These squat giants scarcely wobble in gales which would cause firs and spruces to topple wholesale. Instead, any twigs which grow beyond the level canopy during calms are killed back during storms to give a stag-headed skyline. In the more constant windiness of the seaside margin such defiant gestures are seldom made, the trees 'lying down', with roots to windward, and putting up a dense growth of truncated boughs whose outermost twigs loop sandwards.

Each tree protects the one behind, so that each can aspire to grow a fraction taller than the last. The innermost reach to 15 feet, their lower branches stifled and dying in the communal shade of the massed crowns, to produce an open-floored plantation. The jumble of steep-sided sandhills gives an undulating floor to the forest but the discrepancies are ironed out above because the trees in the sheltered hollows are able to reach up to the 'wind ceiling' specified by their more inhibited neighbours on the summits.

Hailing from the dry, goat-denuded sands of the Mediterranean, the Corsican pine is well fitted to withstand the worst that the moister sands of Margam can do to it. The slightly asymmetric cones are borne in whorls of up to five and there may be three generations on the tree at once. In winter the youngest are no bigger than peas and the oldest are beginning to fall, not usually opening their woody scales to release the winged seeds until they do. The leaf canopy is dense, effectively excluding most of the indigenous dune flora but sheltering a plethora of pine-wood fungi unusually rich in both species and individuals, considering the paucity of organic matter in the original substrate.

Of the commoner native plants, the big tumps of sharp rush seem least able to tolerate any shade, but polypody ferns nestle in gaps of the ground-hugging canopy to seaward. Gladdon iris produces livid, purplish blooms in quite deep shade, the encapsulated orange seeds peeping from ruptured fruits in August and turning scarlet by November. Marram and sand sedge get progressively wispier under the trees and the normally succulent sea spurge and biting stonecrop produce such delicately elongated growths as to be almost unrecognisable.

Ivy creeps across some of the pine-clad sandhills, as in more stable deciduous woodlands, but leaves of the low-dipping brambles turn yellow in Autumn, unable to face the gloom of winter in this scrap of evergreen forest. Moss carpets get partially covered by pine needles, but struggle through into spring. Near the woodland edge the moss provides a seedbed for winter annuals, and seedling swards of dove's-foot cranesbill, mouse-ear chickweed and hairy bitter cress take over in November and December.

July is the time of orchids and 1979 was a bumper year for these. A riot of pyramidal orchids appears around the wood margins, a few pale heads among the rich magenta. Sprouting in shade too sombre for any other plant is a loose carpet of overgrown twayblade orchids and broad helleborine, a few of the last devoid of all chlorophyll, their leaves the same creamy hue as the half-opened flowers. Although more shade-tolerant than most orchids (and flowering later), broad helleborine is also common in the open slacks among whispering drifts of maroon-tinted marsh helleborine. One of the choicest species to survive into the 1980s is star of Bethlehem (*Ornithogalum umbellatum*), its white flowers streaked with green, like snowdrops.

During winter fungi are the biggest source of interest—and profit for those who dare to pick for eating. Puffballs stay mostly just clear of the wood, small heath puffballs (*Lycoperdon ericetorum*) penetrating furthest in, *L. hiemale* (now *Vascellum pratense*) remains outside with the majority. Wood blewits, a gastronomic delight, come in the most appetising hues of mauve. These, too, have suffered name changes recently. For long known as *Tricholoma nudum,* they have passed through *Lepista nuda* to *Rhodopaxillus nudus* in the last few years, only the nudity persisting.

Most striking, for size, number and colour, is the red-flecked "peaches and cream fungus" (*Tricholomopsis rutilans*). This pushes sturdy six inch toadstools up through the blanketing pine needles from hidden stumps. The cap is bell-shaped at first and a reddish carmine, but flattens as it expands, the downy red flecks separating to show a tawny layer below. Gills on the underside are a splendid contrasting yellow. The grisette (*Amanita vaginata*) is edible, but too much like the death cap in appearance for any but the expert to risk. The little *Clitocybe fragrans* smells pleasantly of aniseed.

Dead and dying trees support clusters of yellow honey fungus (*Armillariella mellea*) which are probably the cause of their death. Others growing directly upon the wood are *Gymnophilus penetrans*, penetrator of Gymnosperms, *Mycena alcalina*, which belies its name by smelling of nitric acid, and some of the common bracket fungi and orange slime fungi. Nine other species, which have no popular names, are included in Figure 31. Many of these fungi are peculiar to

31. Autumn fungi of sandy coastal pinewood (identified by Roy Perry). Top: three large: *Melanoleuca melaleuca*, *Stropharia aeruginosa* and *Tricholomopsis rutilans*. Upper middle, four small: *Lepiota cristata*, *Omphalina pyxidata*, *Mycena alcalina* and *Gymnophilus penetrans*. Lower middle, three large: *Lactarius rufus* (slayer), *Amanita vaginata* (grisette) and *Russula sardonia*. Bottom, four small: *Clitocybe fragrans*, *Lycoperdon perlatum*, *Bovista plumbea* and *Hygrophorus niveus*

151

coniferous woods and it is interesting to speculate where they might have come from to populate this outlying habitat of their choice.

This dark pinewood is not without its animal life. Grey squirrels build their dreys in the upper branches and nibble at the endless succession of pine cones, but contortions of the topmost pine shoots are more likely to be the work of salty winds. Squirrels will strip the bark, sometimes killing a sapling by ring-barking, but the free-range ponies of the 'moors' behind leave precious few saplings for their attention. Brown hares trot in from the dyked fields and rabbits find the stabilised sand just right for burrowing.

A pair of kestrels occasionally occupies an old carrion crow's nest and piles of feathers show where small birds have fallen victim to the resident sparrow hawks. With so many moribund trees, this is a woodpeckers' paradise and the timber is pocked with neat circular nesting holes and the regular pits made by their chisel beaks while searching for wood-boring insects and centipedes.

Goldcrests and coal tits are an expected feature of the sombre pinewoods, but blue and great tits, blackbirds and thrushes are there too. Big flocks of starlings move out to scavenge on the gruesome waste tip with crows and gulls, while linnets and goldfinches move in to harvest the seeds of marginal herbs. Others flying by are more strictly denizens of the adjoining water meadows—curlew, lapwing, golden plover and snipe; reed bunting, sedge warbler, yellow wagtail and cuckoo.

Pied wagtails belong to a later phase of this man-made landscape, pottering hopefully around the apparently barren shores of pools formed in abandoned gravel diggings. Even the woodiest of forty-foot rootspreads cannot stand against the steel-jawed monsters which have withdrawn from the beach to exploit the burrows. The waste tip may yet help to avert an inroad of the sea onto the denuded acres.

The moonscape of bare-edged pools and sand heaps is short-lived and soon softens into something more Earthy. Sand is porous, so the pools are not filled by surface drainage, but by dipping down into the water table. Hence the occasional un-nerving sensation of quicksand underfoot at their edges. This instability leads to a slumping of sides to middle at the least provocation, so that quite deep pools tend to shallow and level out, with loss of water if the water table drops in dry spells.

All ponds, by their very nature, are impermanent, but Margam's sand pools are shorter-lived than most. Some dry out annually and carry transparent green flecks of the liverwort, *Riccia cavernosa* on their damp floors. This was a new record for Glamorgan when discovered in July 1980, although locally common in parts of the Brecon Beacon's reservoirs which dried out during 1976. With it on the Margam sands are silvery wisps of the moss, *Bryum argenteum*, and red goosefoot seedlings, germinating as the water recedes. Later come

26

27

29

30

28

Plate VII   PLANTS OF MARGAM SAND
DUNES—*Author*

26. Common gromwell
27. Dewberry flower and fruit
28. Goatsbeard

29. Variegated horsetail and
     sand timothy grass
30. Knotted pearlwort

Plate VIII   RESIDENT PLOVERS AT BAGLAN—*Keri Williams*

   31. Top: Lapwings or green plovers in flight
   32. Bottom left: Lapwing at nest
   33. Bottom right: Ringed plover and Spartina grass

154

attractive radiating clumps of knotted pearlwort starred with dispro-
portionately large flowers and, later still, the brookweed, in little rows
aligned along former shorelines.

Pool vegetation varies from year to year, being sparse in 1977 and
1979 but lush in 1978 and 1980. The constant inward sludging, coupled
with a slight tidal rise and fall of fresh water pushed up by salt water
beneath, may serve to keep the shores of some plant-free, but
gelatinous algal masses form readily in the centres. These lead on to
ferny carpets of harsh-fronded stonewort (*Chara vulgaris*) speckled
with orange reproductive bodies.

Floating tangles of small pondweed produce nutlets at the surface
and water crowfoot forms delicate rafts, but there is little else in the
newer pools. Older ones remaining full become bordered with great
reedmace and common spike-rush; ones with a tendency to dry out
support water horsetail, jointed rush and curled dock.

The fully vegetated slacks are nothing to do with the gravel diggers
and are as floriferous as any in the county. A special feature among the
more usual colonies of early and southern marsh orchids are the
fragrant orchids (*Gymnadenia conopsea*). These, with their longer,
narrower flower spikes, have the most delicious perfume, savouring of
clove oil. The tubular spur containing the nectar is also long and
narrow, so that the flowers can be pollinated only by certain night-
flying moths, and the scent becomes more powerful at dusk to attract
them. Fragrant orchids often emerge from a loose matrix of marsh
pennywort leaves, along with the fleshy spikes of adder's-tongue fern.

The seven week drought in early spring, 1980, which preceded the
wettest summer for 73 years, proved too much for the bee orchid
rosettes, most of which withered and blackened, so that few flowers
were produced that year. Another feature of 1980 was the white-
flowered red clover, its heads a very different shape from the ordinary
white clover alongside.

Viper's bugloss always throws a few spikes with white or pink flowers
instead of the usual rich blue, and the more delicate blue of the tall field
cranesbill can be a joy in midsummer. 1980 lacked the usual brilliance of
restharrow and lady's bedstraw along the junction of pinewood and
water meadow—probably because of a change of farming practice from
hay-making to grazing—which also cut the cowslips and green-winged
orchids off in their prime.

Animal life in the gravel diggers' pools is more prolific than plant life
and two of the commonest species pose problems of arrival. Wandering
snails (*Lymnaea peregra*) are present in profusion, with plenty of jellied
egg capsules to supply the next generation if the water lasts; but how did
they get there? Once arrived, there is no shortage of algal food and they
scarcely bother to retire from public life into their capacious shells when
disturbed.

Daphnia, the water flea, is a more convenient size for hitching a ride on bird or insect, and is present in hundreds of thousands, forming dense swarms above the *Chara* beds, where they change the water colour from yellow to brown. Where there is prey there will be predators, and lively little bugs, *Plea leachi,* abound, buzzing back and forth through the *Daphnia* hordes in a dense, soupy suspension. These, and the rest, can fly when adult, so their almost spontaneous arrival at the new source of food presents no mystery.

Lesser water boatmen (Corixids), which are larger than *Plea,* are present in more modest numbers, and there was an influx of back-swimmers (Notonectids) in 1980. Dragon and damselflies hunt over the pools, but are strong fliers and may have spent their aquatic youth in more mature dune slacks further inland.

At least two kinds of mayfly nymph occur, one shrimp-like, with banded body tapering to the insertion of the three long tail prongs; the other shorter and chunkier, with tail appendages more widely splayed. White midge larvae undulate from short lengths of sandy tube, jaws chomping sideways and sand-coloured gut contents visible through the transparent body wall.

Water beetles come in various patterns, from the little *Potamonectes depressus* to larger Dytiscids, both larval and adult, though *Dytiscus marginalis,* the great diving beetle, has not been seen in the new pools. Some hang from the surface film, others pop up periodically to renew their air bubble for underwater breathing.

More beetles arrive by accident during their dispersal flights in late May and early June. One of the commonest is the scarlet poplar leaf beetle (*Chrysomela populi*), which flies high above the treetops of nearby birch spinneys—scarlet specks against the blue. These frequently land on the pools, but take no harm, scuttling blithely across the surface film and up a water horsetail stem to an elevated take-off point.

The larvae of these resemble those of ladybirds and can be seen almost throughout the summer, as there are usually several broods. They hatch from brown egg clusters laid on the underside of creeping willow leaves, and their pinky orange bodies bristle with black spines. Like ladybirds, they are unpalatable, but they have a very novel way of showing it.

Provoke a larva with a gentle prod and a blob of white liquid appears immediately at the tip of every spine. This is pleasantly aromatic or oppressively tarry, according to taste, and contains salicyl aldehyde—a chemical produced by the sallow on which it feeds, and cleverly taken over by the vegetarian larva as a deterrent to insect predators. Fortunately this poison does not find its way into the bloodstream to poison the user, but is absorbed and stored in glands on the back. Blobs of fluid are sucked back again and conserved for re-use if not brushed off in an encounter. Only after many prods will the trick be abandoned. A lot of energy, which might otherwise go into growth, is devoted to the maintenace of this defence system, hence the elaborate mechanism for conserving the ammunition.

Its utilisation is even more fascinating in the pupal phase. The pink segmented chrysalis with black spots has no aldehyde glands, but the sloughed larval skin is retained at the uppermost end of its body and this still has the poison sacs intact. Provoke the pupa and it wriggles, the motion squeezing the glands, so that the old poison comes seeping down as a protective cloak! In adulthood the scarlet colour is enough to warn off would-be predators.

Other more genuine water beetles come zooming in from the mature slacks, to row swiftly to the depths in search of living quarters and egg laying sites. A few alight in error on shining artefacts which simulate water—sheets of polythene and metal straying from the tip—and slide across the surface in a laughable attempt at swimming. Some skate to a standstill, compose themselves and get airborne again. Others career straight over the edge and seek the darkness beneath to cover their confusion.

Accidental arrivals include young hopper phases of the common grasshopper (*Chorthippus bicolor* var. 'striped') with white patternings on their backs. These are very buoyant, making uninhibited hops from the surface film with no plants to push off from, and arriving safely back on terra firma. Froghoppers and leafhoppers are equally adept at pool crossings afoot.

Pools were swarming with tadpoles in the early summer of 1978. Perhaps there were slacks here before, which the amphibians homed back to for the frenzy of the communal mating, so that the new ones were readily accepted. Frogs have moved away by late May—back to the damp mossy hollows and thick ground cover of the inland slacks. Toads stayed on, squatting lethargically under old timbers in shallow hollows scooped from the sand. Some were sand-coloured, some dark and some reddish, the 'erythristic' form: all were drier-skinned than one expects to see a frog, although inhabiting the moistest retreats available on the open sandscape.

There was plenty of food at hand without budging from the dark hideouts which they shared with larval and adult beetles, woodlice and millipedes. No doubt they relieved the tedium by venturing abroad under cover of darkness. No tadpoles were seen in 1979 and the little toads hopping round the pool margins were all yearlings. These were feeding on smaller prey, principally gnats and midges 'hatching' from aquatic larvae.

Bird footprints along the pool shores are sparse. It seems there is little life beneath the sand to attract avian predators, but a green sandpiper dropped in during August, 1978. The registered tracks of foxes are commonplace, these night hunters padding along the water's edge, with signs of occasional scuffles interrupting the ordered sequence of pad marks.

The foxes bred on a shrub-covered dune ridge hard by, where the cubs could be watched playing among burnet rose and dewberry and foraging out along the steelworks tip for canteen waste, but the ridge was half eaten away by diggers in 1977 and the family moved elsewhere, probably to one of the surviving sallow dingles.

The break in the waste tip opposite the pools gives the foxes free access to the seaward dunes, where there is a good population of long-tailed field mice for the taking. Caches of nibbled hazel nut shells along the eroding face of the regressing dune ridge here are unexpected, as the nearest hazel trees are a long way inland. Nuts must drift down the rivers and strand here due to vagaries of tidal currents, to be gathered up by the industrious mice. So few people visit this stretch that the normally nocturnal rodents can be watched at work in broad daylight. Short-tailed field voles burrow through the moss mats much further back and bank voles are mainly to be found in thicker vegetation around the inland slacks.

Partridges, however, although nesting at the margins of the damp birch-sallow spinneys, can be flushed from the seaward dune crest. They come here to feed on the small beetles which make such heavy weather of scrambling up the steep sand slopes, the hairy St. Mark's flies resting on the grass blades and the ants and spiders which scurry in pursuit of those less fleet of foot. Later in the year the partridges feast on the seeds of marram and other dune plants, leaving lobed, walnut-like dung pellets on the sand, quite unlike the coiled droppings of red grouse. Their decline in Britain as a whole is due to changes in farming practice, but they continue to thrive on the unfarmed sandhills.

Inland from the tinkling, breeze-ruffled waters of the bare new pools, the wind whispers across the plant-muffled surface of mature slacks. The scene alongside is no less rich than that at Kenfig, with the same stands of sun-gilded orchids and round-leaved wintergreen; the same fugitive beauty of butterflies and moths and the dreamy meanderings of sand wasps and hover flies.

The tranquility is broken at times by police motor cycle training sessions—transferred here from Kenfig with the establishment there of the local nature reserve—and private motor cycling. Permission is needed, however, to cross the railway shunting yards from the Kenfig Trading Estate under the new M4, and few walkers come to savour the brittleness of sun-warmed grass, where crisp blue skies are splintered with bird song.

Aristocratic herons from Margam Park stand sentinel on the dune crests when the roar of machines is stilled: cuckoos pursue their search for meadow pipits' nests to foster their young and skylarks shout from the firmament as though nothing had changed since the great sand blows of the Middle Ages.

Whitethroats are still increasing after the countrywide crash in numbers experienced in the early seventies, when drought struck their wintering grounds in the Sahel Zone of the Sahara. Linnets, wagtails and wrens forage across the hummocky landscape, where the air can be soft as thistledown, while green woodpeckers add their frenzied chortling to those blustery days of pewter-grey sea and scudding sand particles.

Snipe can be flushed from beds of spike-rush and variegated horsetail where sand level drops to that of the water table near the railway. Lapwing rise in agitation at the least intrusion when their precocious young are newly out of the nest and bowling across the moss swards on twinkling legs.

The shallow pools are full of insect life, with great diving beetles lording it over the smaller Coleopterans, while backswimmers (Notonectids) dwarf the front-swimming water boatmen (Corixids). Negro bugs (*Thyreocoris scarabeoides*) fly in like round black tortoise beetles, showing little demarcation of head from body. Scarlet water mites churn to and fro among submerged stems while pond skaters scoot across their sun-flecked ceilings. In this limited part of the burrows "The snail's on the thorn, God's in his Heaven and all's right with the world"—so far.

12 DIMINISHING ALLUVIAL FLATS

Industrial encroachment on the Coastal Plain at Baglan and Margam:
rich communities of dykes and water meadows

A chronicler writing of the Baglan/Margam area in 1684 describes "Excellent springs. . . . at the foot of prodigious high hilles of woods, shelter for ye deere. . . . about a mile distant from an arm of the sea. . . . and washed almost around with salt water, is a marsh whereunto the deere. . . . resort much to by swimming". Today's fallow deer

159

which roam through Margam Country Park and Margam Forest on the mountain behind, find little woodland cover on the seaward face of the hills and would risk their lives crossing the M4, A48 and main line railway to forage on what little remains of the marshes at their foot.

Some of the coastal levels had been drained by the Romans 1500 years before that early account, but the Roman ditches had long since clogged with peat. In the early Middle Ages the plain had been farmed by the monks of Margam Abbey, although, by 1326, the abbot was complaining that much of the land near the shore was becoming worthless because of inundation by sand. More land was granted to the abbey in 1383 as compensation for that lost.

By the nineteenth century the main drainage channels supplementing the Rivers Afan and Kenfig were the three Mother Ditches. The Upper Mother Ditch, now swallowed up by Eglwys Nunydd Reservoir, which it leaves to seaward of the British Oxygen Company (BOC), was the landward of the three. The Middle and Lower meandered close together and all were interconnected by an arterial system of cross ditches and a capillary system of drains. Their level was controlled by sluices.

Much was under the jurisdiction of the Mansels of Margam, and when they planned a duck shoot, the fields were flooded to attract more wildfowl. An old farmer still tells of how, as a boy, he would drive his father's cattle out to pasture and look back an hour or so later to find the whole area under a foot of water. (The Steel Corporation maintains a dam across the River Kenfig near to one of the old key sluice gates.)

During the 1960s sizable remnants of the alluvial water meadows were still intact, criss-crossed by a system of regularly cleared dykes. These lands were known as "moors", although they have few plants in common with the true moors of the hills, where the peat is acid, and not neutral to alkaline as here. The term has a historic significance and refers to the fen peat built up from reeds and other swamp plants. On the similar Cardiff "Moors" up-channel peat used to be dug out and sold for horticultural use—as it still is, on a vast scale, from the Somerset Levels, which are the larger twin of the Welsh coastal "moors" on the opposite side of the Bristol Channel.

Winter commuters on the A48 through the 1960s can scarcely have missed seeing the wheeling, wailing flocks of lapwings which shared the Baglan Moors with ponies. Often the bulk of the flats was flooded and other birds flocked in—curlew, oyster-catcher, heron and gull—to populate a chequer board of silver meadows dissected by half-drowned hedges marking the position of hidden dykes.

During the 1970s the wintering bird flocks were squeezed closer and closer to the willows and reeds bordering railway and highway, by an advancing tide of rubble moving just ahead of the expanding Aberafan housing estate. Impeded drainage and choked dykes made life uncomfortable for the ponies and the restless, undulating flocks of linnets, although welcomed by wading birds and bird watchers.

But the lapwing/linnet era is ending: there can be no respite now for the Baglan Moors. Flowering rush and insectivorous butterwort have gone under: breeding shelduck have gone away. Still, at the dawn of the 1980s, the remnant of springtime pasture is bright with kingcup, greater bird's foot trefoil, lady's smock, yellow iris and orchids. The golden carpet of upright buttercups sprinkled with ragged robin and ox-eye daisy is a legacy of overgrazing by livestock which spurned the taste of the buttercups' poisonous alkaloids, allowing the plants to romp away unchecked. Hoof tracks and wheel tracks left by receding waters retain their own aquatic flora into summer; tiny micro-habitats in a larger whole.

Bountiful Nature provides a partial healing cover even for the waterless waste of slag and clinker. Here can be found the least toadflax (*Chaenorhinum minus*), which is usually a plant of railroad chippings, and a larger mauve toadflax, *Linaria repens*. Tiny rue-leaved saxifrage and taller narrow-leaved hemp nettle sprout from the rubbly expanse as they do from the pebbly storm beaches around Aberthaw.

Strangest of all, perhaps, are the reed shoots, pushing through the sterile matrix with exemplary determination, from rhizomes permeating the water table far below. This is Baglan's last defiant gesture—until alien weeds start bursting from the imported soil of suburban gardens.

Part of the Margam Moors five to six miles further south along the desecrated coastal plain are still intact and still superb, but even this fragment has been halved since 1975, in spite of the economic climate which caused such big cut-backs in the steel industry. Concrete rafts, black infill, new coke ovens and other lofty structures swallowed up another three quarters of a mile during the second half of the decade. The remaining relic is precious as an outlier of the English Lowlands clinging precariously to the skirts of the Welsh Uplands, and offering a westerly haven to easterly flowers.

It should be spared, as an oasis of an unrepeatable landscape where the "Garden of Wales", as the Vale of Glamorgan is so aptly called, peters out into the once more rugged West. The Wentlooge Levels between Cardiff and the Severn Bridge are similar but less rich, and these also are threatened by drainage and industrial development as soon as the money can be found.

The lost acres had built up on alluvium deposited behind the coastal sandhills. As the salt washed out, reedbeds succeeded the saltmarsh and the dead remains of many generations accumulated to form a fen peat mixed with pale clayey silt. Some of the reedbeds persisted to the end; other parts, where tall marsh orchids grew in profusion and rare fen

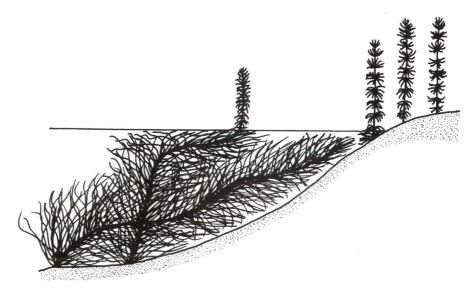

32. Underwater and emergent shoots of marestail

orchids in ones and twos, were usually flooded only in winter. Rank summer growths died back in autumn to reveal an old ridge and furrow system from past agriculture, with water spreading back along the shallow downfolds where the rich tilth was parted by the circling plough.

The vegetation of the seventies was rough grazing, comprising tall oat grass, cocksfoot, crested dogstail and Yorkshire fog; this supporting Herefords and Friesians as well as ponies. There was a rich meadow flora with yellow pea, agrimony, yellow rattle and goatsbeard, and close to two hundred species have been recorded on a sunny July afternoon. Cowslips bloomed along the dykes and the abundant clovers tempted flocks of wood pigeons down from the sky to feast on the tender leaves.

Remarkable differences occurred between the plant life of different dykes, this probably depending on the accident of what happened to arrive first after they had been cleared. One was full of brooklime, which was seen nowhere else, the dominance of stonewort (*Chara*) in iron-fouled ditches was probably the result of selective survival rather than the luck of arrival, although stonewort is typically a coloniser of new habitats.

Other pioneers in newly cleared dykes were Canadian, curled and fennel-leaved pondweeds, water starwort and ivy-leaved duckweed, all of which were suppressed if nutrients from animal dung boosted the lesser duckweed to form a light-excluding raft across the surface.

162

Broad-leaved pondweed had the same effect, but could be topped by two of the area's specialities, bogbean and marestail. Marginal water horsetail and water plantain were interspersed with purple and yellow loosestrifes, forget-me-nots and lesser spearwort.

The three floral gems of the dykes, buried along with the bee orchids and primitive moonwort of the dunes, all, happily, survive into the 1980s south of the beach access road. They are flowering rush, frogbit and arrowhead: a trio of related plants found on Crymlin Bog and its bordering Tennant Canal but in very few other parts of South Wales. All are south-easterly species, more at home in the Norfolk Broads and canals of the Low Countries than on the Celtic Fringe.

Glamorgan's best stand of flowering rush, at Cadoxton near Barry, was destroyed when its pond was replaced by a municipal rubbish tip in the early seventies. That in a prized corner of the Severnside Levels disappeared with the installation of a sewage pump. Margam's biggest colonies were close to the old southern border of the steelworks where rose-tinted flower heads swayed gently above a floating film of oil. Lying on the water surface as it did, this oil caused them no harm, being well above root level where it might have been absorbed.

The "Atlas of the British Flora" shows only one more westerly site for flowering rush—in Anglesey, one for frogbit—in Carmarthen, and two for arrowhead—in Pembrokeshire and Anglesey. Frogbit is locally abundant on the Wentlooge ditches east of Cardiff but grows scarcely anywhere else in Glamorgan. Arrowhead has more easterly outliers in the Glamorgan Canal near Cardiff and the Monmouth Canal near Newport. On Margam the leaves suffer from what appears to be salt scorching, but flowering is unimpaired.

Other, less spectacular, plants of this "Little England Beyond Wales" include the true bulrush or clubrush (*Scirpus lacustris*) near its western limit, all Gower plants being the smaller, greyer *S. tabernaemontani*. Distichous sedge (*Carex disticha*) has not been found further west in Glamorgan, although growing in a few parts of Dyfed and Anglesey. Prickly sedge (*Carex muricata*) and blunt-flowered rush (*Juncus subnodulosus*) are other unusual species of the dykes. The water speedwell is *Veronica catenata* and there is lesser as well as greater bur-reed here, marsh foxtail and reed sweet grass.

Sodden areas become spread with the Turkish towelling flowers of bogbean in June, when early marsh orchid and southern marsh orchid are at their best, with pyramidal orchids on drier hummocks. A superb cowslip meadow is of very different calibre from the rough pasture of the main complex, where selective grazing by animals leaves coarse tufts of ragwort and thistle. This is old, unploughed water meadow, traditionally mown for hay and grazed only as aftermath, when the cowslips and green-winged orchids have finished flowering and the spotted orchids are past their prime. Splendid stands of meadow cranesbill and musk mallow merge into the greater splendour of the dunes where sand spills inland from the coastal burrows.

Slender, tasty shaggy-caps or lawyer's-wigs (*Coprinus comatus*) are a conspicuous feature in summer, when the flesh is still firm and white in the puffballs (*Vascellum pratense* and *Bovista plumbea*). Fairy ring champignons (*Marasmius oreades*) and *Psathyrella* can also be seen from June on, but the ivory white *Hygrophorus niveus* seldom appears before September. *Fuligo septica* is one of the slime moulds which spend a mobile youth unsure whether to be plant or animal, but finally organise themselves into little spore packets that are definitely fungal.

Three-spined and ten-spined sticklebacks live in the dykes and are fed upon by heron and kingfisher. Heron imprints in the ginger sludge of ferric hydroxide flooring a few of the ditches confirm that even those fouled by iron can support life in these neutral to alkaline conditions. In the acid waters of the South Wales Coalfield both fish and invertebrates are more sensitive to this type of pollution, which affects them in the same way as suspended coal dust, coating the fish's gills and making life impossible for some of their prey animals.

Tadpoles cluster about the stems of great water dock, some of them falling prey to great diving beetles. Pond skaters take smaller morsels from the surface, while ever-hungry nymphs of dragonfly and damselfly patrol the muddy depths. Horseflies and midges emerge to prey on the warm-blooded, and fragile white plume moths mingle with the more familiar cinnabars and burnets.

Black-headed gulls started to breed in the slacks of Margam Burrows quite close to the River Kenfig in the 1890s—the first ever to do so in Wales. Influx into the now more typical sites of bog and moorland in Mid Wales began in the early 1900s. During the 1920s and 30s they also bred more or less continuously in Kenfig Burrows, and later in the Eglwys Nunydd Pools which preceded the reservoir. They have gone from Kenfig long since, and the pair which failed to rear its brood by the Kenfig River in 1977 was the first to try in 40 years, but the colony persisted at Margam.

The birds moved north and occupied islets in a shallow, oil-sullied pool in the 1960s and 70s, but this lay in the path of extensions to the Abbey Steelworks. Impeded drainage in 1976 initiated a 4 feet rise in water level which increased the size of the pool threefold, but left sufficient tussocks for them to carry on nesting. The oiliness lessened, as much was being recovered and burned by then. Hedged about though they were by tips and artefacts, the gulls' spruce feathers were scarcely soiled and their lives apparently unaffected, but it all proved too much in the end and they are there no more.

164

Other dwellers in this area watched and filmed over the years by Alan Pickens and Sydney Johnson have fared no better than the black-headed gulls filmed by Colonel Morrey Salmon in 1911. The kestrels, crows and woodpeckers which nested in the fire-killed pines used for target practice during the last war have lost their habitat entirely, as have the goldfinches and yellowhammers which occupied the low scrub of white poplar saplings and elder which sprang up on burned ground near the Tower Farmhouse (a former hunting lodge of Margam Estate, now buried). The stonechat, wheatear and ringed plover sites in the dune grassland have been covered over, but the last two can make do with artificial rubble habitats just as well.

Many of the dykes were poisoned during the extensions, so that the moorhens died or were driven from their waterside homes. Plants on the banks were killed, so offered scant cover for the yellow wagtails, sedge warblers and reed buntings which were part and parcel of the summer scene until 1976 and whose nests were sometimes kicked out by ponies. Some of the remaining grassland was unsullied, its greensward being in heartening contrast to the brown strips along the channels, so skylarks and meadow pipits continued to nest as before, and the odd covey of partridges could still be flushed, but snipe no longer rear their young in the tussocky marsh.

Some, no doubt, of all these species will find territories south of the beach road, but their numbers will be sadly diminished. Sedge warblers left no stretch of suitable habitat unoccupied in the early seventies. Their territories were contiguous and a walk along a dyke would produce a series of cock birds taking up the declaration of land ownership as the notes of their neighbour died away. A few pairs of grasshopper warblers and reed warblers were nesting then, also white-throats in the bramble patches with wren, robin, dunnock, blackbird and song thrush.

Yellow wagtails were among the less usual of the nesting passerines and some of these were hard by the steelworks. The repetitive "swee-swee" as they carried food to the nest with the undulating flight characteristic of all wagtails, was an image-provoking sound which helped to dim the insalubrious visual impact of their environment.

This choicest of birds like *Butomus,* choicest of flowers, co-habits quite successfully with industrial enterprises, given the little bit of necessary leeway. The nesting sites which the species clung to in Cardiff and Swansea Docks were in dry grassy areas which were probably much wetter when their ancestors moved in in pre-dock times, but it is doubtful if they have nested in Cardiff Docks since the mid 1960s. Their Cadoxton (Barry) site has been taken over by a factory and on Crymlin Burrows they are right in among the oil storage tanks.

Spring migrants fly in from the Channel and linger on the coastal strip to feed before moving on to the hills, so they can be seen here a week or so ahead of their arrival in North Glamorgan. A cuckoo was spotted as early as 8th March in 1973. Normally chiff-chaff and wheatear are among the first, making a landfall in the second and third weeks of that month.

In 1972, before the rhythm of life was disrupted north of the beach road, willow warblers were first seen almost a month later (April 13th), with swallows and sand martins on the 18th: sedge warblers and yellow wagtails on the 22nd. Swifts were around by May 1st and whitethroats and blackcaps were not spotted until the 3rd June, but were probably about before. In that year the grasshopper warblers of mid-June were not seen again. Coot, moorhen and, possibly, water rail, still nest here, but the herons which appear, up to seven at a time, are probably from Margam Park.

Winter is quite as eventful birdwise. Snipe occur then, sometimes twenty-five together, though only a few pairs breed now. Curlew and lapwing come in big numbers in winter, with some staying on into summer. Golden plover and redshank winter on the marshes and a green sandpiper may drop in on passage. No redshank nests have been found, but the lovely sounds of the birds' courtship displays are to be heard in April, and the sharper notes of their alarm calls later on, suggesting that a few must rear their families here. Usually the only duck seen now are mallard and teal, both of which breed.

Big flocks of fieldfare and redwing come in the colder months, when kingfishers are more likely to be present and the numbers of pied and grey wagtails are augmented. Birds of prey seem more active at this season, and freshly killed corpses include those of teal, black-headed gull, lapwing, starling and meadow pipit. Buzzard, kestrel and sparrow

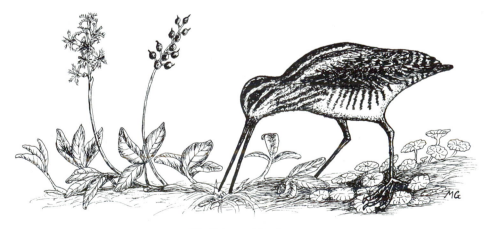

33. Snipe and bogbean

166

hawk and the occasional hen harrier, peregrine and merlin are the killers. A great grey shrike turned up in November 1972.

Water voles and brown rats tunnel in the banks of the dykes and moles throw up their mini-volcanoes from less waterlogged soils. Hares frisk in the March sunshine, where young rabbits will later be out at play, running the gauntlet of weasel and fox.

The grass moors terminate at their southern end in a spinney of young trees bordering Margam Burrows, where sea sands have been blown inland right to the railway. This area is seldom visited, and is probably richer in wildlife than Castle Wood at Kenfig. Diversity diminishes temporarily in both during bouts of cattle grazing.

Other mammals live here and the soft mossy balls of voles' nests can be found pulled out of ferny banks by foxes or crows. What was probably the summer nest of a dormouse was discovered on a visit with Arthur Morgan in late May 1978. If this is what it was, it will be the first record for West Glamorgan, the only other certain site in the triple county being near Caerphilly in Mid Glamorgan, with an old, unconfirmed report from Berry Wood in Gower.

The nest was conspicuously pear-shaped, made almost entirely of stripped honeysuckle bark and tucked among the woodbine stems five feet up a tree trunk. It contained small oval dung pellets and one black flea—which might have proved diagnostic had we managed to catch it! There were none of the nutshells or large seed remains that might have been found in autumn, dormice living on softer buds and shoots in early summer, even young honeysuckle leaves, until the blackberries and nuts ripen. Their winter nests are constructed below ground, among tree roots.

Trees are mainly downy birches, with a central hollow occupied by grey sallows and floored with yellow flag, kingcup, ragged robin and water figwort. The spinney is advancing south to swallow up a dune slack, transpiration from the increased leaf canopy drawing water from the sandy soil to initiate a general drying out. Creeping willow, once dominant of the slack, persists, along with twayblade and angelica, but the round-leaved wintergreen, St. John's worts and vetches are giving way to more shade-tolerant enchanter's nightshade, wood avens and lesser celandine. False oxlips are sometimes to be found, the primrose parent rarer than the cowslip, which is pleasantly abundant.

Toppled trees may reveal horsehair woven into the sheeps' wool linings of twiggy crows' nests built ten feet from the ground, while wrens' nests tucked in crevices of contorted trunks can be almost entirely of moss and hair. One was of honeysuckle, but differed from the suspected dormouse nest in having a substantial lining of moss and down. There is usually little differentiation of layers in the nests of small mammals.

Phlegmatic toads and summering smooth newts can be found under old logs, while ditches and pools yield a fine crop of dragon and damselflies. Particularly plentiful in May and June 1978 were broad-bodied libellulids, the chunky torsos of the males resplendent in powder blue, the females in yellow, with strong ginger veining at the base of the gauzy wings. Large red damselflies were also numerous, their slender crimson bodies narrowly striped with yellow and with a penultimate band of black. Both spend a lot of time sunning themselves on bramble leaves, the libellulids often wiping their huge compound eyes, cat fashion, with their forearms as they bask.

These noble insects are parodied at this season by the craneflies, with their feebler powers of flight and no greater efficiency when settled, for all that exaggerated length of limb. Reddish ones with legs less fragile than most are *Ctenophora atrata*. The adults vary from yellowish-red to blackish-red and the young stages live in rotting timber on the woodland floor. Other bright craneflies breeding here in damp wood and leaf mould are *Limnophila ferruginea*. These were indulging in mating flights, with tails attached, in late May, one of each pair yellow with a dorsal line of black specks, the other orange with a continuous black line.

Next down for size are the scorpion flies (*Panorpa communis*) the males with unmistakable bloated red tail hoisted over their backs to look more menacing than it is. Bluebottles mate busily on bramble leaves, preparing for the almost endless succession of oval white eggs which are squeezed from the female at the slightest whiff of anything edible, the more unsavoury the better. Red-tailed and buff-tailed bumble bees find the intensely blue flowers of Buxbaum's speedwell irresistible.

A bumble bees' nest of grass was found among tenuous stems of creeping willow struggling to live in the dark under the collapsed wall of a caravan. Such artefacts pose a visual intrusion to the visitor but are accepted by the wildlife for their intrinsic worth as shelter, from the elements and from predators. The bees' nest was surrounded by several feet of darkness in all directions, while being freely accessible through the mesh of twigs with no recourse to burrowing on the part of its makers. Black sand-hunting wasps with orange middles hover over the sand surface, where iridescent purple-bronze *Necrobia violacea* beetles scuttle among the sand cat's-tail grass.

On good days in May and June the borders of the spinney are alive with butterflies, some foraging out over the marsh, some over the dunes. Common blues are everywhere, with rather fewer small coppers and small heaths. Brown argus and dingy skipper are more special and there is a good population of wall browns, meadow browns, orange tips and small whites.

Plate 10   SAND DUNE SLACKS AT MARGAM—*Author*

44. Plants colonise old gravel diggings: steelworks tip beyond

45. Round-leaved wintergreen (*Pyrola rotundifolia*) in a bed of creeping willow

46. Drifts of marsh helleborine orchids fill the slacks

47. Two young newts found sheltering under an old log

48. Long-spurred fragrant orchid

49. Crimson form of early marsh orchid: fungal rust on leaf

50. Pendent buds of broad-leaved helleborine orchids

169

51

5

53

Plate 11 MARGAM MOORS IN 1980—*Author*

51. Margam Moors and south-east end of Steelworks
52. Large bindweed scrambles into the willow tops
53. Part of a fine stand of meadow cranesbill
54. Tall umbels of flowering rush grow in wet corners
55. Rafts of rare frogbit float on the dyke waters

54

5

It can be a revelation just to sit in such a place when the sun is high in the blue vault now no longer tinged with the Steelwork's special brand of red dust, and watch the life teeming all about, oblivious of the industrial holocaust. Though we cannot always set our sights on unsullied scenery in this mechanised world, we can try to gear our senses to appreciate the multiplicity of interesting creatures which live their little lives successfully in spite of all the forces ranged against them.

Part Four

Wildlife and Industry

Large white butterflies

A crack in the pavement is all a plant needs to put down roots. An old fashioned lamp standard makes as good a nesting box for a tit as any hollow oak. It is not the parks but the railway sidings that are thick with wild flowers.

Richard Mabey in "The Unofficial Countryside."

13 B.P. CHEMICALS: THE GENTLE GIANT

Exploiters and survivors, birds nesting on towers, plant and animal colonisation in areas treated annually with herbicide. Gradation from vesiculate slag seaward to sand dune and landward to marsh. Open water of the old Baglan Canal.

THE forces ranged against the wildlife within the perimeter of British Petroleum's Chemical Works at Baglan would seem insurmountable, but plants and animals are not defeated that easily. Biologists have a catch phrase, "Nature abhors a vacuum". If there is a niche where life is possible, life will flow in. The petrochemical works embraces many ecological niches, and life has flowed in generously.

Resembling a space rocket station in daylight and lighted battlefleet by night, the installations are widely spaced, with room between for newcomers which have learned to exploit man and room around for old stagers which have learned to tolerate him. Because most of the chemicals are inflammable, weed killer must be used to reduce the fire hazard. Thus the winter scene savours of a lunar landscape, but a visit at the peak of flowering time in June proves that non-risk plants, like the juicy cushions of stonecrop, thrive on this treatment—rejoicing in the lack of competition from those which have succumbed.

Four main habitats can be distinguished in the plot of land occupied by the self-styled "Gentle Giant". The area under heaviest pressure is where the primaeval soil has been buried beneath vesiculate grey slag from the Margam Steelworks and where herbicides are applied annually in February or March to curtail plant growth. Sand blowing from the dunes and flats to windward alleviates the austerity, giving a gradual transition to the second type of community, which is a relict dune system. This includes the remnants of the partially infilled pond which appears on the maps at the base of Witford Point—a pond no longer except in prolonged periods of heavy rain, but with an ameliorating humidity which sponsors an oasis of plenty on the half vegetated sands.

The inner part of the establishment was erected on marshy flats in 1967-68 and shows a similar gradient with increasing distance from the hub of activity. There are fewer installations, but a vast area was spread with clinker in case it should be needed and this grades out through the third habitat, where the soil water table is sufficiently high for hardy aquatics to push through.

174

The fourth habitat has the appearance of true alluvial marshland but is, in fact, no such thing. A water colour painted in 1806 by William Payne shows the whole of the area to have lain under the tidal waters of Baglan Bay, which lapped to the foot of the steep Coalfield hills. Relating the painting to the modern Ordnance Survey map, it depicts a view northward from the point marked "Old Refinery", across a wide expanse of water to that marked "Steelworks", the site of which, now derelict, was then occupied by a bustling copper works. Some of the area referred here to Baglan Bay is now ¾ mile from the nearest infiltration of the sea into the Neath Estuary.

Infilling occurred with the coming of the main-line railway in 1850 and the railway engineers made very sure, with their extensive coverage, that there should be no tidal inroads onto the iron way. They brought the dump to a height where fresh water seeped in as the salt water was pushed out—the level lying around the mean of the summer and winter water tables.

In the ensuing 130 years, plant growth has been sufficiently vigorous to produce a deep layer of silty black fen peat over whatever material was used. This has remained neutral to alkaline in reaction, supporting none of the acid-loving heathers and the like which are sneaking in along the Tennant Canal towpath through the neutral fen peats of Pant-y-Sais and Crymlin Bog.

The marshland is threaded today by a string of pools marking the line of the old Baglan Canal—not thought of in the artist's day, but later linking the Duport Steelworks at Briton Ferry with Margam. It is bordered along the north by a broad, concreted dyke to seaward of the railway and the less determinate line of the Mother Ditch, which is scheduled for annihilation in preparation for the next major change—the coming of the local section of the M4 motorway. The triangular "Lagoon" to the north-west belongs to the Afan Borough Council and receives the drainage waters from Baglan Moors.

Although not virgin, the marshland is superb and among the best that is left of a once extensive community. This it owes to the absence of grazing ponies and public access, with its unfortunate corollary of trampling, picking and general disturbance. The "Gentle Giant" has nurtured this gem, unwittingly, in its bosom: the last of its kind in Glamorgan: but cannot now avert the tragedy of its slipping from our hands beneath the unremitting tarmac of the impending motorway.

This valuable wetland could have provided unrivalled opportunity for comparative studies with the Magor Nature Reserve in Gwent—the final ungrazed relic of the other alluvial system this side of the Bristol Channel on the Wentlooge Levels beyond Cardiff—but it seems doomed to pass beyond our ken.

The surviving fragment, if not pounded to pulp during the influx of road-making equipment, will have to start afresh and is unlikely to be big enough to form a viable ecological unit for more than a few of the smaller organisms. This area, stolen by man from the sea in 1850 and reclaimed gently, unnoticed, over the years by the forces of the wild, is to be stolen again, so that commuters on the A48 to landward of the railway can have the choice of commuting instead on the parallel M4 to seaward.

It would be inhuman and unperceptive not to question the wisdom of such three-lane highway duplication, when it entails the loss of a little breath of heaven which could have carried a rich heritage of the lost Glamorgan into the future; a lifeline between the old road/rail links to the north and the new industrial complex to the south. The orchids and irises, it seems, will not be allowed to blaze on through the centuries, to the uninhibited chattering of sedge warblers and croaking of frogs, to show our children (and theirs), that we were not wholly unmindful of generations yet to come. Water rail and crested newt, drinker moth and skipper butterfly, will no longer be living their undemanding lives in this small corner, which would scarcely be missed by the society that has appropriated so much of their ancestral territory along the grey flank of the vast housing estate to the east.

While certain of the marshland creatures cannot change their ways sufficiently to live in close contact with new developments, others can, and appear to enjoy doing so. Caradoc, the crow, was quite an institution during the late seventies. He was a sorry-looking specimen, moulted feathers failing to regenerate as they should, and he was fed so many goodies by sympathetic employees that he took most of them off to hide. Unless the ground was frozen hard, he would dig a scrape in which to place his horde and cover it with an old works glove, polythene sheet or any handy artefact. This was no idle pastime. He remembered his caches and was seen returning to retrieve his gains.

Some of his kind nest regularly on the pylon-like lighting towers, one of 1980's three resident pairs occupying the top platform of the West tower of the Benzene Concentrate Plant. Masters of flight, crows have no need to land into the wind, like 'planes and albatrosses, but have an adequate stalling and braking system of their own. It is not hard to sense their enjoyment, as they rollick in downwind, twisting and turning on the breeze. Jackdaws, too, nest in the buildings and towers, the tallest of which reaches to 520 feet.

Several pairs of kestrels have bred on the lighting towers and more substantial concrete cooling towers, using the ledge on these where the overhang commences and a door allows the man climbing up the outside to continue his ascent within. Others nest on the flare stack where the surplus hydrocarbons are burned off, and repair work on the stack had to be rescheduled in 1979 to avoid disturbing them.

Starlings can cope with rebuffs more easily. A thousand or so flock into the towers to roost in autumn and maintenance gangs on night shift work within an arm's length of the speckled throng. Any disturbance causes the birds to flap off into the outer darkness, but they are soon back. Many nest on pipes, and in any suitable hole, indoors or out, as in the old workshop, where they keep company with house sparrows. By 1980 black redstarts had been seen on the PVC plant for three years in succession.

Buzzards are not resident, but a pair comes to circle in the thermals above the cooling towers, which produce a useful updraught and manufacture their own microclimate 1,000 feet above. There is no shortage of rabbits on site for them to hunt, nor of small passerines for the sparrow hawks which occasionally visit.

Two pairs of peregrines living in the Neath Valley come this way at times to hunt, and Terry Otterski has had the good fortune to see food being passed between a pair in mid-air. The tiercel came in with a fat wood pigeon in his talons and the falcon flew out to meet him, passing 20 feet below. As he dropped the offering, she somersaulted, catching it neatly in upturned claws to bear away, back to the nest.

Pied wagtails comb the site in numbers, picking insects and spiders from crannies in the honeycombed slag, and one has been known to pit its puny strength against Caradoc's. Others walk the water lily leaves in the ornamental pond by the administrative block canteen, like mini jacanas or lily trotters. Water onion, bogbean and others help to create an aquatic micro-habitat here which is utilised by more than the golden carp and pond skaters.

Areas of rubble are seldom quite devoid of vegetation and there are even a few of the notoriously pollution-sensitive lichens on the windward corner. Liver brown fruiting discs of *Lecanora dispersa* with scalloped white rims, are tiny enough to be overlooked—and to be little affected by atmospheric fallout—and are quite common on the slag fragments. In pollution-free areas the discs grow embedded in a grey thallus: here they are connected merely by a dark stain. Orange *Xanthoria parietina* is depauperate, but persists, and may receive an extra boost from nitrogenous fallout which others of its kind get from bird droppings.

Olive brown sheets of *Ceratodon purpureus* moss cover considerable areas of the most insalubrious substrate, winter and summer alike, but the silvery sheets of *Bryum argenteum,* so common on town pavements, appear only where blown sand fills the crannies. Spreading fronds of *Brachythecium albicans* come in among pioneer grasses as the deposit meets over the surface. Soft black residues of poly-iso-butylenes (PIB) (used as the basis of adhesives and as oil additives) have begun to weather and mix with sand, and are readily accepted as a rooting medium by hardy pioneers.

Loose carpets of rue-leaved saxifrage and thyme-leaved sandwort are sprinkled across them by the end of winter and coltsfoot flowers alleviate the overall blackness in March. By June the yellow stonecrop is at its best, in neat spherical pin cushions 4-6 inches across. Normally these circles would grow on, unevenly, around obstacles and competitors to coalesce. Here they are cut off by the next application of weed killer, but have set an abundance of seeds by then to start the cycle over again.

Germinating in the shelter of these radial growths, the little peas of hare's-foot clover have produced sizeable plants covered in soft pink flower heads by June. The short dead spikes of evening primrose have given rise to red-tinged leaf rosettes, while seedlings of annual wall rocket, lesser dandelion and annual meadow grass have got away. Velvety grey leaves of great mullein and pearly everlasting pop up here and there; weld, mignonette and creeping speedwell follow the lorry tracks, their seeds brought by the tyres and benefiting from the moist shelter of the furrows. Some are nibbled by rabbits, but the golden discs of stonecrop remain unscathed. Not for nothing has this been dubbed wall pepper. The acrid sap which deters rabbits, may also reduce insect attack. Sap-suckers, generally, tend not to favour those succulent plants with the inconvenient tendency to accumulate harmful residues. The plants are able to dilute these to innocuous concentrations in their copious cell sap, where they are beneficial as insect deterrents.

There is, however, nothing wrong with the nectar and the stonecrop flowers were buzzing with insect visitors in June 1980. Pollen baskets of the portly buff-tailed bumble bees (*Bombus terrestris*) were packed with rich yellow pollen. With probing tongues 8.2 mm. long, these would have fared equally well on the bird's-foot trefoil flowers, but not so the *Andrena* solitary bees. These, with a reach of only 2.7 mm., are important pollinators only of open flowers like the stonecrop, sea holly and yellow parsnip.

34. Ringed plover and yellow stonecrop

Sawflies of the family Tenthredinidae were probably there for the pollen, their chief food when adult: the parasitic wasps of the family Evaniidae may have been on the lookout for *Andrena* bees to parasitise. Bee-mimics, *Volucella bombylans,* had joined the throng. These are hoverflies, but are hairier than most and with a reddish tail, resembling very closely the bees they are aping. (There are several different forms mimicking several different kinds of bumble bee.) The association is closer than just mimicry, as the larvae live in the nests of bumble bees or wasps as scavengers.

Cynipid gall wasps were seen here, far from any possible host plants in which to produce their galls. Only by such wanderings can new habitats be reached and many must fall by the wayside in pursuit of the common cause. One of the marsh fly group, *Helcomyza ustulata,* had almost certainly got blown off course by the wind. This is a species associated with seaweed along the shoreline and unlikely to wittingly explore inland.

Beetles, as well endowed with wings as bees, sawflies, wasps and flies, were, nevertheless, only to be found crawling through the miniature forest of stonecrop 'trunks'. Here were two-spot and seven-spot lady-birds (*Adalia bipunctata* and *Coccinella septempunctata*), little black weevils (*Apion* sp.) and the carabid or ground beetle, *Amara aulica.* The Melyridae were represented by *Psilothrix nobilis;* the Oedemeridae by *Oedemera lurida,* relative of the more familiar thick-legged flower beetle.

Common field grasshoppers (*Chorthippus brunneus*) spurting blithely across the empty slag, epitomised the contempt felt by all these lowly organisms for man's attempts to annihilate the plants on which they depend. Close on their heels, with amelioration by sand-blow, came Capsid or Mirid bugs, *Amblytylus nasutus.* These are plant suckers, green to match their feeding substrate, but with the wing cases too short to cover all the transparent wings, and imparting a double diamond pattern.

With plant-sucking 'blackfly', they live where bird's-foot trefoil is able to take over from stonecrop as dominant on the deepening sands. The odd thistle wafts in at this stage of the succession and the seeds of small annuals like sea fern grass and dune fescue. With the arrival of more sand, marram and sand sedge appear to stabilise it, and from then on the scope widens. Heath dog violet and common pearlwort flower in spring, heralding the showier evening primroses, with their yellow petals shivering in zephyr breezes like a flock of tethered brimstone butterflies.

Sap-suckers, too, increase, with green, long-bodied, long-legged *Chorosoma schillingi* bugs creeping through the marram bases like mini-stick insects. Most of their family, the Rhopalidae, are red or black, and a less handy shape for life among wiry, close-set grass shoots.

179

Spittle bugs (*Philaenus spumarius*) favour the thistles, and adults in an area near the works were emerging about a fortnight before expected in 1980, in spite of the prolonged spell of cold weather, possibly as a result of a local rise in temperature. All the possible colour morphs were seen except black, and any such industrial melanism would have been of no service to them against their pale, sandy background. They have need to make themselves as invisible as possible, because the wasps which parasitise them do so in the adult phase, unable to cope with the froth surrounding the larvae.

Some of the 'cuckoo spit' is in the bottom of the marram clumps, with aphids, weevils and woodlice. Black speckling of old leaves and stems shows where other plant bugs have burrowed inside to pass the winter—as eggs, larvae, nymphs or adults.

Common swift moths (*Hepialis lupulina*), whose caterpillars feed on the roots of grasses and the like, venture in and there are plenty of Micro-lepidoptera of the family Nepticulidae. Small brown flies with distinctively pointed wings belong to a species of *Lonchoptera*.

Red mites scamper everywhere on the sun-warmed slag, overstepped by Daddy-long-legs or harvestmen. Black and white zebra or jumping spiders (*Salticus scenicus*) stalk their prey, catlike, making prodigious leaps for their size: of as much as 6 or 8 inches. They wear their four front eyes like headlights and sidelights and retreat to silk-lined havens in the bubble holes of the furnace waste—which supplies a maze of hidey holes for yellow-bodied spiders, black ants, banded *Helicella* snails and others.

Creeping cinquefoil advances as abrasive clouds of knee-high sand come to rest. Parasitic broomrape blossoms where its only possible hosts are rest harrow or coltsfoot; bringing the total of flowering plants to a round twenty. Another twenty come in on the deepening sand drifts: common storksbill, blue fleabane, sea mayweed and sea spurge among them. Grasses, clovers and rambling shoots of dewberry begin to mat the mobile surface and rosettes of three kinds of ragwort and three of plantain get established.

A brown hare was startled from a form where shaggy vegetation met across its back and the rabbits had left enough upstanding stems to act as songposts for stonechats. Two pairs of wheatears nested quite close together here in 1980, one under a discarded sheet between adjacent railway lines and one in an old rabbit burrow. Their mode of foraging necessitates an open plant cover and they cannot feed in the ranker growths of the ungrazed marsh.

By the sandier track leading to the old pond, earwigs scuttle among dove's foot cransbill and square-ended, long-snouted *Tortrix* moths flip out from underfoot. By early June there are a few laggard caterpillars of five-spot burnet moths (*Zygaena trifolii*), cocoons of six-spot burnets

(*Z. filipendulae*) and flying adults of cinnabar moths (*Thyria jacobaea*), whose caterpillars will later infest the ragwort. While so doing, they ingest the ragwort poison, senecin, storing it in their bloodstream and passing it on to the moths, whose red and black warning colouration is no more of a hoax than is the black and yellow wasp-striping of the young. Provoke a cinnabar moth and a blob of yellow fluid will appear at the mouth, while the wings spread to show the 'red for danger' signal. Such distasteful morsels can afford to fly as slowly and indeterminately as they do: few birds will have a second go!

The red and black burnet moths are also stuffed with poisons (including cyanides) and are blessed with a biochemical mechanism which prevents them from poisoning themselves. The five-spot burnets are the sub-species *palustrella* which flies in May and June and feeds on common bird's-foot trefoil when young. The subspecies *decreta* flies in July and August over marshes and feeds on marsh bird's-foot trefoil.

Members of the *Brassica* group on these sands use precious energy in equipping themselves with poisons as insect deterrents—but for cabbage white butterflies these act as an attractant. The mustard oils are volatile and floating molecules impinge on the sense organs in the butterfly's antennae, so that she can home in on the right sort of plant to lay her eggs. The ichneumon wasp, *Apanteles glomeratus*, which lays its eggs in the ensuing caterpillars, is also attracted by the essential oils—so effectively that entomologists think the large white butterfly might be extinct in Britain as a result, were it not for the annual influx of migrants.

The ubiquitous seven-spot ladybirds also store toxins. The speckled bluish larvae are less warningly coloured than the adults, but able to exude a drop of resinous fluid when attacked, this gumming up the predator so that it has to spend the next few hours cleaning itself. Usually it doesn't try again!

Sea stock began to increase around 1974 and, by the end of the decade, there were several hundred plants along the riverward edge of the works. Rabbits eat them down to the ground in hard weather, but their anchoring root systems can be enormous and a well-established stock sprouts unabashed from the beheaded base.

The partially filled pond towards the river mouth has been contaminated by hydrocarbon residues, but the rich flora and fauna show how much more highly the wildlife rates the enhanced humidity of the narrow depression than the lost purity of substrate. The only free water after the seven week drought of April and May 1980 was in an old metal drum lying on its side, but there had been sufficient for the rearing of tadpoles, and large frogs of other years squatted contentedly among the yellow iris and woody nightshade in early June.

A common lizard sunned itself on a weathered timber among common horsetail and the very rare sand lizard existed on these dunes in the late 1940s and early 1950s—but has been seen recently on only one of the dune systems on Gower. Rabbit burrows penetrate the sandy banks.

Southern marsh orchids rear brilliant spikes of flowers fully 5 inches long, glowing like tumblers of weak blackcurrant cordial with the sun behind. The plentiful soil water favours marsh arrow grass, soft and jointed rushes and sea sedge, giving a hint of brackishness. Drier parts support yellow wort, rock cress, dune pansy, silverweed, yarrow and a host of others. A brown rust fungus, *Puccinia calcitrapae,* speckles the leaves of creeping thistle.

Five kinds of butterfly were abroad here on 12th June, 1980: common blue, brown argus, wall brown, hedge brown and small white. A green-veined white was about on 27th June and delicately pencilled yellow shell moths hovering round the hemp agrimony. Red, white and black gold-tail moth caterpillars munched assiduously at the young dewberry leaves. Another 'woolly bear' with orange stripe along the back and faint speckling on the flanks was a white ermine, chewing holes in the centre of fleshy coltsfoot leaves instead of taking the easy way in from the edge.

Heavy thunder showers and hailstorms during the previous fortnight had replaced some of the lost water and yearling frogs were flipping everywhere. A big streamlined water beetle, sliver-flat and smoothly oval, scrabbled around the edge of a pool with reddish legs working overtime. Had this flown in, seeking a habitat to lay its eggs, or was it preparing to fly out in search of more permanent water?

Prize among the beetles was the bee chafer (*Trichius fasciatus*) sipping nectar from a hemlock water dropwort umbel. This is another bee mimic, with black and yellow wing cases too short to hide the furry yellow tail. Almost as broad as long, and lethargic enough to allow handling, it was, nevertheless, a high flier when it chose to take off. Another potential master of flight was the common Sympetrum dragonfly which sat around awaiting a mate.

Drone flies (*Eristalis tenax*) and sun flies (*Helophilus pendulus*), which emerge only when the sun is shining, are two of the Syrphid hover flies which hum motionless above flowers and perform extraordinary feats of flight. Both have 'rat-tailed maggots' living in submerged black mud or organic matter as their larval stage, the rat tail being a telescopic breathing tube in three segments, like a radio aerial, which can be retracted or extended to reach the surface, depending on water depth.

Shiny greenbottles, *Lucilia caesar,* share the flowers with the Syrphids, while Asilid flies, *Philonicus albiceps,* which ape digger wasps (also present) leap from underfoot to settle a few feet away.

Scintillating red and green ruby-tailed wasps (*Chrysis ignita*) are about, these slipping into the nests of solitary bees to lay their eggs when the owner is out.

Sleek bunches of ruddy tassel galls sprout on the few clumps of jointed rush where jumping plant lice, *Livia juncorum,* have laid theirs. Funnel spiders sit patiently at the mouths of their funnel web traps waiting for some unwary insect to blunder over the trip wires and topple in.

The marsh inland of the works merits a chapter in its own right but includes much of what has already been mentioned in that on "Diminishing Alluvial Flats". Diversity increases as the overlying slag thins to allow wet soil nearer the surface. Its height is not very different from that of the Works, where the water table is only 2 feet below floor level at high tide. On raised ballast carrying railway lines there are feathery stands of pale toadflax, mats of rough clover (*Trifolium scabrum*) and cushions of stonecrop. Elegant sprays of mignonette sprout in June with wild carrot to follow. Ox-eye daisies overshadow the annuals and dewberry creeps in from the edges.

The major dry parts are sparsely vegetated levels where lapwing and ringed plover sit on clutches of cryptically speckled eggs and carry food to spherical, long-legged chicks bowling round among scattered vegetation tufts. These grade into shaggy grassland dominated by tall oat grass, cocksfoot and couch. In between is a good average limestone grassland flora with kidney vetch and purple tare, centaury and yellow rattle, hemlock, chervil and yellow parsnip, woundwort, knapweed and mugwort.

Showers of plant hoppers of the Delphacidae and Cicadellidae can be disturbed from the sward, the Deltocephalines with triangular heads. Members of the Reduviidae are predatory, blood-sucking bugs, their formidable beak curved back under the body when at rest. The leaf hopper, *Zyginidia scutellaris,* is one of the few of its sub-family, Typhlocibinae, to be found among grass rather than trees. It punctures the upper surface of leaves to suck the green contents from the palisade cells, leaving them blotched with white. Some of the cuckoo spit on the grass is produced by *Neophilaenus lineatus,* but the most spectacular of the plant bugs is the red and black fire bug, *Cercopis vulnerata,* whose nymphs feed on plant roots.

Other root feeders are the leather jackets which lie, fat and sluggish, in tunnels under stones. Some have already metamorphosed into craneflies by May and June. A chafer or scarab beetle which lays its eggs in dry dung and pupates in the ground is *Aphodius fimetarius.*

Large and small whites, small coppers and small skippers, small tortoiseshells and painted ladies dance in the sun. June 1980 was exceptionally good for migrant painted ladies, these possibly fleeing hither from the prevalent bad weather on the continent. Common heath moths (*Ematurga atomaria*) and *Crambus* grass moths are here, with yellow shells and prettily-shaped blood vein moths (*Calothysanis amata*) and the first of the summer's silver Ys (*Plusia gamma*) in June.

Outsize caterpillars of drinker moths (*Philudoria potatoria*) disport themselves on upstanding stems, orange-flecked 'woolly bears' with black tufts at either end and white ones along the flanks. Darker and hairier are the garden tigers, *Arctia caja,* which, like cinnabars, produce moths with gorgeous warning colour on the hind wings.

Worker wasps begin to emerge in June, too, and the robin's pin-cushions caused by the gall wasp, *Diplolepis rosae,* burgeon on the dog roses, changing from orange to crimson. Solitary wolf spiders lurk in pear-shaped, silk-lined chambers at ground level, with egg sac clamped firmly beneath. By late June many broods of spiderlings have hatched from the cobweb purses slung among the flowers. In repose they bunch together, but a gentle touch sends them radiating in all directions.

Seen at the peak of flowering, the main marshland could best be described as an amalgam of orchid glades and willow tumps. The rich wine colour of the southern marsh orchids is interspersed with the paler hues of common spotted orchids—the second parent of the outstandingly vigorous hybrid swarms. Long grass is topped by ragged robin and marsh bedstraw, the kingcups and cuckoo flowers gone; mint and meadowsweet yet to come. Downy fleabane brightens beds of hairy and false fox sedges between splaying tufts of giant fescue and the odd sea buckthorn bush. There are tiny reedbeds, no wetter than the rest, with a few *Lipara lucens* cigar galls, and patches of creeping willow low to the ground.

Most of the willows are goat and grey sallows, rounded growths averaging 5-8 feet high in 1980, with grassy corridors between. Alders are rarer and larger and downy birch so scarce that few of its usual insect predators have managed to locate it. This did not apply to the sallows, which can support almost as good an invertebrate life, size for size, as oak.

Willow leaf hoppers tend to be phloem feeders, plugging into the veins, so the leaves have none of the white stippling caused by the mesophyll feeders which pierce the epidermis to suck the green contents from individual cells. In Britain they confine their attention to willow and poplar, except for one, which will accept maple as host. Three of the kinds identified are *Cixius nervosus, Idioceros lituratus* and *Kybos* species.

More conspicuous in 1980 were the willow leaf beetles, *Galerucella lineola,* which had caused such havoc the previous year on Crymlin Bog, but had merely reduced the leaves to broderie anglaise texture this

184

year. Mating and egg laying were in progress on 12th June, the bigger female with wings raised to show part of the segmented abdomen, the smaller male with shiny black penis large out of proportion to the rest. The cream-coloured eggs were being deposited in circular clusters of 12 to 20 and about half the leaves of badly infested bushes carried clusters of eggs and adults. By 27th June there was scarcely a beetle to be seen.

Metallic green dock leaf beetles, *Gastrophysa viridula,* scuttled over the dock leaves below, some of the gravid females so portly that their pace was slowed and their decorative wing cases forced up by the load of eggs in the bloated abdomen. Speckly figwort weevils, *Cionis hortulanus,* with black velvet tuft on the 'withers' ambled in mounted couples on the leaves of water figwort in June.

Gold tail moth caterpillars (*Euproctis similis*) are again present, feeding on the sallow leaves this time. Their warning colours tell of noxious bristles—grown by the caterpillars, incorporated in the chrysalis, wiped off by the female moth on her bushy tail and deposited over the new laid eggs—one armoury of weapons sufficing for all four of the life stages. The moths, which fly at dusk in July and August, are white and ghostlike.

Black and green sawflies of the Tenthredinidae, rest their striped legs among the willows and Braconid wasps are also about. Two Tabanids are on the lookout for a drink of warm blood as the summer matures. Clegs (*Haematopota pluvialis*) are distinguished by their mottled wings, horseflies (*Chrysops relictus*) by their glowing green eyes. The female (the one which sneaks up quietly and does the damage) has orange flecks on the dark body. Males sip nectar from flowers of the carrot family.

Exquisite golden-eyed lacewings flutter among angelica and chervil and elongated scorpion flies with dappled wings wave ineffectual red tails aloft. Elongated *Tetragnatha extensa* spiders stretch themselves out along narrow reeds, head downwards, with long legs extended fore and aft and a smaller mid-hind pair clasping crosswise. Brown-lipped hedge snails crawl into the willows and clamp on in numbers about 3 feet from the ground.

Willow warblers nest among the willows, sedge warblers among the sedges and a family of reed warblers was abroad on 27th June 1980. The grasshopper warblers seen in early spring probably do not stay on to breed and chiff chaffs are rare. Song thrushes, blackbirds, dunnocks, robins and wrens breed, yellow wagtails may still do so and the odd grey wagtail was to be seen in 1980. Pied wagtails nest and one, preparing for her second brood in this year, had gathered a wad of sheep's wool as big as a ping-pong ball, so that she failed to see where she was going and flew a zig zag course to the nest site!

Young great tits line up on branches to be stuffed with leaf hoppers and weevils when the 'rope hanging' caterpillars are all used. Blue tits comb the budding tips of bramble for aphids to deliver to even more spherical young and whispering parties of long-tailed tits blow in at times to join the home-bred ones.

Reed buntings are characteristic, the males resplendent on their modestly elevated song posts, and yellow hammers call for their 'little bit of bread and no cheese' among the sallows. Greenfinch, chaffinch and linnet poke for seeds throughout the year and goldfinches build up from a few in midsummer to sizeable charms harvesting the teasel, thistle and evening primrose crops in autumn and winter.

Skylarks and meadow pipits nest in the more open parts, moorhens in the seclusion of waterside herbage. Curlew, oyster-catcher and grey plover shelter in hard weather, but this is not one of Glamorgan's golden plover haunts.

Those most secretive of marsh birds, the water rails, bring off chicks successfully and six eggs were spotted in the nest in 1979. Like the mute swans, they are around all the year, but it is not every year that the swans manage to rear their cygnets on the Lagoon Pool. Mallard fly in occasionally but are not known to nest and teal have not been seen. (The clutch of goose eggs found in 1979 was a hoax!) There are said to be as many as 20 lapwings nesting and, by late June, their fleet-footed young are abroad, becoming suddenly invisible at the appealing command from above when intruders are about.

Foxes produced a family of cubs in 1980 in a secret earth and another family of four or five visits occasionally. Juveniles, unused to disturbance, may be momentarily petrified when nearly stepped on. Feral cats are quite common, nursing their litters of kittens in old rabbit holes. They were introduced by construction workers to keep down rats and mice, and these are still about to sustain them, along with young rabbits and leverets. Most are wild and unapproachable and, apart from the odd pet, are likely to be tag-eared and battle-scarred. Field voles tunnel in thick herbage and some of the water vole holes in the old canal bank have mounds of excavated material underneath the size of an average molehill. Genuine molehills occur, but neither hedgehog nor bats have been seen and there has been no live-trapping to reveal such as shrews.

Rudd, eels, minnows and sticklebacks have been recorded in the string of pools, but the water is too scant to supply all their needs. They remain small and the avidity with which they rush at fragments of bread cast upon the waters, suggests that they feel undernourished. Batches are caught at intervals for release into the Neath and Tennant Canals. Smooth newts and rarer great-crested newts, which are also present, were rescued and transferred to the Tennant Canal when a pool was to

Plate 12　PORT TALBOT OLD
　　　　　 FRESHWATER DOCKS IN
　　　　　 1980—*Author*

56. A riot of pink crown vetch flowers in July (*Coronilla varia*)
57. Sickle medick massed with yellow pea flowers (*Medicago falcata*)
58. Yellow horned poppy finds rubble dumps as accommodating as pebble beaches
59. Natural regeneration on old wharves (the broom and gorse ablaze with flowers in Spring)

56

57

58

59

187

Plate 13   CURLEW IN ACTION—*Keri Williams*

   60. Drinking
   61. Gulping down a shore crab
   62. Scratching chin
   63. Wiping beak over preen gland
   64. Washing wings
   65. Finishing the bath with a good shake

188

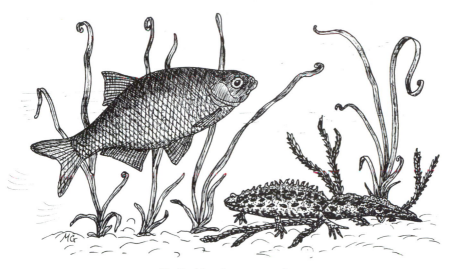

35. Rudd and great crested newt

be filled in and hundreds of frogs and toads were dredged up when the lagoon was being cleared.

June 1980 saw striped blue *Aeshna* dragonflies zooming over the peat-stained waters, with three kinds of damselfly. *Ischnura elegans* with banded blue tail was commonest, but the bluer *Coenagrion puella* and small red *Pyrrhosoma tenellum* were almost equally so, the last, particularly the females, with more black on them than the large reds of the Margam Moors. All three species were flying in tandem, mating and egg laying.

David Edwards of BP keeps an eye on freshwater happenings and is engaged in a study of the microscopic aquatic life which provides for the dragonfly nymphs via larger creatures, from water beetles to worms. Submerged larvae of caddis flies and Chironomid midges contribute to this link in the food chain, but probably not the scuttling water mites with their warning red coloration.

More sedentary life includes leeches, Planarian flatworms and green Hydra, *Chlorohydra viridissima* with starred tentacles. Open cones of bell animalcules, *Vorticella microstigma,* retract at a touch, on spiralling stalks, and jelly-like moss animalcules, *Cristatella mucedo,* reproduce in three different ways; by budding, by releasing ready-hatched larvae and by producing tough, seedlike statoblasts able to carry them through the winter.

Among the Crustaceans are Ostracods and *Cyclops;* among the Rotifers bell-shaped *Synchaeta pectinata* and 'bristle-backs', *Chaetonotus larus;* among the Protozoa the two well-known 'classroom types', *Amoeba* and *Paramecium.* Some of the prettier of the

189

microscopic green algae which may contribute seasonally to the 'pea soup' water blooms are Desmids such as *Closterium ehrenbergii* and the colonial spheres of *Eudorina elegans* and *Volvox globator*.

As lesser pools dried up in the spring 1980 drought, the water life unable to fly away was stranded, the best preserved remains being tall spired shells of moss bladder snails (*Aplecta hypnorum*), shorter ones of wandering snails (*Lymnaea peregra*) and bigger ones of great pond snails (*L. stagnalis*). Some of these pools, scrunchy with deposited lime, appeared to hold thousands of empty caddis tubes, but these proved to be fragments of grass stem enveloped in prettily scalloped lobes of tufa—the original stem often rotted away to leave a parody of Crinoidal limestone. On pool beds exposed for long, the tufa had disintegrated to a white powder and was pierced by an abbreviated flora of small-flowered forget-me-not and creeping yellow-cress, with marginal silverweed.

Several score *Butomus* plants held pink heads high among yellow flags, bobble-laden bur-reed and sea sedge in the biggest remaining fragment of the Baglan Canal. Common spike rush was advancing into the water, but the rare slender spike rush (*Eleocharis uniglumis*) was found only in the slack-like depressions. Like the patches of variegated horsetail topped by oval orange cones on slender necks, these savoured more of dunes than of marshes.

Pools on rubble nearer the works showed fine stands of water horse-tail, great reedmace and seaside bulrush, with a scattering of parsley water dropwort in a matrix of lesser spearwort. Others, more ephemeral, were devoid of large plants and were ideal nurseries for wriggling mosquito larvae. Undesirable? Perhaps, but these are perfect bird food and every privilege has a price on it.

How much are we willing to pay to sustain these life systems? Allow the pools to lie and there will be aquatic life for waterfowl: allow the scrub to develop and there will be leaf hoppers, beetles and caterpillars for woodland birds: allow rank grasses to clothe the banks and there will be flowers for butterflies and cover for foxes and hares.

The Baglan Bay site is a microcosm which tells the whole story. The message which comes through is twofold. Preserve the habitat and Nature will respond lavishly: destroy it and she will demonstrate how resilient and forgiving she can be—up to a point. The advance of the minions leaves us in no doubt that she could be our ally in promoting a better world if we choose to let her.

(I am grateful to Colin Pitts of BP Chemicals for making my visits to the works so profitable and pleasurable, to Terry Otterski and Noel Dorey-Phillips for information about the birds, David Edwards for a list of freshwater organisms and Gerry Nixon of University College, Cardiff, for joining the survey and identifying the more obscure invertebrates.)

14 WILDLIFE OF THE GREAT ABBEY STEELWORKS AT PORT TALBOT

*Uneasy compromise:man-made niches for plants and animals:
a wealth of bird life*

WHEN the iron and steel industry moved from the uplands of Mid Glamorgan to the coastlands of West Glamorgan, it posed a serious threat to one of the triple county's richest natural communities. The move appears at first to have been from one barren tract of land to another: from bleak unproductive moorlands of the northern Millstone Grit to wet, sandy wastes emerging from the sea.

Speaking biologically, however, only the moors are barren, with their vast repetitive acres of rough grazing and little species diversity. These we could have spared for industry at little cost, apart from the inevitable loss of uplifting mountain views, but the ore ran out. In shifting to the coast to use imported ores, the new works sprawled across the sort of acres which are everywhere under heavy pressure, because of their convenient flatness or their value as farmland when drained. Steel we must have, and jobs, but there is a price to be paid.

It was inevitable that the Abbey Steelworks, largest in Europe and stretching along nearly three miles of coast, should come here: there is scarcely another part of Glamorgan with that amount of flat land. What we need to remember in future planning is that smaller enterprises can occupy smaller sites—preferably those already ravaged by earlier industry or given a synthetic face-lift, as in the Swansea Valley's admirable rehabilitation scheme.

The policy of covering unspoiled countryside with new industrial concerns, while pouring money into the conversion of derelict land into new countryside, is both thriftless and short-sighted. Our pathetic attempts to reinstate a pale replica of the landscape diversity our ancestors knew, would be laudable if we were not destroying the real thing as fast as we create the sorry imitation. More far-sighted planning for the best use of limited land resources can save the God-given beauty and halve the costs, necessitating work on far fewer sites. Such economies are now being written into the county structure plans.

Mediaeval man had need to protect his beleaguered settlements from encroachment by the wilderness, holding at bay with walls and moats the swamps, forests and sands; the hungry deer and wolves. Today we must protect the dwindling amount of wilderness and animal life from the urban sprawl, which creeps insidiously out from any industrial nucleus. It is the outer fringes which are often the most deplorable waste: part abandoned farmland, part shack, part dump, in a derelict limbo of uncertainty between town and country.

This limbo is often a write-off from the aesthetic and amenity point of view, but can be surprisingly rich biologically. A thought-provoking exercise is to consider how readily many plants and animals accept the new regime, ignoring the ugliness and making use of any artificial quarters or food sources which measure up to their requirements. It is man they avoid rather than his works.

Whilst a vehicle is a more blatantly un-natural part of the environment than a person, it is outside the ken of instinctive reaction patterns and more readily accepted by wild creatures—enabling naturalists to watch lions and farmers to shoot rooks. An opportunity to wander round part of the Abbey Steelworks illustrates this truth to a nicety.

Those who earn their living there are mostly divorced from the wildscape, unaware of the life about them, and they are ignored in their turn. They do not root out primroses like some of the leisure-seeking public, persecute predators as a gamekeeper might or filch birds' eggs with our urban cherubs. There is a state of laissez faire and birds and mammals go about their business untroubled by the din, while plants creep inexorably across untrodden corners.

The richer the habitat to start with, the greater the potential for invasion. A lump of discarded slag in the bleak, abandoned 'ironscape' of Dowlais Top near Merthyr Tydfil will support scrappy *Polytrichum* moss, *Cladonia* lichen, sheep's fescue grass and little else. A similar lump at Port Talbot could give a home to lush mallow, lady's fingers and willow herbs, and might have a wheatear nesting beneath or a

36. Redshank on mud banks

ringed plover on top. Their kind will outlive the Steelworks, so long as we leave them survival space during our occupation.

A former employee of the Company, who was by no means ignorant of the creatures all about him on the site, is Alan Pickens, and much of what follows is the result of his painstaking daily observations over the years.

Forming, perhaps, the most unpropitious habitats of all, are the roofs of the buildings, but life can succeed even here if given the time to establish. Bituminised roofing felt is first colonised by close growths of moss, which cradle biting stonecrop among their moisture-retaining shoots. The minerals essential for flower formation are lacking, however, unless gulls nest on the roofs, and supply these in their droppings.

Herring gulls formerly nested on the melting shop and old coke ovens, where they were as immune from human disturbance as on the remotest of the Heritage Coast cliffs. The buildings were pulled down in the mid-seventies and 1977 saw the gulls established instead on top of the cold mill—82 pairs bred on roofs here in 1975; 80-90 in 1977, and a pair of kestrels joined them in 1980.

Goldfinches, chaffinches and linnets nest on the tanks bordering the computer block and the cold mill as well as in adjacent trees. They feed on a sequence of weed seeds, those of evening primrose, teasel and thistle carrying them well into winter. It is joy to watch the busy flocks at work on the thistles, juggling the plumed seeds round in the beak and nipping off the silken parachute to drift away, so that some, at least, of the wind-borne thistledown is not a source of further infestation.

Starlings and house sparrows nest on the steel structures of the cold mill and general stores, the open ends of pipes providing delectable homes for the starlings. Steam pipes are a traditional roosting site for starlings at Cardiff and Llanwern Steelworks. These are not birds to suffer cold feet when man's domestic animals or artefacts can be used to good advantage, and it is these which we most often see on the backs of sheep, with their toes tucked deep in the woolly fleece.

They have learned quite painlessly that window sills of city buildings make roosts quite as acceptable as ledges of lonely cliffs, and have gained warmth in the doing, from urban central heating systems. This is evolution in action.

1975 saw a group of opulent sparrows taking time off while embryos developed unaided inside their eggs and naked chicks remained cosy without being brooded. They had built their untidy nests behind the lagging of steam pipes in which the temperature was 400°C. It was pleasanter to sit outside in the cool and chat among themselves. Time enough to take up the threads of housekeeping again when the chicks started demanding food. Even at this stage life would be easier than for

193

their country cousins (not that house sparrows are ever far removed from the domain of man). The Port Talbot chicks would not be using precious calories to keep out the cold.

Birds such as gull, starling, sparrow and crow will survive longest wherever we continue our headlong rush into complete industrialisation. 'Adapt or perish' is a fundamental law of survival. They, like the steel workers, have learned to 'strike while the iron's hot'.

A pair of ravens, largest of our British crows, sometimes nests on a tower in the works, foraging out over the tips and shores. Others bring off their chicks on the Guildhall in Swansea, working the Oystermouth beaches for carrion: yet others occupy a working quarry at Ogmore, accepting with equanimity the intermittent blasting calculated to scare the wits out of any bird of the wilderness. Yet it is not so many years ago that ravens epitomised the wildest tracts of mountain, moorland and sea cliff, and such proximity to man would have been inconceivable.

Ravens are Corvids and Corvids rank with gulls as our most intelligent and adaptable birds—less slavishly tied to the instinctive behaviour that governs the lives of all. Jackdaws are great exploiters of domestic chimney pots. Only the beautiful red-legged chough has failed to come to terms with the changing world, the few survivors having retreated from the clamour of industrial South Wales to the West Wales cliffs.

Pied wagtails need little persuading to come indoors to winter roosts on roof rafters and overhead pipes, moving out to include the insects of roof mosses in their daytime foraging. These can be territorially belligerent to the extent of fighting their own reflection in the wing mirrors of parked cars, but at Port Talbot it was a grey wagtail which indulged in this energy-consuming pastime—until the mirrors were covered with a pair of old gloves!

Blue tits and great tits frequent the trees around the cold mill canteen throughout the year and are joined by gossiping groups of long-tailed tits and goldcrests in winter. For such scraps of warm-blooded life as these, with their large surface to volume ratio, loss of body heat can be critical during the cold months and any man-made warmth is greatly appreciated.

Sedge warbler, blackbird, song thrush, dunnock, robin, meadow pipit and reed bunting may all nest close to the buildings. Willow warblers, chiffchaffs and young wheatears turn up in August and September, some lingering into October.

Meadow pipits flock in fair numbers in winter, skylarks less frequently, although a group of forty to fifty has been seen. These last can often be heard singing on the waste ground bordering the Sinter plant and between here and the old harbour—an area from which partridges may be flushed.

194

Swallows and sand martins arrive in mid-April, flying in from Eglwys Nunydd Reservoir to the south in small flocks, the passage lasting from three to seven days. Swallows and swifts abound during summer and wrens and mistle thrushes are about then, along with jackdaws, rooks and carrion crows. The gull flocks are augmented by common gulls in winter and extra lesser-black-backs in summer, when the number of black-headed gulls falls off. Buzzard, kestrel and, rarely, a harrier, may be seen overhead and other casual passers by are heron, cormorant and lapwing.

There is a fair-sized reedbed in the works where mute swans may use the same nest in successive years. Coot and moorhen are always to be seen and sedge warbler and reed bunting sing and probably nest, along with dunnocks and meadow pipits. Stonechats are successful in bringing off as many as six young some years.

Ringed plovers breed annually on the seaward side of the waste tip, trotting along the sun-warmed tarmac of the haul road to lure intruders from the nest. Wheatears lay their eggs at the landward base of the tip where a jumble of brickbats provides suitable crevices. Such a luxury was hard to come by in the pre-existing dunes and marshland, when their need for nesting burrows was supplied by a vigorous population of rabbits.

Foxes trot nonchalantly among the coal wagons by the tippler pits and can sometimes be seen on the skyline from the beach below. They no doubt help to keep down the rat population and compete with the resident weasels and kestrels for smaller rodents.

A good sized rabbit warren has been constructed in the oldest part of the tip, within the works. Rabbits and wheatears often co-habit, as here, because these birds cannot forage effectively unless the turf is kept short by grazing. Both feed across abandoned parts of the coal dump adjoining their living quarters—uninterrupted through the daylight hours. Rabbit nibbling is sufficiently close to allow low growths of acrid, unpalatable biting stonecrop to dominate the area without being swamped by taller species. The mats produce a blaze of yellow flowers, which look particularly fine against the background of coal dust. Others doing only slightly less well here are bird's-foot trefoil, lesser yellow clover and storksbill.

The sparse grass swards bordering the hard core roads through the works are made up largely of rat's tail fescue with some common bent, these turning the colour of ripe barley in midsummer. Along with all the expected annuals—sandworts, pearlworts, stitchworts and chickweeds—are vetches, peas and clovers, the little blue fleabane and the larger yellow fleabane in unusually dry situations. Spikes of rayed and unrayed knapweed, agrimony, goatsbeard, white and yellow melilot and scarlet poppy add touches of richer colour. Lesser broomrape and bee orchids grow on sands near the marshalling yards, the fungal partners in their roots making life possible in the disturbed, infertile soil of this area.

A hundred and twenty six species of flowering plants have been recorded within the confines of the Steelworks. This is more than in an average well-established plant community. The inevitable disruptions suffered occasionally serve to keep the habitat open, with room for newcomers to germinate and grow, if only temporarily.

There is no traffic on the several miles of waste tip, which consists of many things, from furnace cleanings and contractors' rubble to old iron, tyres and the contents of wastepaper baskets with left-over lunches to attract gulls, crows, daws and starlings. Parts have the texture of liquid tar, parts of solid tarmac; some is powder fine, some gravelly. The vegetation (if any) depends on what has been dumped, and tends to grow in strips, following each consignment.

Tall spikes of great mullein are a striking feature, with Oxford ragwort, which bears the name *Senecio squalidus* because of the places in which it habitually grows. It is far from squalid in itself. Over most it is the unselective docks, thistles, nettles and plantains which hold sway. Usually there is a sharp change at sand level to beauties such as musk mallow, viper's bugloss and sea convolvulus. Do what we may to create squalor, Nature forgives and does her best to hide our synthetic nastiness with her natural loveliness. If we defeat her in our own time we shall be the losers and she will triumph when we are gone.

Not all natural organisms are able to cope so well in the concrete jungle. While hardy ones are moving into the Steelworks, pollutants are moving out and pushing the more sensitive ahead of them. Many lichens are particularly vulnerable to air-borne sulphur dioxide and an assessment of the lichen density and species diversity can indicate the extent of industrial pollution.

Brian Pyatt has carried out a survey to windward and leeward of the Abbey works, to see how Port Talbot's lichens have fared. He found the 'lichen desert' around the works to be quite small—just over $1\frac{1}{2} \times 4\frac{7}{8}$ kilometres—possibly because atmospheric pollution is not severe, possibly because the pollutants are quickly dissipated by the strong sea winds, and funnelled up the valleys to leeward.

Different species exhibit different degrees of tolerance, and it is usually those adhering most closely to the substrate that can cope with the greatest sulphur dioxide fallout. These are the crust-forming or crustose species. More loosely adherent, lobed ones, the foliose forms, tend to occur further from the source of pollution, in what may be termed the struggle zone, while upright, branched or fruticose ones live furthest away, these having more of their vulnerable surface exposed to the poisons in the air.

196

Plate IX   MARSH ORCHIDS OF BP's PETROCHEMICAL WORKS—*Author*

34. Top left: Southern marsh orchid with flat lip
35. Top mid: Hybrid marsh orchid with long bracts
36. Top right: Early marsh orchid with folded lip
37. Bottom: Cluster of marsh orchids in damp dune depression

Plate X RODENTS OF INDUSTRIAL SITES—*Keri Williams*

38/39. Above: Field mouse: long nose and ears and protruding eyes for night foraging

40/41. Below: Brown rat: close-up shows tick and tick bites on ears and sand on whiskers

38

39

40

41

198

All will grow faster, larger and thicker and produce more spores having a higher percentage viability in a purer atmosphere, but the more upstanding will tend to smother the others when all are growing well. There thus ensues a gradual transition from sparse crustose or 'incoherent' powdery forms, through foliose to fruticose-dominated lichen communities. This will be complicated by aspect and microhabitat, with the more sensitive sometimes occupying the side of a wall facing away from the works, while quite different ones occupy the other side, these possibly exhibiting dark necrotic spots or edges to the greyish fronds.

Generally lichens need plenty of sunlight, but a certain amount of overarching vegetation may prove beneficial in filtering off some of the toxic particles as they drift groundwards. 104 species of lichens were identified during the Port Talbot Survey, but only five of these were found in the Margam kilometre square by the works, as against forty three in the kilometre square south of Glyncorrwg, 14½ kilometres north-east.

Lecanora conizaeoides, one of Glamorgan's most pollution-tolerant lichens, is abundant at Port Talbot but is readily overrun by spreading, wavy-edged slabs of *Parmelia saxatilis* further away. The powdery grey growths are largely confined to such areas of fairly high pollution, possibly because of the absence of this sort of competition, but perhaps because they have an actual need for the sulphur compounds in the pollutants—a suggestion supported by the finding of the species near sulphur springs in Iceland by Bailey.

Lichens are slow-growing and long-lived. When adhering to rocks, walls or tree trunks, as they so often are, they need to be efficient at picking up minerals from blown dust or any other available source. If these minerals are toxic, they have no ready way, such as leaf-fall, of getting rid of them, so the progressive accumulation will usually prove too much.

Two others of this genus, *Lecanora campestris* and *Lecanora dispersa,* are among the five most smoke-resistant species at Port Talbot, along with *Lepraria incana* and *Squamaria muralis. Lecidea macrocarpa,* the orange *Xanthoria parietina* and the already mentioned *Parmelia saxatilis* are usually the next to appear, but fairly well away from the worst of the sulphur dioxide fallout, or avoiding the horizontal surfaces on which the particles are most liable to settle.

Pollution can affect lichens in several ways. Smoke in the air will cut down the amount of light available for food manufacture by photosynthesis. Sooty deposits can cause physical damage by clogging the breathing pores or chemical damage by bleaching the green chlorophyll and upsetting the osmotic balance of the cell sap. Sulphur dioxide mixed with rain water becomes sulphuric acid, which can acidify the

37. Cormorants on posts

substrate so that lichens often grow best on limey surfaces like concrete and mortar, where this acidity will be neutralised.

The clouds of red dust which no longer hang over the works on still, humid days as once they did, contain iron oxides (haematite and magnetite). These travel less far in the atmosphere, usually not much more than three kilometres, even to leeward, so have a more localised effect. They are less active chemically but tend to coat otherwise colonisable surfaces and smother existing growths.

The shift of the main source of pollution southwards during the past twenty-five years is reflected by the appearance of more young lichen colonies in north-west Port Talbot and at Sandfields across the River Afan, these including some old man's beard lichen (*Usnea*) which is among the least smog-tolerant. To the south-east at Brombil, old established colonies are dying away.

These humble organisms, part fungus and part alga, have taken on a new significance in recent years. Usually overlooked, seldom understood and possessing no vernacular names, lichens have proved so sensitive to the purity of the air we breathe that they can be used as an early warning system. Where there are no lichens, it behoves the planners to find out why, before others, more highly regarded, begin to suffer injury.

15 OPPORTUNIST EXPLOITERS OF
PORT TALBOT'S FRESHWATER SITES

Mouth of the River Afan: freshwater docks; their birds and ungrazed turf: the Steelwork's Reservoir

APART from those few tell-tale dunes at the river mouth, there is no more sand visible around the lower Afan today than there was in 1186, when Theodoric's Hermitage stood there, or when this became a grange of Margam Abbey around 1227. But it has been very different in between. The arrival of an all-enveloping cover of sand is thought to have been at least as early as 1300 AD, in the mighty sandstorm that brought into being the great dune systems at Pennard and Penmaen on Gower, 13 miles away, and buried two churches there.

Theodoric's Hermitage 'Stood on almost the extreme point of a narrow strip of land having the Severn Sea on the West side and an estuary on the East, up which the tide raced for three miles, measuring from the opening on the shore between the sandhills', not from low water mark out across the wide stretch of beach. This must have brought estuarine conditions to (and along) the foot of the old sea cliffs, represented now by the steep face of the Coalfield hills backing the coastal plain.

Alongside were the coastal marshes, and we read that 'Coch, the hermit, owned land in the Marsh of Afan near the shore'. So the old sea cliff was already separated from the open sea by a marsh, which came to be held against the sea by a line of dunes, much as the Nicholaston cliff at Oxwich on Gower is today. Even those massive Pennant Sandstone cliffs at Margam were buried at one time—beneath subsequent deposits of Triassic rocks long since worn away again, to give what is termed a 'resurrected landscape'.

In 'Notes on the Granges of Margam Abbey' we read: "At high tide the Granges of Theodoric and Le Newe Grange were separated by a width of tidal water of half a mile, and truly picturesque the scene must have been on a calm summer's day with the background of Margam Mountain rising abruptly from the plain several hundred feet and clad with oaks right to the summit, with this stretch of water on the plain'. Alas those vanished oaks.

Another writer paints a less idyllic scene: 'The roaring tide on one side and the tidal estuary close up on the other; the circling wheeling gulls and other sea-birds with their raucous cries, the spindrift scudding

201

past the dwelling, the strange continuous roar or din which we hear at times, as the breakers fall and dash upon the hard flat sands in rapid succession: these sounds echoed back from the mountains and altogether mingled, seem to fill the bowl of heaven with a curious roar, which creates a feeling akin to awe, and must in those lonely days have added to the sense of desolation'.

Theodoric's Grange lay preserved beneath the sands for nigh on 600 years, from 1300 to 1898, its clay and mortar undissolved and its iron unrusted beneath the protective blanket. It was excavated, then lost again beneath the sands, to be re-exposed in 1949 by a dredger, working on the Steel Company's Abbey Site.

The dune country still extant to the south of the Steelworks suffers sandblows still. In one night of storm during the 1950s a big whaleback dune at Margam moved inland as much as 10 feet, sand sheeting off the top to be deposited to leeward.

There is rock below, but a long way below. Professor Anderson reports on a series of borings between the Neath and Margam Works which show the rock surface under the coastal flats to slope from Ordnance Datum level a mile and a half inland to 100 feet below O.D. at the present shoreline. The Afan is one of the buried valleys revealed by the borings. It lies south of Port Talbot Docks, where the modern river was still flowing until it was re-routed round the north of the docks in early industrial times.

Where ancient travellers floundered across the quicksands at the 'treacherous Ford of Afan,' the river is no more. It is now diverted, tamed and narrowed, cutting deep and muddy between confining banks of stone and hard core. Flood waters which once raced headlong to the sea are used by our urbanised society before ever they get that far.

The heavily buttressed sea lock on the eastern curve excludes salty waters from the dock, which nestles into the western loop of the river immediately upstream. To the south the bank has been continued sea-ward—as one of the massive walls of Port Talbot's new deep water harbour—but the river still empties into the modest, firm-floored river-mouth haven tucked against the northern angle of its great successor.

As the tide ebbs a central spit of industrial rubble appears in the haven, separating the dark mud of the river channel from the bright sand of the old harbour. Edible periwinkles, humbug-striped as well as black, leave sinuous feeding trails across the petrified purple swirls of furnace slag, and rough periwinkles glow orange among shiny brown wracks and chalky white barnacles.

Glistening drifts of coal dust riffled across the sand show that all is not well yet with the river, but this flows much cleaner than once it did. Before the Industrial Revolution, the Afan was one of Glamorgan's salmon rivers, along with the Tawe and the Taff, and the archives tell us that 37 salmon and well over 500 migratory trout were caught in the lower reaches in 1706.

Then came the physical impedimenta and pervasive pollution of industry and returning fish were repelled. Matters improved with the decline of the coal industry in the 1950s, but particulate matter continued to swirl seaward from the coal washeries until 1970. Now the mine effluents come down only occasionally, washed from riverside slag tips by heavy rains.

Salmon are still not tempted, but the beginning of the November 1979 rains saw a fine run of sewin or sea trout up river—over the first weir, which is submerged under many feet of water by the in-flowing tide, and on in a headlong passage to the second. High tides top this weir too, but, for the most part, the fish must proceed via marginal fish passes which are smaller than optimum size, the stepped pools shorter and shallower than they should be.

A lot of water is drawn off just above this weir to supply the Steelworks, and sewin make the passage upstream to the spawning grounds only when the deficit is made good by floods. These carry the appropriate smell of the home river from the hills and sluice away sedimented coal dust which would otherwise blanket the river gravels, preventing the free circulation of oxygen that is necessry for both fish eggs and prey animals. Suspended particulate matter in excess of eighty milligrammes per litre of water can also impair the fish's own respiration, by coating the gill filaments with sludge. The non-migratory brown trout of the upper river suffer the same hazards, and there is constant restocking by the Afan Valley Angling Club to keep the numbers up.

Grey mullet are as much a feature of the Afan as they are of the Thaw, surging up in their thousands with the tide on occasion, a tumbling mass of silver bodies breaking surface as they go. These need salt and run best during droughts, when the incoming tide is scarcely diluted. They have usually neither ability nor desire to climb the second weir into fresh water, but the odd flounder finds its way up—and even out into the docks feeder canal, where it does not inevitably succumb to the lack of salt. Both flounder and mullet can tolerate wide fluctuations in water salinity and, if acclimatised slowly, can learn to live in completely fresh water.

Fishermen squelch into soft black river muds among the moored boats to dig for bait, but no plants grow down there. Only where the mud is thinner over the stabilising rock walls near the top of the tide do salt marsh plants occur, principally the disc-headed sea aster and sea spurrey, with a grey fringe of sea purslane above.

Behind the slag and rubble path which tops the western river bank rabbits excavate tunnels into pure sand—well upstream from the tiny, wind-whisked marram dunes at the river mouth and hidden beneath ordinary grassland vegetation. Plants are mixed, with hare's-foot clover, storksbill and evening primrose from the dunes, sea beet, sea mayweed and wall rocket (*Diplotaxis muralis*) from the walled embankments and a medley of others, with yellow rattle, yellow toadflax and bladder campion.

This whole area north-west of the river mouth was once dune country —playground of the Rhondda mining communities, for whom it was the most easily accessible watering place. Families came by train, through the Blaengwynfi Tunnel, until well after the Second World War, alighting at the seaside station of Sandfields. A natural lake provided boating and paddling facilities and the spacious sandhills could accommodate the whole population when the incoming tide drove the holiday-makers up from the beach. Now there are no sandhills, no cosy picnic spots, no lake and no railway—only a vast, unending housing estate backed by hundreds of acres of grey rubble where the last of the ponies are being ousted from the water meadows.

Port Talbot Dock, now disused, leaves the Afan on the outer, deep water side of a loop to the east, as does Briton Ferry Dock from the Neath. It is four-lobed but undivided, the combined basins comprising the biggest single dock in Wales. They formerly accommodated boats of up to 8,000 tons, dealing first in coal and pitprops and later in steel, but were closed in 1966.

Since then the last of the salt has been washed out and the big area of fresh water serves as a reservoir for industry, a training ground for sea cadets and a wintering place for wildfowl. The two principal sources of water are the river flowing down the steep-sided valley of Cwm Dyffryn from north of Maesteg and the old docks feeder leaving the River Afan at the second weir. Most of this last is actually used for industrial purposes, the weir having been heightened when the Steelworks replaced the more modest riverside tin works.

It is a meagre stream of compensation water which now enters the western arm of the dock, through a spinney of well grown alder, willow and sallow, and out through a reed bed into the open. The flow is brisk at first, with long shoots of river crowfoot streaming out with the current and emulated by generous bunches of two foot long roots splaying from bramble tips which dip into the water.

The pace slows in the wooded swamp. Here marginal ground flora diminishes from thicket proportions to bare leaf mould or open water in the gloomy interior, where contortions of the gnarled tree bases are reminiscent of a mangrove swamp. Fungi thrive on the time-battered trunks in the airless humidity: bright orange slabs of *Phlebia radiata*, lighter yellow clusters of sulphur tuft (*Hypholoma fasciculare*) and overlapping, vari-coloured fan-shaped shelves of *Coriolus versicolor*, which bears the charmingly appropriate name of 'Turkey tails' in North America.

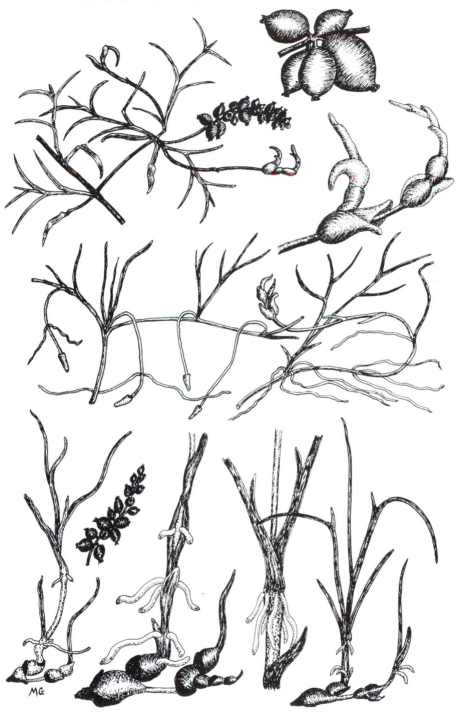

38. Fennel-leaved pondweed. Nutlets and tuberous winter buds which supply food for water fowl.
Top: Late summer. Middle: Autumn and winter. Bottom: Spring

Osier and Japanese knotgrass hog much of the light which penetrates into clearings, but there are herbs too, with giant horsetail, water pepper, angelica, hemp agrimony and yellow flag. Water seeps out from this rushy hinterland through a shoreline reedswamp with patches of great reedmace and a fringe of winter-brown sea sedge, before reaching the open dock. Submerged aquatics are represented chiefly by curled pondweed and some of the narrow-leaved pondweeds, whose severed fronds drift up against marginal hemlock water dropwort, gipsywort and tansy.

Fat nutlets produced by the pondweeds in August persist into winter if not eaten and are joined in October by firm, food-packed stem tubers. These serve the plant as turions or winter buds from which new shoots will sprout in spring, but they also provide a rich source of winter food for water fowl, along with the fruits, and tempt many birds in to feed, as at Cadoxton Pond behind Barry Docks.

Chief takers in mid-November, 1979 were pochard, 50-60 strong, with smaller flocks of tufted duck, mallard and teal, ten to a dozen of each. Coot were present in strength, as on all Glamorgan's coastal waters, with a few bouncy little grebes, diving and surfacing among them and resident moorhens yapping from the reeds.

Most of the eight cormorants drying themselves out on the central piles were youngsters of the year, with so much white on their fronts that they could have passed for South Africa's white-fronted variety *lucidus* of our common (and almost cosmopolitan) black *Phalacrocorax carbo*. Only one shag was seen, and this kept itself to itself. The four mute swans had not yet been called upon to share their foraging with visiting whoopers and bewicks.

A snipe burst from cover and zig-zagged over the breeze-ruffled waters, past a heron standing contemplatively among the bulrushes. The greater black-backed gull atop a central prominence kept a fierce, unrelenting eye on all about. The remainder of its kind consorted with herring gulls here and on the gravel river shoals, leaving the nippier black-headed gulls to wheel and tumble at the harbour mouth and squabble over the miscellaneous food items tipping over the weirs or churned up below.

A big flock of chaffinches commuted between the swamp woodland and the riverside, this containing birds of both sexes, their plumage flushed yellower than in summer. Bushes were used only as a retreat; they fed on the ground. In the carr woodland they systematically worked the soil beneath the fluffy fruiting heads of gone-wild michaelmas daisies (*Aster* sp.). On the riverside they fed mostly where the fruits of sea aster fell, but a few were searching midstream mud-banks for stranded water-borne seeds.

206

The chaffinches seemed incongruous companions for the oyster catchers and ringed plovers which probed these muds for animal life, but they were not the only land birds. Jackdaws, carrion crows and starlings were there too, collecting sedentary and transported goodies. Blue tits and wrens pottered in riverside bushes and a kestrel hovered over the trampled, rabbit-grazed turf near the river mouth carpark.

Thick, ungrazed swards of cocksfoot and red fescue around the dock held far more kestrel food. The rank growths, full of ox-eye daisies, yarrow and knapweed, were riddled with vole holes, but the day-foraging voles were effectively hidden without ever having to burrow down into the soil. There were no rabbits here.

Rabbits and field voles can be mutually exclusive, voles preferring to tunnel through the grass bases above soil level, their highways often marked by strips of dead grass where the blades have been severed from their roots. In the average rabbit-grazed sward the tops and bases of the grass leaves are one and the voles must go underground.

Empty straw-coloured cocoons of burnet moths persist on the grass tops through the winter and woolly bear caterpillars, possibly those of ruby tiger moths, are still abroad in December. On mild winter days slugs emerge from their lairs to tuck into the soft flesh of the late toadstools and the big terminal leaflets of kidney vetch show where leaf miners have been at work. By mid-July cinnabar caterpillars are about, sometimes racing over the ground in search of fresh ragwort plants to nibble, and there are butterflies of many kinds, particularly graylings and small skippers.

Although based principally on an infill of hard core, the rank growth around the dock contains as wide a range of plants as old natural grassland—even wider, because it includes acid communities among the more general neutral to alkaline ones. One of the brightest in mid-summer is crown vetch (*Coronilla varia*), which is also a feature of Barry and Cardiff docks. *Lychnis coronaria* is also established.

This augurs well for the many acres of rehabilitated rubble and tip material being contoured and reseeded throughout industrial South Wales at present. The most important factor favouring this well established secondary grassland at Port Talbot is almost certainly the absence of hungry mountain sheep, which can slow down a plant succession almost indefinitely, and hold it at an early phase of sparse moss and wispy grass.

Early successional phases occur at Port Talbot too, where material has been excavated at intervals between the western dock basins, sometimes to as much as 12 feet below the marginal strip of land left at the water's edge. There is a ready source of seed to recolonise the denuded sections, and grassland species take over again, unchecked by sheep or rabbits, leaving little time for the usual early influx of arable weeds.

Indeed, these scraped zones show some of the choicest flowers of the whole complex, with splendid stands of great mullein and evening primrose, open swards of delicate pale toadflax and white campion and pebble beach plants such as yellow horned poppy (a rarity in the county now) with sea beet. Most colourful in midsummer are rest harrow and others of the pea tribe, meadow vetchling, yellow and white melilot, sickle and black medick, red and white clover and various vetches.

Areas which have had longer to settle down contain fennel and wild parsnip, carline thistle and yellow toadflax, teasel and yellow cinquefoil. This phase leads on to one which equates with a true limestone grassland, having wild carrot and field bindweed, red bartsia and yellow rattle, hedge bedstraw and goatsbeard. Wild mignonette, hare's-foot clover, sand sedge and even a little marram, suggest that beach sand must be incorporated in places.

The later, acidic, stage may arise as a result of leaching of minerals or may be initiated on slag which was more acid in the first place. Somehow the Scottish heather and fine-leaved heath, gorse and broom, bracken and sheep's sorrel, seem out of place in these rich lowlands, savouring more of the austere hill country of Mynydd Margam, which frowns down upon the ravaged plain below.

A skin of soft black peat develops in places, with moorland mosses and scarlet-tipped lichens, North America's 'British Soldier' *Cladonias,* as on a genuine heath. Deeper humus builds up in sheltered hollows to support sizable broad buckler and male ferns, but their delicate fronds miss the mitigated woodland micro-climate as soon as they reach out of the depressions, their tips becoming brown and salt-scorched.

The Steelworks reservoir between the south-west corner of the steel sheds and the coke dump, supplies another freshwater habitat which wildlife has not been slow to colonise. During its excavation a buried village was discovered. The Dutch firm carrying out the job pumped the original sandy hollow full of sea water and pushed the liquid sand suspension northwards to build up the level for the works. All the water ran out of the hollow leaving a firm base, and, 20 feet down in the hole, was the village which had been overtaken by the sand. It is now under the waters of the reservoir.

These hold much particulate matter, but are not too opaque to support some of the narrower-leaved pondweeds and a weft of green algae on marginal rocks. A small reed bed occupies one corner, while greater willow herb and yellow iris root in the bounding wall with a fringe of dune plants above.

Pochard and tufted duck are the main wintering wild fowl, as in the dock, most of the vegetation being too deep to be reached by up-ending dabbling ducks. A smew turned up in November 1979. The gently

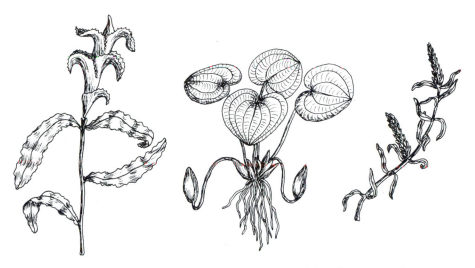

39. Winter buds of curled pondweed, frogbit and Canadian pondweed

sloping sides are too cluttered with plants to entice waders, but suit the moorhens admirably. Mute swans are attracted, up to seven at a time, with a pair well established most summers.

Coot spend much of the winter here. Gorse, dewberry and creeping willow at the water's edge are not too sparse to provide twiggy perches for stonechat and yellow hammer, and the lower cover harbours wren and dunnock.

Weasels hole up in the stone embankment and the grasses and clovers tempt rabbits to lollop across the coke tip from their burrows in the waste dump and graze along the banks.

First (in 'modern' terms, speaking geologically) there was the ancient forest described in Chapter I—which came to light on the foreshore here during the excavation of the deep water harbour in the 1960s, but only when the sand finally ceased sludging in to the excavation from the seaward side. Centuries later mediaeval villagers plied their trades here and grazed their livestock on the sweet marsh grasses.

Then came the great sand blows, and later the great industrial invasion. Now, in this little corner borrowed back from heavy industry, water, the basis of all animate things, forms the nucleus of a microcosm of new life, from microbes to mammals.

When the Steelworks has ceased to function and the reservoir has silted up or been swept away, there will still be life here, perhaps terrestrial, perhaps marine. Such landscapes are among the most finite in this finite world of ours.

16 NATURAL INVADERS OF DOCKLAND

Seaweeds, invertebrates and birds of Swansea Docks and Port Talbot deep water harbour

THE great expanses of beach which offer neither let nor hindrance to the stirring onslaught of the waves, give sanctuary only to specialised sand dwellers able to burrow. Where dock basins dip back into the shelter of the land or harbour walls encompass a haven of stiller water outside, the scope is widened. The concrete, boulder-buttressed wall of Queen's Dock, Swansea and the great new sea wall around the deep water habour at Port Talbot offer a more secure foothold.

Seaweeds can withstand the pull of tidal currents when there is something firm to cling to and these in their turn give shelter and stability of habitat to animals living among them or seeking refuge in crevices beneath. Thus Swansea and Port Talbot support outlying populations of rock-dwelling organisms whose nearest contemporaries may be several miles away.

At Swansea small periwinkles (*Littorina neritoides*) penetrate into a region of little splash well above mean high water of spring tides, where they browse on lichens. Their small substance contained within the pointed spiral of the blue-black shell can subsist on very little and the encrusting black 'inksplash' lichen, *Verrucaria maura,* supplies most of their needs. They have evolved much further towards life on land than the other periwinkles which cleave more closely to the ancestral medium of the sea. Indeed, their gills have been replaced by lungs, so that they are air breathers and virtually independent of submergence by the tide.

Some, however, live further down, almost to the mean high water mark of neap tides, where they meet the uppermost of the rough periwinkles. Here they will probably be dependent on sporelings of the Welsh laver (*Porphyra umbilicalis*)— a filmy red seaweed from which laverbread is made—and the green sea lettuce (*Ulva lactuca*), in the top of the zone dominated by the brown bladder wrack (*Fucus vesiculosus*).

Sand smelts (*Atherina boyeri*) weave among the weeds growing from the walls of Queen's Dock. Sedentary acorn barnacles (*Chthamalus stellatus* and *Elminius modestus*) grow upshore, the latter spreading further down to overlap with two other kinds of barnacle, *Balanus balanoides* and *Balanus crenatus*. *Elminius* travelled from Australasia by ship, arriving in Southampton Water around 1940. By 1947-48 it had reached West Wales and penetrated up the Bristol Channel. It enjoys

40. Sand smelts and carragheen 'moss'

the swirling silt of the great estuary and is at its best up-channel from Barry to Cardiff, although settling also on the cleaner shores of Gower.

Chthamalus is a southerly species in Britain, *Balanus balanoides* a northerly one. The slightly lopsided *B. crenatus* is a common fouler of ships' bottoms and the object of much scraping when the old sailing vessels came ashore for careening and today's larger craft to dry dock. Its fouling activities waned when the dock waters were warmed up by effluent from Tir John Power Station in the 1930s, as did those of *Elminius modestus,* but another species, *Balanus amphitrite,* arrived by chance from the sub-tropics and took over. This, however, is dependent for survival on the hot water being spewed into the dock and thrived only until the 1950s. Reduction of temperature to something nearer the norm in 1961 led to its replacement by native barnacles again and common limpets.

From the 1930s when the power station was functioning, it drew its cooling waters from King's Dock and expelled them into Queen's Dock, much warmed. Water temperature in the fifties rose to as much as 30°C (88°F) in summer, eliminating many of the expected native animals and preventing others from breeding, so that their numbers were maintained only by new individuals moving in from outside.

Among those waxing fat and multiplying in the added warmth were other problem species—the destructive wood-boring shipworms (*Teredo*) and gribbles (*Limnoria lignorum* and the newly arrived, sub-tropical *Limnoria tripunctata*). The first is really a two-shelled Mollusc, called shipworm because the shells are reduced to a small but highly efficient drill for boring into timber piles and wooden ships, while the body is long, naked and wormlike. The commonest species, *Teredo norvegica,* can reach a foot long and is a serious pest in untreated marine timbers. Consuming the wood as it tunnels, the shipworm grows ever bigger, so that the pier or pile becomes honeycombed with broad, lime-lined tunnels. There is little indication of this outside, as the

211

teredos are tiny when they first burrow in, making holes not much bigger than those of the gribbles. As a result of the increased activity at Swansea with the warming of the water, timber jetties had to be replaced with concrete ones.

Gribbles have the appearance of woodlice less than ¼ inch long, but they usually live in colonies, so that timbers can become gribble-riddled. Like pill bugs, they roll themselves into balls when upset. Teredos and gribbles were quick to arrive and were presenting problems to harbour engineers soon after the opening of the power station in the thirties.

As the newcomers came by ship, most were automatically ship foulers, which impede progress and raise fuel consumption by increasing frictional drag. Two of Swansea's new arrivals were sea squirts, *Ciona* and *Ascidiella,* two others were tube-building worms, *Hydroides incrustans* and *Mercierella enigmata,* a fifth was a branched Polyzoon, *Bugula neritina.*

Others with no fouling propensities reaching Queen's Dock by boat, included the Mediterranean crab, *Brachynotus sexdentatus,* and the Caribbean mud crab, *Neopanope texana-sayi,* neither of which had turned up anywhere else in Britain. In 1961, when the hot water output was reduced, these warmth-loving crabs began to diminish, though some lingered till 1969. The homely native shore crabs, *Carcinus maenas,* lost that idle tropical holiday feeling and got down to the serious business of breeding, where before they had been unable to. With the power station out of commission, it is to be expected that other organisms will revert to normal, after this interesting sojourn with organisms from kindlier latitudes. Cooling waters expelled into the open Bristol Channel, as off Aberthaw power station, are soon dispersed, the heat dissipated and wildlife little affected.

Edible periwinkles (*Littorina littorea*) are abundant on the walls of Swansea Dock, with a few flat periwinkles (*L. obtusata*) and rather more rough periwinkles (*L. saxatilis* ssp. *rudis* and ssp. *neglecta*). To most of us these look the same, along with two other subspecies recently differentiated by workers in Pembrokeshire. The separation hinges on their apparent inability to breed together and their preference for different types of habitat. They cannot be identified without dissection, as the diagnostic feature is the number and arrangement of knobs along one side of the male penis!

Beadlet anemones and edible mussels are the only other common animals in the mid-tide zone at Queen's Dock. These increase among downshore boulders, where a predatory population of dog whelks prowls among them, feeding mainly on mussels, and preferring barnacles to anemones.

Keeled tubeworms (*Pomatoceros triqueter*) build curvaceous limey tubes on concrete, boulders or the shells of others. Serrated wrack

42

Plate XI   BIRDS OF INDUSTRIAL SITES—*Keri Williams*

42. Top: Swallow at nest
43. Bottom left: Willow warbler at nest
44. Bottom right: Starling in speckled winter plumage

43

44

45

46

Plate XII   BIRDS AT THE WATERSIDE—*Keri Williams*

45. Top: Stock dove drinking   **46.** Bottom: Moorhen nesting

214

(*Fucus serratus*) overlaps with bladder wrack here alongside one of the two 'carragheen mosses', *Chondrus crispus*.

There are threats to life more serious than those posed by the dog whelk. By 1977 parts of both Swansea and Port Talbot Docks had become so polluted that all the animals disappeared. Way out in Swansea Bay more 'abiotic mud' was discovered; black, smelly and devoid of all detectable life.

Research vessel 'Ocean Crest' established the existence of currents which could have brought these pollutants out from the docks. Diagnosis is the first step to cure. The sea is too beneficent and unknown an ally to monkey with in this way: such knowledge must be used to make amends.

The only other bits of hard-standing offering comparable conditions between Mumbles in the north-west and Sker Point near Porthcawl to the south-east are the jetties at Port Talbot, where the British Transport Docks Board completed Britain's biggest deep water harbour in 1970, with accommodation for ships of up to 100,000 tons.

There is a tremendous population of small periwinkles here, withstanding considerable battering by waves on the outside of the breakwater but far fewer inside, where they extend neither so high nor so low. In spite of their small size, they thrive on the buffeting and high oxygenation, always favouring the more exposed sites. Rough periwinkles are rather more abundant inside than out.

There are three species of barnacles inside and three outside, but these are not the same. *Chthamalus,* the 'star' barnacle, revels in the exposure of the outer face, but appears not at all on the inner side in comparable transects made by Dr. Tony Nelson-Smith in 1974, a few years after the breakwater was built. On the inside it is largely replaced by the bigger *Balanus perforatus,* which is centred further downshore. Like *Chthamalus,* this is a southern species but is even more addicted to the warmer waters and was almost wiped out in Glamorgan during the icy winter of 1962-63, but made a successful if rather patchy come-back in the seventies. *Balanus balanoides* and the Australian *Elminius* are abundant on both sides of the breakwater.

Limpets, mussels and keelworms occur in both the Port Talbot transects, the limpets commoner and extending higher on the seaward face. Seaweeds, on the other hand, prefer the shelter of the inner side, where a thick cover of bladder wrack mingles with spiral wrack (*Fucus spiralis*) towards the top and egg wrack (*Ascophyllum nodosum*) around mean tide level. Sea lettuce and the related 'green strings' (*Enteromorpha*) are prolific here, no doubt boosted by inflowing fresh water. The latter is sometimes called 'gutweed', one of the commonest species being *Enteromorpha intestinalis,* named for the irregularly bloated intestines which it is supposed to resemble. Welsh laver is common more or less throughout, though represented only at the top and bottom of the rock wall outside, where downshore sea lettuce is the only other weed.

Cooling waters from the steelworks empty into the harbour to simulate something more tropical and teredo borers are here too, tunnelling into the wooden piles. They may well have travelled here from the Red Sea, cemented to the iron plates of a tanker.

During the construction of this great harbour in the late 1960s, silt was reported on many shores to the west—even as far as Port Eynon in west Gower, but the stirred sediments have settled back to normal now. Part of the beach inside the harbour is of peat, scored with little branching runnels which become filled with drifted sand. Fishermen dig for bait here, particularly for ragworms (*Nereis diversicolor*) and lugworms (*Arenicola marina*). Shore birds were quick to discover the new source of food. Almost as soon as the harbour was built, the peat had a sufficiency of life for both bait diggers and birds.

Turnstone and dunlin arrive as early as the first week of August in some years, the last still wearing the conspicuous black bellies of their summer breeding plumage. Curlew, bar-tailed godwit and snipe are not far behind, while oyster-catcher, ringed plover and sanderling are often about. New feeding opportunities are seldom left unused for long and these birds are establishing a pattern of behaviour which, pollution permitting, can continue side by side with the unloading of the massive ore carriers.

Terns were among the first to cash in on the altered microhabitat, arriving in large numbers on passage almost as soon as work began on the sturdy walls. It seems likely that the heavy stones thundering into the water stirred up food which was to their liking.

Large flocks of terns are exceptional in Glamorgan, with two hundred the usual maximum in the best of the traditional sites (Kenfig, Whiteford Point and Worm's Head), but in 1971 a thousand odd were feeding near the new breakwater on Margam Beach during their trek south. They had the sands to themselves, the lofty waste tip and cavernous pits receiving acid wastes from as far away as Llanelli, proving an effective deterrent to walkers on the beach.

Common terns usually arrive as early as June and continue numerous, with three hundred in mid-June 1977, when nine sandwich terns were also present. Small numbers of arctic terns, little terns and even the rarely seen black tern, visit from mid to late Summer. 9th May 1978 saw some roseate terns here and a fulmar was spotted on 1st June that year.

Little gulls have been recorded here most autumns since the late sixties and Mediterranean gulls turn up spasmodically. Common gulls move in from the north and Port Talbot Harbour usually yields the maximum kittiwake numbers outside their breeding terrain of Gower—with seventy five in mid-June 1977 and fifty on 9th May, 1978.

216

Sometimes the harbour yields food for man as well as birds. On one occasion a sizeable shoal of mackerel, chasing small fry into the harbour on an outgoing August tide, found itself stranded in an ever diminishing pool as the water ebbed beyond an outer shoal. Synchronised movement of the perfectly aligned regiment of green-striped backs changed to a churning jumble of leaping quicksilver as the pool became more fish than water. Mackerel have to keep swimming in order to breathe, lacking the ability of most fish to pump water over the gills when at rest: but this time there was no water to swim in. The naturalists called the fishermen, who came to bale them out in buckets.

Usually only starlings and carrion crows exploit the land invertebrates among the coltsfoot and mayweed of the upper harbour wall. Above this at certain seasons the man-made ground of slag and cinders becomes partially covered by a yellow-green moss carpet. The chief moss is *Bryum bicolor,* a species which also does well on the slag heaps of the Coalfield and owes much of its success as an early coloniser to the many little leafy buds or gemmae which sprout among the leaves and form new plants when they get detached. Such a moss cover will shelter a fauna of springtails, tardigrades and other small fry to form a food source for larger animals. Roving flocks of pied wagtails, meadow pipits and skylarks forage here throughout the winter and wheatears are about some years until as late as mid-October.

41. White-fronted geese

217

Shorebirds and their invertebrate prey have had longer to find out about Swansea Docks than about Port Talbot and the open coast outside is richer in species, so that bird watching can be very rewarding in Swansea's rather unprepossessing dockscape of concrete, mud and rubble. Mr. D. Chatfield has kept daily bird notes in the docks over the years and recorded no less than seventy species of birds during 1965-69, forty-five of them of regular occurrence.

Gulls, of course, are here in plenty, even, occasionally, the rare little gull, but no species breeds. Common terns drop in on autumn passage every year, a few at a time. Up to twenty cormorants arrive most days at dawn and linger till dusk, but shags are scarce, and seen only in winter. Red-breasted mergansers come into Queen's Dock occasionally but other duck and shelduck are rare, geese unrecorded and great crested grebe seen only once during the five-year spell. Passing grey heron and mute swan are not usually tempted down by the murky waters.

Oyster-catchers are fairly regular on the mudbanks in groups of a dozen or so and flocks of several hundred pass overhead at times. Ringed plover potter on the mud up to twenty at a time and the odd few pairs show signs of breeding among the masonry rubble, distracting intruders with their characteristic 'broken wing' imitation. Turnstones are part of the normal scene on rocks by the sea wall, up to seventy or more together and at any time of the year. Other waders are rare; dunlin and redshank, curlew and whimbrel and the very occasional little stint. Common sandpipers move through during autumn when their normal freshwater habitats in the hills become excessively chilly.

Inland birds seem oblivious of the inevitable noise and clamour of dockland. Kestrel and little owl breed here and green woodpeckers spurned their ancestral woodland for a month-long stay in this urban environment. Meadow pipit, rock pipit, skylark and pied wagtail nest in the area, along with wren, dunnock, stonechat and wheatear. The much rarer yellow wagtail also nests in the docks some years.

Chaffinch and linnets breed but the other finches come mainly to forage in winter. The inevitable house sparrow and starling are resident, as are species more rightly associated with woodland—blackbird, song thrush and robin, willow warbler and blue tit. Swifts, swallows and house martins comb the upper air for food in summer: fieldfare and redwing sweep over in rustling flocks in winter, but are not usually tempted earthwards. Crow and jackdaw rear their broods here in company with some 25 pairs of feral pigeons. Collared doves, on their great advance from south-east Europe, were first spotted in the docks in 1969.

That seventy different kinds of birds choose to inhabit or visit this triangle of urban activity, sheds a bright ray of light onto the worst that may yet befall us environmentally. Birds have no aesthetic likes or dislikes. A habitat that can offer a living is a habitat worth occupying. The most urban locality may be brightened by bird song so long as the paving is not so neat as to eliminate all the weeds and creepy-crawlies on which these erstwhile denizens of a very different world depend. Sightings may be of the most noble. 31st August 1976 brought an osprey to Swansea Docks: twelve days later a great skua was seen off Port Talbot Docks. A pair of ravens was nesting on Swansea's Guildhall by 1975 and the latter years of the seventies go into the ornithological archives as the years of the peregrine in Swansea's city centre.

Part Five

The Brighter Side of
Nature Conservation

Water Rails

All too often the case for conservation is misrepresented or ignored, because it is virtually impossible to place a monetary value on such features as habitat diversity and species density. Thus the balance of the equation tends to be weighted in favour of increasing agricultural productivity.

Tim Clarke in "Friends of the Earth Habitat Campaign" (Ecos 1(1), 1980).

17 EGLWYS NUNYDD RESERVOIR: GLAMORGAN'S LARGEST BODY OF FRESH WATER

The old Morfa Pools; their wild geese and rare mudworts. Siting and water quality of the Steelworks Reservoir; water plants, molluscs, fish and tadpoles

CONSTRUCTION of the 250-acre Steelworks Reservoir near Eglwys Nunydd Farm in 1962 completely changed the character of the south Margam Moors inland of the railway, but the indigenous wildlife suffered only temporary defeat. It was superb before, as an adjunct to the grazing grounds of the white-fronted geese displaced by the coming of the Steelworks: but it became repopulated—after the trauma of dredging operations—as a feeding area for wintering wildfowl. Ornithologists have been able to piece together a fascinating story of opportunism and exploitation of the new environment by this group of animals, which are much more than the creatures of instinct that some animal behaviourists would have us believe.

'Eglwys Nunydd' signifies the church of the nuns, later converted to a farmhouse, and lying to the south of Margam Abbey. Tradition, largely refuted, has it that the two were connected by a subterranean passage — very handy...... 'Margam' is thought to be derived from a character called Morgan, but the historians have not yet decided which one. 'Morfa', the pools around which the wild geese had centred, is the Welsh word for sea marsh—appearing again in such well-known names as Morfa Harlech in West Wales.

White-fronted geese had flown into Morfa Mawr, the big marsh, from time immemorial, to escape the winters of Northern Russia and Siberia— until the upheaval of the building of the Steelworks after the second world war almost completely annihilated their habitat. The coming of the London to West Wales Railway must have disrupted their routine, but they recovered from this and 2,500 came in the winter of 1939-40 and 2,000 in 1941-42, these representing a substantial proportion of the European race. (Others fly from Greenland to winter on Tregaron Bog in West Wales, but such birds are exceptional in South Wales, with the first certain Glamorgan record at Whiteford Point in Gower on 23rd February 1977.) From a trickle in mid-October, the flood of geese built up to a peak in November and set out on the return flight in March, to utilise the short Arctic summer to the full.

222

Poachers took their toll during building operations, and numbers were down to 300-500 in 1946-47, with none at all the following year. As things settled down, a few began to drop in around Eglwys Nunydd Farm again, up to 50 in January 1949 and 1950, increasing to 90 in 1953 and 100 in 1954, but back to 43 in 1956 and then to none.

In the exceptionally hard winter of 1962-63, 150 birds were counted around the starkly bare reservoir, then in its first winter and not yet 'grown in'. At this time there were 300 geese in the Ogmore Valley and 250 in the Thaw Valley. A few, after a flight of many hundreds of miles to escape the Siberian winter, failed to cope with the mini-Siberia which they encountered on the Atlantic sea-board and died in their tracks, frozen to Welsh soil. When snow lay again, in January 1966, a small party of 22 turned up briefly and moved on. It is likely that we, rather than the geese, are the losers. By flying on up the Bristol Channel, the cohorts can partake of Sir Peter Scott's hospitality on the Dumbles at the Slimbridge Wildfowl Trust Grounds, where all their needs can be satisfied. Wales's loss is England's gain.

Right through the 1940's the reed-fringed Morfa Pools played host to big flocks of wintering ducks as well as geese, particularly teal, wigeon and shoveler. These are dabbling ducks; upending in the reedy shallows for their food. The big flocks tempted down by today's deeper, man-made reservoirs and docks are more likely to be diving ducks, such as pochard and tufted duck, which can reach to the depths when feeding. Tufted ducks bred at Morfa Pools, along with the three dabblers, and there were also nests of lapwing, redshank and little grebe, sedge warbler, reed warbler and reed bunting.

There is no reason to believe that the flora of the pools was any poorer than that of the Margam Moors today, and there are records of such delectable items as frogbit and great water dock, with bordering sea dock *(Rumex maritimus)* and marsh ragwort *(Senecio aquaticus)*. Botanically the region is most famous for the rather inconspicuous but rare mudworts, three kinds of which were discovered here by Eleanor Vachell in 1935. These, although belonging to the noble company of the foxglove family, produce only tiny rosettes of leaves—along open stretches of shoreline which are subject to drying out in summer. They form succulent swards, resembling those of the much commoner shoreweed *(Littorella uniflora)* and, like these, they favour areas which are puddled to pulp by livestock, so that larger herbs cannot reach up to shade them. Vachell reports that thousands of plants were growing for a third of a mile along the open, cattle-trodden northern shore of the West Pool; so thickly as to look like grass; while only a few were found among the reeds bordering the East Pool. Many produced runners, as does the shoreweed.

Although reputedly annuals, with seedlings appearing in January, the plants will overwinter, and they will bloom as well under water as above. This is something the shoreweed cannot usually do, but its leaves respond quite as readily to fluctuations in water level. Stalks of the spatulate or spoon-shaped leaves of the ordinary mudwort (*Limosella aquatica*) will grow to six inches long as water level rises, their blades floating on the surface, but the juvenile leaves of young plants have no blades, being awl-shaped or subulate. In *Limosella subulata* they remain this way throughout life. This species has recently been re-named *L. australis*, the Welsh mudwort. In the 1930's this rarer kind was present also at Kenfig Pool and Crymlin Bog, but is seldom seen at either. Only when droughts take the water level as low as in 1976 are the two mudworts accessible at Kenfig Pool. In that year both were seen to be doing well. The only other known site in 1935 was by the Glaslyn River in North Wales, and 'The Atlas of the British Flora', published in 1962, marks only one other for Britain—quite close to the Glaslyn. 'Common' mudwort is far from common, with fewer than a score post-1930 records in Great Britain and Ireland.

The suspicion that the needle-leaved mudwort might be a juvenile form of the other was dispelled by Kathleen Blackburn, who examined Margam plants and found *Limosella aquatica* to have forty chromosomes in the cells, *L. subulata* twenty and the half-way type thirty, lending support to the supposition that this more vigorous form was probably a hybrid between the two.

By 1950 the pools were filled in and built over and the mudworts disappeared, along with the geese. Meanwhile a subsidence over an old

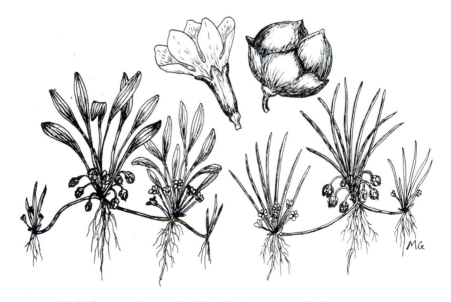

42. Ordinary mudwort and (right) Welsh mudwort with flower and fruit

224

colliery working away to the south-east at Eglwys Nunydd brought a shallow pool into being in the late 1930s, and this gradually enlarged until it came to occupy twenty-five acres. The four breeding duck from Morfa came to breed here—and were joined by a pair of pochard in 1950.

Steel production was using up to twenty thousand gallons of water per ton and direct supplies from the River Afan and River Kenfig proved inadequate during dry spells, now that water formerly pumped into these rivers from working collieries was lost with the closure of the mines, in which it remained.

The 250-acre Abbey Steelworks Reservoir was constructed to boost the inflow and lay along the old course of the Upper Mother Ditch, which was diverted to flow between the western impounding wall and the complex of railway sidings to seaward. This embraced the subsidence pool, but neither this and the old mine-workings cutting across from near Pyle, nor the underlying geological fault cause any leakage. The reservoir deepened from a gently sloping shore on the inland side to twenty feet along the western boundary when first full in 1963, but the level has been raised several times during the sixties and seventies, and by 1980 both bird life and plant life had dwindled because of insufficient shallows.

As often in lowland lakes, the waters are eutrophic or rich in nutrients, in contrast with the average upland reservoir. In this instance they are a deal more eutrophic than they should be, much of the intake coming from a point on the River Kenfig about three kilometres downstream from the discharge of an overloaded sewage works.

By the time the much enriched water reaches the reservoir, the oxygen deficiency due to fungal and bacterial respiration during break down of the sewage sludge is largely overcome and the products of decomposition are available for recycling through another food chain.

This begins with millions of cells of the blue-green alga, *Anacystis aeruginosa*, which is a notorious 'bloom former'. The light-excluding rafts comprising the algal bloom can be several inches thick over the surface. Although at least the upper layers give off quantities of oxygen during photosynthesis on sunny days, little of this gets dissolved in the water. Instead it bubbles to the top and fizzes off into the atmosphere. Dead cells sinking to the bottom can cause an actual oxygen deficiency, due to the respiratory needs of the organisms which achieve their breakdown.

Another hazard has been created when the purple-green rafts get banked up by the prevailing wind against the extraction point where they clog the screens, sometimes making the reservoir virtually unusable during the summer months when the need is greatest.

Such over-eutrophication is a common problem where water is taken from enriched lowland courses of rivers instead of barren, stony reaches

near their sources. It proved impossible to eradicate the algal bloom at
Eglwys Nunydd, but the problem was overcome in 1979 by constructing
a new extractor away from the leeward area of accumulation.

In a comparative study of South Wales lakes in 1974 David Johnson
gives physical and chemical data for the waters of Eglwys Nunydd and
Kenfig Pool, which are contrasted in the following table with those of a
traditional type of upland reservoir near the source of the Taf Fechan in
the Brecon Beacons.

Analysis of lake waters (parts per million). After D. N. Johnson, 1974

Location	Area (acres)	Greatest depth (feet)	Status	Total hard-ness	Cal-cium	Mag-nesium	Chlor-ide	Phos-phate	Nitrate	Sul-phate	pH
Eglwys Nunydd Reservoir	250	c.20 +	Lowland eutrophic	135	75	60	44	0.15	?	85	8.9
Kenfig Dune Pool	70	14	Lowland eutrophic	113	95	18	35	0.15	0.3	?	7.5
Neuadd Reservoir, Brecon Beacons	59	72	Upland oligo-trophic	23	18	5	7	?	0.13	9	6.8

The two coastal lakes lie at 25 feet and 20 feet above sea level in the 40
inch rainfall belt and show a much richer chemical make-up than the
Neuadd Reservoir, which is at an altitude of 1,506 feet and suffers more
than double this amount of rain (82 inches annually).

This reservoir is smaller but deeper than the coastal ones, so a smaller
proportion of the water is warmed and lighted by the sun. Plant growth
is also inhibited by the paucity of nutrients worn from the surrounding
Old Red Sandstone and stony soil of the steep valley sides. The lowland
sands, alluvia and imported material of the reservoir banks have more
to give in solution.

The coastal waters, especially those of Eglwys Nunydd, are alkaline
and hard, the mountain waters slightly acid and soft. Hardness in Kenfig
Pool is mostly from limey material, probably dissolved from the shell
sand of its lining: in the Steel Company's Reservoir there is more magnesium—and more than nine times as much sulphate (from sulphurous
industrial compounds) as in the mountain reservoir—and three times as
much as in Roath Lake in Cardiff.

The effects of the sewage is not very apparent in Johnson's figures for
nitrogenous compounds and phosphates, but these fluctuate seasonally.
During algal blooms much will be tied up in the plant cells and not
measurable, but will be released into the water again after the death of

the algae. Chlorides from blown sea salt are most evident in the broad, wind-ruffled expanse of Eglwys Nunydd, and may help to account for the higher alkalinity here.

The mineral quality of the water is manifested mainly in the microscopic flora and fauna. Larger plants are usually dependent on the extent of shallow water and most of the banks descend too steeply at Eglwys Nunydd to support much growth. Even species such as water milfoil, water starwort and the pondweeds, which can have a free-floating existence, prefer to be anchored in the mud, at least when young. Some of these can get out of hand.

Vigorous growths of water bistort were already causing a problem by 1965 and again in 1979, with fluctuating densities in the years between. Rooted plants will reach up through 5 feet and more of water to interfere with fishing and sailing, two of the activities practised on what has become a multi-purpose lake, large enough and rough enough to provide some pretty heady yacht racing when the wind is off the sea. Indeed, the adjacent M4 is one of the few stretches of motorway to be furnished with airport-style funnels and gale-warning signs. Winds like those which brought the sands in the thirteenth century still blow on occasions.

In 1968 the Steel Company of Wales made a Nature Reserve agreement with the Glamorgan Naturalists' Trust relating to the northern corner adjacent to the Crematorium, where shelving shores and marginal spinneys made this a more promising exercise than in most parts. Much the most profitable section floristically and zoologically was the shallow outlying bay in the east, but this was swallowed up at the coming of the motorway in 1974. Nevertheless, the greatest overall natural history interest is scattered throughout, in the form of wintering wildfowl. Power boats are banned, to the benefit of all users, so the reservoir is a first class example of a happy partnership between industry, amenity use and nature conservation.

3,000 bushes were planted in 1971 among grasses clothing residual soil heaps in the Nature Reserve corner. Scarcely had these found their feet when they were blasted by the salt-laden gales of May and June, in what we laughingly refer to as the 'summer' of 1972, when Glamorgan had autumn in spring, with young leaves crisped and bronzed for many miles inland from the coast. All the leaders were 'scorched' into immobility. What could have been a disaster for tree saplings, proved to be no more than a beneficial pruning for bush saplings, which branched the more profusely from undamaged bases to give good ground cover.

Willow, hawthorn and guelder rose comprised the bulk of the planting, and were shooting well by August of that dreary summer—in spite of being so smothered by coarse grass that visitors were often quite unaware that their parked cars were straddling a future spinney!

Some of the young birches not so hidden were nipped off by sheep until these were kept out by the installation of cattle grids in the autumn. (The excluded animals were not so short of food that they learned to roll across the grids, as sometimes happens in the hungrier hills.) The little bushes took a pounding during motorway construction, but 1,000 more were planted and time is a great healer. The 1980's should provide a respite for plants to grow out and animals to move in.

At the end of the first decade, in that same year of 1972, no less than 178 species of flowers and ferns were found in and around the reservoir. This is adequate testimony to the value of the community before disturbance and its resilience in adapting to the man-made habitat. Marestail and bogbean were among the few members of the indigenous marsh flora which failed to find their way to the new lake shore during this first ten years. The grass seeds mixture used produced some elegant newcomers like crimson clover. Precocious annuals and hardy perennials occupying regularly spaced niches in the concrete facing of the steeper banks seemed a hesitant parody of a more formal garden theme.

There are unlikely to be as many as 178 species by the end of the second decade in 1982. The main deficiency will probably be in the flora of the shallows, both because of loss of area and rises of water level. Less serious will be the loss of successional phases of the land-based vegetation of the banks. Many opportunists which arrived and prospered in the early days are being progressively squeezed out as the long-term dominants settle in and close their ranks.

Less and less spiked water milfoil and water crowfoot are stranded as feathery carpets on the summertime mud below the shoreline fringe of hairy sedge. The five common pondweeds persist, along with celery-leaved buttercup, blue skullcap, sneezewort and most of the colourful components of the Margam Moors flora.

Both marsh yellow cress and creeping yellow cress are here; nodding bur marigold and trifid bur marigold and the hybrid *Mentha* x *verticillata* as well as water mint and corn mint. Marsh woundwort throws both white and pink flowers. There is pale persicaria *(Polygonum lapathifolium)* in addition to water bistort, water pepper and redshanks; plicate sweet-grass *(Glyceria plicata)* as well as flote grass and reed sweet-grass.

Water bistort has such a hold that it romps away from the depths out through the shallows and across dry land, where it pushes short red and yellow shoots through the limestone chippings of the tracks. Here it is joined by a dwarf, red-leaved version of lesser water parsnip and trip-wires of purplish reed rhizomes many yards long, which lose their way in the swamp and trail out over the hard core. The production of red pigment in the reeds arises from the effect of light on parts which are usually underground. In bistort and parsnip leaves it is more likely to be the result of local drought.

Reed sweet-grass *(Glyceria maxima)* monopolises considerable portions of the reedswamp south of the reservoir—holding its own against the taller and more aggressive reeds only by virtue of the earlier shoot growth in spring, which enables it to occupy frost-bared areas undisputed. Cattle and ponies are partial to its sweetness, so grazing by these can favour the cause of the less palatable reeds.

To live among either, subordinate plants must be aggressively robust to reach the light of day, or early maturing, to make the most of it before the canopy closes overhead. Those succeeding in the first category include angelica, meadowsweet, teasel, iris, great reedmace and branched bur-reed (see sketch of white-fronted geese for the last two). Plants in the second category are epitomised by kingcup and lady's smock.

As the plant life settles in, so do the animals. Peter Dance carried out a survey of the molluscs during the seventh summer. His specimens were gathered from the mud of the doomed eastern bay, but there are hopes that representatives of the eleven species identified may have found refuge in other parts.

Wandering snails *(Lymnaea peregra)* and common ramshorns *(Planorbis planorbis)* were those most often met with browsing among the pondweeds. The marsh snails *(Lymnaea palustris)* have a more pronounced shell spiral and the ear pond snails *(Lymnaea auricularia),* a south-westerly species, have a shell shape between the two.

White ramshorns *(Planorbis albus)* were present, and also smooth ramshorns *(Planorbis laevis)*, these constituting a new vice-county record. They are local in their distribution, found usually near the sea, but mainly in Northern England, with few Welsh examples.

Jenkins's spire shells *(Potamopyrgus jenkinsi)* weave pencil-thin trails through the mud, as in practically all Glamorgan waters since their apparently spontaneous appearance in the middle of last century. They were first discovered in brackish areas, but started migrating inland to fresh water about 1893—in defiance of the fact that only one male specimen has ever been found and the female might have proved a trifle inhibited. The phenomenal spread is remarkable: perhaps the parthenogenetic production of offspring with no prior need to seek a mate has helped. The viviparous birth, with the young born alive, has eliminated the need to search for something solid in a mobile expanse of silt on which to place the egg capsules. Laver spire shells, the marine counterparts of this species on the Bristol Channel muds, have solved this problem by laying their eggs on each other's shells!

One of the delicate bivalves found at Eglwys Nunydd is an orb mussel *(Sphaerium),* the others are pea mussels *(Pisidium).* The short-ended

P. subtruncatum is likely to be found anywhere. The quadrangular *P. milium* likes its water clear, but not moving fast enough to dispel the mud of the bed. Henslow's pea mussel *(P. henslowanum)* is confined to this sort of hard, limey water.

Fish food is quite adequate to sustain a healthy population of brown trout and rainbow trout for the fly fishermen, but the reservoir has not been stocked with coarse fish. It is rated highly as a trout fishery, and young fish are bred in floating cages, which must have puzzled many a passer-by on the motorway. Trout are put into these as fingerlings and are fed on fish pellets, which they pounce on like a mob of piranas. At ¾ pound weight they are ready for release. 1979 was a bad season, but disabled fishermen, permitted to bait their hooks with worms, were able to pull out numbers of big eels.

These had no doubt missed their way when migrating down the River Kenfig for the long journey to the spawning grounds of the Sargasso Sea. The 250 acre cul-de-sac in which they found themselves can offer them a good living, but not the conditions to propagate their kind. Those not too well grown, may provide prizes for visiting herons if they choose to lie in the limited shallows.

One highly prolific food source in the isolated pools and inlets of the north-east are the tadpoles. In late May 1973 the reedmace pool north of the Yacht Club H.Q. contained astonishing hordes of these. Hundreds of thousands thronged against the banks in wriggling phalanxes, unable to go anywhere because of the regiments pressing in behind. Such a glut is seldom seen in Glamorgan waters. In spite of the local population pressure, the animals must have been feeding richly, as all had well developed hind legs kicking futilely against the press of fat, glistening bodies—at a time of year when less opulent tadpoles of impoverished upland waters were only half this size and of very basic personal statistics. Identification at the tadpole stage can be tricky, but by that September infant toads were more in evidence than frogs.

230

18 EGLWYS NUNYDD RESERVOIR:
AS A WILDFOWL HAUNT

Microhabitats and feeding methods of diving and dabbling ducks.
Other water birds, passerines and mammals of the shoreline

USE of the new reservoir by water fowl got off to a bad start during the frigid winter of 1962-63, when even those birds retreating to salt water to feed found their habitat partially ice-bound, with sizeable floes up-channel towards Cardiff. Many died on the Eglwys Nunydd ice or the iron-hard banks, but this was no fault of the reservoir, which has offered sanctuary to progressively larger flocks through the years.

By February 1963 over 80 coot had converged to graze the frost-crisped grass atop the steep banks, but a dozen more were frozen rigid in the shoreline ice. Emaciated bodies of starlings, lapwings, gulls and skylarks were scattered across the banks, and even their favourable ratio of body weight to radiative surface did not enable all the mute swans to conserve sufficient body heat to stay alive.

Whooper and bewick swans, geared as they are to the high Arctic, seemed more able to cope, although entitled to expect better than this after flying so far to the ameliorating influence of the Gulf Stream. Pochard and mallard stood miserably on the ice, shoulders hunched against horizontally driven snow, or alighted in good faith, to skate dizzily to an unpremeditated standstill. Sufficiently large flocks of pochard and coot paddled around the centre of the reservoir to keep this ice-free.

February 1965 offered kindlier conditions, but it was still cool. The bird watchers shivering on the bank and envying the water fowl their unassailable insulation in that cold grey expanse, were surprised to learn that the water was, in fact, warmer than the air. Large bodies of water buffer extremes of heat and cold and on this occasion water temperature was 37°F and air temperature 36°F.

Coot were there by the hundred, swarming up and down the steep embankments at a shambling run, with wings aflutter. They preferred the grass sward for feeding, but the wind-ruffled water gave greater seclusion from disturbance, so they shuttled to and fro. Diving duck were in the majority, with 50 tufted duck and as many as 22 goldeneye, although these are usually more solitary. Several cormorants had flown in to vary their sea-food diet with a soupçon of trout and eel.

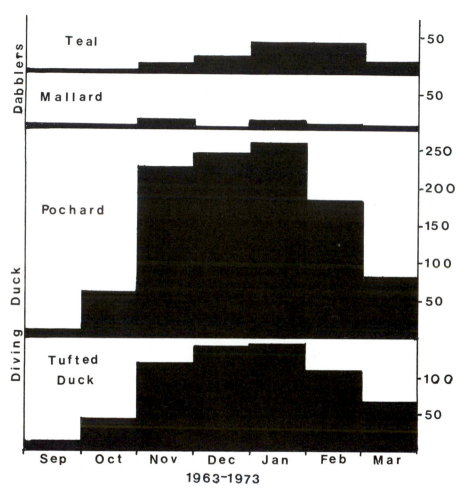

43. Average overwintering population of the four commonest duck species on Eglwys Nunydd Reservoir during its first decade (after Edington)

John and Ann Edington have assembled the figures for duck flocks over the first decade, and their monthly averages for the four commonest species are presented here diagrammatically. The two divers were in the ascendancy, with twice as many pochard as tufted duck, and dabbling mallard and teal in more modest numbers. Shoveler do not appear until January and reach an average flock size of 16 in February, although 170 divided their attentions between here and Kenfig Pool in February 1973. Goldeneye peak at an average of 13 in March. Wigeon like to graze on short grass, which is restricted about the reservoir and monopolised by coots, and their monthly average did not top 5 during the first ten years.

232

In 1977 the maximum count of pochard was down to 120, while tufted duck stayed at 150, but both may reach to 400 on occasion. Teal and mallard were up to 73 and 45 and were topped in this year by shoveler, which remained at about 90 in January and February. Wigeon, present at both ends of the year, peaked at 17, goldeneye at 26.

Gadwall took refuge here through autumn and winter, as many as 60 together after Christmas. There were rare sightings of long-tailed duck and scaup: also eider duck, at the eastern end of their usual flight range, although one bird strayed right up to the River Rhymney in this year. A smew turned up towards the end of 1979. Other unusual visitors are pintail, ruddy duck, red-crested pochard, garganey, red-breasted merganser, goosander and shelduck.

The bare expanse of water looks homogeneous, but each duck species is using it differently, as surely as each buck species seeks different foods at different levels in the African savanna. Its size and the lack of shelter around its margins makes Eglwys Nunydd one of the roughest areas of fresh water in South Wales.

The naturally shelving shore of the north-east is on the lee side, so receives the greatest battering by waves, which have cut a bank several feet high in places, leaving nothing but barren gravel at its foot. This restricts the habitat available to the shore feeders which formerly thronged on the eastern bay, protected by its own causeway to windward and thus escaping wave scour and catering generously for moorhen, water rail, waders and amphibians, as well as dabbling duck.

David Johnson has studied duck feeding techniques, length of dive and habitat selection in relation to shape of bill and positioning of legs, and has pin-pointed some interesting facts.

Pochard is not only the most prolific species, but the least specialised. It often joins the dabblers in the shallows, but dabbles less effectively, and it is the least efficient of the divers: an all purpose Jack of all Trades and the Master of None, with no marked physical modifications of body structure. Tufted duck dive more proficiently, staying down for longer, so that they have more searching time on the bottom. Golden-eye are even better at this, able to dive from rougher water and reach to deeper levels. Their greater efficiency under water is achieved by a backward displacement and shortening of legs—which makes them awkward on land, where they seldom venture. The rare long-tailed duck is the champion diver: the equally rare goosander and merganser are in a different category, chasing fish at intermediate levels instead of having to plumb the depths for bottom organisms.

Data on the foods eaten can be obtained from wild-fowlers, who kill their birds and are thus able to analyse gut contents. Except for the fishing ducks, the range is wide, and usually consists of what happens to be in greatest supply. In other words, most wildfowl are opportunist feeders and congregate where the feeding is richest, exploiting each new food source as it becomes available. Several species may thus be eating together, an unusual situation in Nature because it implies harmful competition, but the chances are they are taking food by different methods from different places. Wigeon are mainly grazers, teal filterers and mallard general purpose feeders, so the goodies are fairly divided when they are working a patch of waterside together.

Quantities of plant seeds find their way into the reservoir—released from underwater pondweeds, falling from bur-reeds and sedges or dropping in from waterside plants. Some will drift against the bank with the wind to be scooped up by teal, either by surface filtering, when head and neck are laid parallel to the water with bill partly submerged, or by bottom feeding, with head and neck immersed.

Other seeds will waterlog and sink deeper, where they are likely to be guddled up by mallard, up-ending, with half the body under water. As with most ducks, animals are taken as well as plants—water snails, midge and caddis larvae from the muds, Corixid water boatmen and shrimps from the middle layers, with planktonic cyclops and water fleas, and stranded midges, flies and spiders from the surface film.

Lighter particles will drift out over the lake where the most efficient filter feeders of all, the shovelers, can sweep them off the top with the lamellated, grotesquely broadened shovel bills acting like vacuum cleaners. They tend to do this under the north bank of Eglwys Nunydd when the water is calm, and on a still day their beaks are scarcely lifted from the water surface. Wave action disrupts this mode of feeding, partly by dispersing and submerging the floating food items and partly by splashing water into the ducks' nostrils. Johnson noticed that the beak is held less horizontally as the water roughens, this bringing the tip lower, among the sinking food, and the nostrils higher, above the splash.

Wigeon, which are partly land grazers and partly water grazers, seem to be in their element on partially flooded grassland, where they can eat well watered herbage with water lapping round their ankles. Their fast pecking rate, like that of teal, probably suggests a lack of selectivity. Anything and everything within reach is grist to the mill within their gizzard.

All the water fowl tend to commute between Eglwys Nunydd and Kenfig Pool, depending on the amount of disturbance. The feeding is richer at Kenfig but the area is smaller, so that it is sometimes difficult to get away from people. Shyer species will feed at night, taking refuge well out from the shore by day.

Geese are uncommon visitors now, but barnacle, brent and Canada geese have been recorded and 13 bean geese passed through in January 1972. 15 mute swans spent part of their winter here in 1977 and some

44. Backward displacement of legs in mallard

have attempted to breed each year since 1970. A trench was dug in 1972 between the bank and one of two nests which had been robbed of its eggs by vandals, in an effort to make it more secure. 7 birds were investigating the site the following spring. A pair tries each year to nest on a tongue of land left by flooding near the motorway, and now an island, but these usually get robbed.

These swans, understandably, have become aggressive, but not in the right quarter. They have chased off great crested grebes which tried to nest there and Syd Johnson watched an amusing David and Goliath incident between swan and dabchick. The cob swan was pecking persistently, but not viciously at the diminutive nesting dabchick which held its ground, lying on its back in the water and scrabbling with its feet in the way that a coot meets attackers. It finally withdrew a little, hurt only in its pride, but was soon back, and the swan mooched off, bored. Little grebes can be seen at any time of the year, with a maximum of 15 in the autumn in 1977.

The great crested grebes chased off by the swans moved into the reeds and brought up three chicks so close to the road that they could be filmed from a car. A bird coming in to relieve its mate on the eggs would often bring an offering of weed for the nest. Its ritual placement would be followed by a bout of mutual head shaking before they changed places.

235

Rafts were installed in the early seventies to tempt the grebes to nest in islanded isolation, but with mixed success. The first got waterlogged and sank unobtrusively from sight. The second, launched in September 1974, was turned upside down in the gales that caused a lot of bank erosion but also brought in some exciting birds—grey phalaropes, white-winged black terns and little gulls. The raft was tethered to leeward of a reed patch: to windward, the reeds might have held it. This was constructed of parallel branches about 2 inches in diameter, lashed together with some leafier twigs on top. This type floats on oil drums and covered with soil and grassy vegetation, proved more lakeworthy.

The great crested grebes' need for large areas of open water is met here, and it is not uncommon to see 9 or 10 about, with some breeding successfully most years. There were 8 present in May 1977 and 11 in November, after the rearing of 4 chicks from 2 nests, with 30 in early October 1978. Both black-necked and Slavonian grebes turned up in that year. November gales of 1977 blew a young storm petrel onto the reservoir (and a leach's fork-tailed petrel onto Kenfig Pool). These little pelagic wanderers must have found the taste of the water rather odd! Great northern, black-throated and red-throated divers provide the occasional thrill in winter and water rails are sometimes spotted among thick vegetation.

The 1973 grebe raft was made use of by a pair of moorhens and Arthur Morgan witnessed an unusual incident between these and some coots on 3rd June. Three downy moorhen chicks were being fed with flies scooped from the surface of the water by a solicitous parent, when a coot intervened. In a brief scuffle the moorhen was separated from its chicks and the aggressor ganged up with another on the family, one of which was taken out of the water and given a good shaking. The second moorhen hopped off the raft and the two joined battle with the attackers, but were soon routed. The more violent of the coots returned to the chick, which it drowned, by treading it under water while raising itself aloft with flapping wings. The remaining chicks escaped unscathed, one to the raft and the other to a patch of yellow flags. Peace descended—with one less mouth to feed.

Little gulls have become quite a feature of Eglwys Nunydd in recent years and can be relied on some time during autumn or spring. The first appeared in August 1964 and they have gradually built up, with an unprecedented 30 in September 1973 and 60 on 12th April 1977. A flock of 23 performed beautifully on 21st May 1973, engaging in ungull-like butterfly flight, low over the water, with swifts wheeling far above. Glamorgan's fifth glaucous gull turned up on the reservoir in early January 1951. Most other records are way before—in 1892, 1903 and 1925, but also in 1949. Lesser black-backed gulls, which formerly migrated south in winter, are now resident throughout the year.

6

67

Plate 14 EGLWYS NUNYDD: THE STEELWORKS RESERVOIR
—68 and 70 Jack Evans, rest Author

66. View over the reservoir to the sea from the edge of Margam Forest
67. Flowering shoots of mare's-tail
68. Magpie moth on lichen-covered bark
69. Nodding bur marigold
70. Elephant hawk moth

68

9

70

Plate 15   MARGAM COUNTRY PARK—*Author*

71. The verdant valley of Cwm Phillip cuts down through brackenny slopes from Margam Forest
72. Fruiting spikes of sweet flag (*Acorus*)
73. Inflorescence of skunk cabbage (*Lysichiton*)
74. Heron's quill feather and regurgitated crop pellet composed of vole fur and remains of water insects
75. Floating and submerged leaves of yellow water-lily
76. Margam Castle viewed across the Middle Lake

238

Black terns have been tempted down increasingly often since the first 18 were recorded in August 1963. The first white-winged black tern was seen in August of the following year—a second record for Glamorgan, the first having been shot at Cardiff in March 1891!

Limited shallows imply limited feeding for waders, which we most often see on 'Wader Point' near the Yacht Club. Solitary common sandpipers feed here in summer and small groups fly in during spring and autumn on their way to and from the hills. Ruff, greenshank, redshank, spotted redshank and dunlin are most evident on autumn passage, the dunlin ridiculously tame. This often applies in the more restricted habitat of fresh water, where a furtive approach is so much easier than on the open mud-flats where dunlin are usually observed. Wood sandpipers appear occasionally and snipe shelter among sedge and iris.

Just once in a while a phalarope can be watched spinning its small feeding orbit on the water surface. Somehow it is always a surprise to see a wader swimming, but phalarope's toes are partially webbed to assist with this mode of locomotion.

Golden plover, lapwing and curlew congregated on the adjacent fields and were a joy to watch in the early years. Perhaps they still do— beyond the intervening motorway—but they are invisible from the reservoir and their wild cries are drowned by the roar of traffic.

The starling flocks which share the fields with them roost in trees during the winter and reeds during the autumn, when these are still in good fettle and the weather not too severe. In the winter of 1955-56 a big new winter roost was formed·in the plantation north of Eglwys Nunydd Farm, but this was only used for two or three years.

Until 1946 starlings roosted in autumn in the reedbeds around the Morfa Pools. The Eglwys Nunydd reedbed roost was not discovered until 1961, but is probably a replacement site. Starlings use another of these temporary seasonal roosts in the reeds by Kenfig Pool. Flocks are swollen in autumn by the large numbers of young fledged, not all of which will make the grade as over-winterers, but there is a greater boost in winter by migrants from Europe.

In smaller numbers on the eastern cornfields at harvest time and an attractive part of the avifauna were foraging flocks of yellow wagtails and meadow pipits, some of both having bred here. Reed buntings and yellowhammers came through in small flocks at this season and again in spring: redwing and fieldfare in bigger flocks in winter, with mistle thrushes, rooks and jackdaws. They still do in the surviving segment of their old haunt.

So many small birds attract the occasional merlin and peregrines have sometimes hunted here in recent years, these more interested in the stock doves, which feed a hundred at a time over the stubbles, in company with the more ubiquitous wood pigeons. A rough-legged buzzard was spotted in March 1978.

A notable recent addition are the tree sparrows, which were scarcely known in Glamorgan till 1961, when the first nest was found in the Marcross Valley further east. A wintering flock of 40 or so fed by the reservoir during the first week of January in 1962. Since then there has been a general consolidation and westerly spread, with breeding in the Eglwys Nunydd spinney from 1970 onwards and flocks of 30 or more gathering from early August.

White wagtails can usually be counted on the fingers of one hand but 25th April 1977 produced unheard of counts of 200-400. Pied and grey wagtails scavenge wave-borne drift cast onto the reservoir embankments. They take the gnats and midges which have drowned: swallows and swifts take them in their prime, both birds reaching flock sizes of 300 in May and June 1977.

Reed warblers nest in modest numbers, sedge warblers more commonly and the occasionally grasshopper warbler is in residence. Lesser whitethroats occur as well as common whitethroats, with other warblers in summer, tits and goldcrests in winter.

When family parties begin to gather after fledging, the blue and great tits feed communally in the reedbeds, but they usually retire to roost in holes and crevices which they appropriate individually. Like others, they run the gauntlet of the resident little owls, which are skilful hunters by day as well as night. Kingfishers, too, move in for autumn and winter when the rather messy family chores are over, but dippers usually stick to the inlet stream tumbling steeply from the Margam Park lakes, turning back as the flow is checked in the marginal pools.

45. Disparity of bills in shoveler (a surface filter feeder) and golden-eye (a diving duck tweaking food from the bottom)

These are profitable mini-habitats for other species, however. 7-8 coots' nests were strung out along their overgrown banks in 1977, with bald-pated chicks still no bigger than golf balls bowling around in August. Although birds of open water and open grassland, coots need the homelier cover of the backwaters for nesting as much as do moorhens, which imprint the mud with their single line footmarks. (These are one of the few birds to 'register' their tracks like a fox.)

Water pipits are spotted occasionally in February or March and may be commoner than the records show, because only the expert is likely to recognise them. More distinctive rarities in the bushy parts are the sparrow sized lesser spotted woodpeckers seen during the 1970s and the winter bramblings, which may stay as late as 28th March.

The north-eastern spinneys yield a variety of such birds, their numbers boosted by the outlying pools, which broaden the range of food items and supply more comfortable drinking space than the choppy waters of the reservoir. This is a good place to watch for mammals, too.

Water voles are the most in evidence and are fully active by day, taking little notice of unobtrusive observers. Scenes from 'The Wind in the Willows' are re-enacted as they beaver away at their food-gathering. The sweetest, most succulent lengths of reed stem lie below water level and foraging water voles will dive to bite these through at the base, then surface and tow many feet of scape behind them to munch in the seclusion of waterside vegetation, for all the world like tiny beavers at their lodge stocking.

Other rodents are less easy to observe, but Arthur Morgan has found harvest mice among the rough vegetation of the banks. He carried out a live trapping programme in the nature reserve in April 1974 to find out what was about. Numbers of bank voles were caught, but no short-tailed field voles and only one probable long-tailed field mouse, which escaped, as is the way of this more agile species. Common shrews were also observed, stoat, weasel and brown hare.

Large bats were present in profusion on 18th May 1973 and others were seen on and off during the summer months but are notoriously difficult to identify as they flit through the half light. A few years later Arthur Morgan confirmed the presence of Daubenton's bats here—a species which also hunts over Newton Pools at Porthcawl and a stretch of the Glamorgan Canal near Cardiff. These are likely to roost in houses and trees in the summer, retreating to the security of caves for the winter hibernation.

Tormented though this habitat is at times, by bitter winds and human turmoil, it yields much pleasure in its quieter moments and will continue to do so as long as we let it.

19 AT THE SEAWARD EDGE OF THE COALFIELD: MARGAM COUNTRY PARK

Topography and drainage, history of the deer park; plants and animals of bracken-clad slopes, grassy plain and woodland plots

THE ancient sea cliff bounding the Coalfield behind Port Talbot dips inland as it passes south to Margam and begins to rise less precipitously from the alluvial plain. Margam Park nestles in the resulting haven and spreads up the flanking slopes to the heights of Margam Forest. The natural beauty has been enhanced over the centuries by the skilful placing of trees and spinneys and the creation of lakes. Its designation as a Country Park in 1977 by the West Glamorgan County Council has brought the attractions of this 850 acres within reach of the ordinary citizen, while still retaining secluded areas of woodland and waterside as a wildlife reserve.

The deeply incised and wooded valley of Cwm Philip runs within the northern and western boundaries, leading drainage waters seaward from the 1,129 ft. (344m.) watershed of Mynydd Margam— the same that feeds the River Kenfig to the south. A little north of the ancient fort on the lesser Mynydd y Castell, it is joined by Cwm Maelog and the two streams flow together into the westermost of the park's three lakes.

The other two lakes are supplied by rivulets springing from aquifers in the Coal Measure sandstones of the park itself. After nurturing two widely different plant and animal communities, their waters pass on, gaining impetus as they tumble down the sharp incline to Eglwys Nunydd Reservoir beyond the M4 motorway, or slide more gently into Coal Brook to the South. This last, along with another draining the eastern margin of the park, empties into the River Kenfig at Pyle.

A tilted isosceles triangle based along the old A48 London to Fishguard road, the Margam Estate reaches from 40 ft. above sea level to 750 ft.. Its history stretches back to its foundation by Cistercian monks as an abbey and monastery in 1147. From the dissolution of the monasteries in the 16th century until the 1970s, it has been in private hands, each owner adding to the elegance of buildings and grounds—as told by John Vivian Hughes in the 1973 bulletin of the Glamorgan Naturalists' Trust. Improvements continue, and the famous Orangery was reconstructed as part of the county's effort for Architectural Heritage Year in 1975.

Furzemill Pond, which is now part of the nature reserve, appears on the 1814 plan, so must be at least 168 years old—with many of the

242

magnificent parkland trees reaching back almost as far. Some of these are reduced to gaunt skeletons, making fitting perches for sentinel heron or buzzard; others are approaching senility, passing their substance on to the hosts of creeping wood eaters which people a woodpeckers' paradise. Yet others are being removed and replaced, the fortunes of the fine park landscape looking fit to prosper under the new regime of public ownership.

The sloping backdrop of the park is composed of Middle Coal Measure rocks, and the scatter of old tree stumps shows that it was once forested. Much has a covering of acidic boulder clay, which is poorly drained in parts and gives rise to rushy hollows and purple moor grass quagmires. Sandstone has been taken from small quarries for building and walling, clay has been extracted for puddling the beds of the lakes and there are some old gravel pits.

Bracken cannot live on exposed or waterlogged soils, but does particularly well on the sheltered, well-drained slope leading down to Cwm Philip, and also under trees. Here the fronds may reach to 6 ft. and more in summer, blanketing down in winter to create a formidable barrier to plants pushing up from beneath.

Bluebells manage somehow, bursting bravely through in April, along with a modicum of greater stitchwort flowers, the rugged leaves of woodsage and a little bilberry or whinberry. Exposed slopes enjoy less of a woodland climate and bracken is more stunted, leaving space for the smaller flowers of common dog violet and wood sorrel. Foxgloves make a fine show in soil exposed alongside the rides, while bird's-foot (*Ornithopus perpusillus*) flowers on the domed anthills with sheep's sorrel and heath bedstraw.

Tawny owls nest in hollow trees and can be heard hooting late on spring afternoons, while barn owls occupy the old buildings. It was in 1919 that long-eared owls last nested here. A little owl may be surprised at a daylight doze in the underbrush. These nest quite low in old tree boles, even on the ground, leaving give-away pellets of fur and plant debris studded with the shiny black carapaces of the beetles which loom so large in their diet. Plenty of suitable prey items can be picked up from the matted moorland grasses in early summer.

The aptly named bumble dor (*Geotrupes stercorarius*), one of Britain's eight scarab beetles, is often encountered, blundering through the grass and toppling to reveal an iridescent, magpie-blue underside and wildly waving legs. These are dung beetles and have to make do with deer dung here, although usually associated with cow dung. He and she work together, excavating shafts under the droppings and hauling the goodies down inside. They eat some and lay their eggs in some, but there is always plenty over, so they function as unwitting recyclers of valuable nitrates and phosphates, bringing these down to the root level of hungry plants.

Minotaur beetles (*Typhaeus typhoeus*) of the same family are distinguishable by the two forward pointing horns of the males, like some fab-
ulous armour-plated minotaur bull's. These prefer rabbit and sheep
dung and both were available in 1978, although the donors of the sheep
dung may have been strays. The handsome, horned he-beetles carve and
roll the dung pellets but do none of the digging.

Bloody nosed beetles (*Timarcha tenebricosa*) are the largest of the
British leaf beetles or Chrysomelids. They are more slender for'ard than
the other two and preceded by long, questing antennae like strings of
beads. Their most distinctive feature is the trio of flat pads on each leg
behind the claw, these tarsal joints being pale fawn below. They are
wingless and flightless, with the wing cases inseparably fused. Another
beetle to be found with these three at Margam is the seven spot
ladybird, but most birds know better than to tamper with these distasteful morsels. Elephant-snouted weevils are more edible and are around
in plenty.

May and June are times of butterflies and moths and a sunny day in
early May 1978 saw countless fast-moving peacock butterflies and the
mating chases of small tortoiseshells. Large and small whites were on
the wing at this time, and through into summer, when the gatekeepers,
meadow browns and wall browns had emerged. Commonest of the
moths in May and June are the brown silver lines (*Lithina chlorosata*).
The caterpillars feed on bracken and there is no shortage of this: so,
although the rather plain little adults prefer to fly only at dusk, they are
constantly being flushed from the fronds by day.

There is less bracken in the low-lying part of the park and the bent-
fescue grass heath becomes starred with tormentil, mouse-ear
chickweed, self heal and creeping buttercup. Much is overtopped by
common ragwort in autumn, while marsh ragwort brightens the wetter
parts, growing with corn mint and water pepper. Ground ivy and
bluebells, which persist best where there is bracken cover to shade their
leaves after flowering, are survivors from a former woodland phase.

Queen bumble bees are on the wing from early spring. The three
kinds most evident in May, seeking provender to feed the first batch of
workers, are the buff-tailed *Bombus terrestris,* the smaller garden
bumble bee, *Bombus hortorum,* and the common carder bee with furry
orange thorax and stripy behind, *Bombus agrorum,* which makes its
nest of grass above ground. Solitary bees home in on the dwindling
waters to drink with ever increasing frequency if a showery spring turns
to a dusty summer.

The first wasps are abroad by May, the population building up gradually to the September fruit harvest. An underground nest may be concealed below an entrance the size of a woodpecker's nest hole, gnawed
through the under-felt of dead grass. A column of wasps four to six

deep was watched emerging from one such near the Middle Lake in August, each carrying a soil pellet the size of a lentil in its jaws. Others were chewing cellulose from a dry stem in the manufacture of paper for the nest fabric, the rim of which was visible a few inches down where the entrance tunnel broadened into the main chamber containing the layers of comb.

Scaeva pyrastri is one of the commonest of the hover flies abroad in May, and likely to be around right through to November. It is wasp-like in appearance, with a double row of yellow crescents on the black body—a colour scheme designed to warn off would-be predators. The eggs are laid among aphids and the residents are joined by waves of migrants from the continent. Adults feed from a variety of flowers and are not put off by the aromatic whiff of water mint.

1978 was a good year for St. Mark's flies (*Bibio marci*) and these were out in hordes in May, the males, with whiskery legs adangle, disporting themselves in desultory clouds while waiting for a female to break cover and run the gauntlet of their attentions.

Gawky craneflies or daddy longlegs (*Tipula paludosa*) with fragile sets of even more pendent legs, can build up to plague proportions by September. Females get busy in summer insinuating their eggs among the grass bases—precursors of the next generation of root-chewing leather jackets. *Tipula maxima,* largest of British craneflies and,

46. Common cranefly on dog rose

indeed, of British flies, occurs in waterside habitats, the flies developing from larvae feeding on lakeside plants.

Margam Estate is graced by old and new plots of deciduous woodland, as well as fine standing trees dotted about the open parkland. The steep, mixed woods and beech hangers of the slopes backing the coastal plain are little disturbed and extend up to about six hundred feet—the upper limit of redstart territories. Many kinds of birds find cover here and diffuse out over the plain to feed.

Beeches seem to predominate in spring when their fresh pea-green leaves are bursting from splayed, gingery bud scales—and again in autumn, when these same leaves (or a replacement crop after insect defoliation) are turning to yellow and bronze. At either end of the year, it is a joy to lie beneath them contemplating the asymmetrical symmetry of the bright leaf mosaic, etched against the peerless blue of a cloudless sky.

Gaudy cock chaffinches come to tweak at the catkins, pulling off the tawny stamen tassels with no ill effects, but depriving themselves of nuts in the fall when they destroy the upstanding sprouts of female flowers. Nuthatches sporting the same shade of blue-grey but paler salmon breast feathers, seek less fibrous food over the smooth grey of the sometimes magnificent beech boles (which may end their days as commendably solid park benches).

A striking feature of the beech, perhaps more than of any other tree, is the non-synchronisation of leaf-appearance. Some specimens will be in full leaf during the first week of May while their neighbours show only a slight swelling of winter-brown buds and others the folded fans of very infant leaves. Bud-burst is spread over a three week period in an average year.

Unfurling of leaves marks the mobilisation of nutrients in the woodland food chain and woodland insects are adept at cashing in on this. Those which fail do not survive to breed their kind. Their life-cycles are so ordered that tiny grubs with voracious appetites are scheduled to hatch from overwintering eggs at the precise time of the unsheathing of tender young foliage. The trees retaliate with a system of staggered opening, so that at least some of their leaves will survive the surge of insect predation. Less fortunate trees may be practically defoliated. Some, like our native oaks, can produce a crop of lammas shoots in midsummer to compensate for lost leaves, though lost photosynthesising time cannot be retrieved and the tree is accordingly weakened. Others, like the introduced sycamore, cannot respond in this way.

Life-giving protein bound up in the living protoplasm of tree leaves must be used, if it is to be used, between May and October. After this it breaks down and is reabsorbed into the trunk and branches, where it can be utilised only by wood borers. Many leaf-eaters can digest only the young, non-fibrous leaves which contain less tannin than older ones. The repercussions of this reach further, triggering the late summer departure of birds which rely on leaf-eating insects, although having no significance for woodpeckers and the like, which subsist on the denizens of more permanent parts.

Beech weevils (*Rhynchaenus fagi*) are a common cause of browning of beech leaves. The 2mm. long adult beetles congregate on the buds in spring as the leaves unfurl, flying from tree to tree to lay their eggs in the soft midribs. Grubs hatching from these are leaf miners, small enough to live within the substance of the leaf. They burrow outwards, eating their way through juicy leaf cells flooded with the rising sap, to form a brown blotch at the leaf edge.

By the end of a month the stages of egg, larva and pupa have run their course and the adult beetle emerges, fully equipped to chew away at more beech leaves through the summer. It is unusual in being able to jump as well as fly. Larvae cannot eat mature leaves, so there is no second generation, the remaining eleven months of the life cycle being spent as adults. The magnificent cut-leaved beech near the abbey is not immune, any branch tip accidentally knocked during the summer of 1979 emitting unbelievable clouds of slender green leaf hoppers.

Interaction between leaf-eating insects and their host plants is chemically very subtle, most insects infesting only one species of tree, even to the extend of differentiating between common oak and durmast oak, or between downy birch and silver birch. *Rhynchaenus fagi* lays its eggs only on beech, *R. quercus* only on oak, *R. saltator* only on elm and *R. rusci* only on birch.

The several species of winter moths are less choosy and their energetic little looper caterpillars can be found dangling on silken threads from almost any sort of tree: which is good news for the tits and other small birds which rely very heavily on them as a source of food for their nestlings.

Some gall wasps have a more intimate relationship with trees and, although we seldom see them, their presence is only too obvious in the fleshy pink oak apples, hard brown marble galls, 'spangles', 'silk bobbins' and 'pea', 'currant' and 'cherry' galls on oaks.

Not all the insects to be found on trees are parasitising those trees. Many are living off others which are, and so helping to minimise damage. Yet others, like *Mesopsocus* species, which are members of the booklice group, are neither parasite nor predator. They live by scraping away the algae, yeasts and other fungi from the bark, often sheltering among lichens, and living with equal success on the quick and the dead.

One of the key features in park management is the herd of fallow deer, which fluctuates in numbers, but is several hundred strong. Its members are endowed with an ability to make light work of barriers erected to contain them—and a good appetite for sapling trees. They use stealth rather than agility when escaping, and the builders of the 7 miles or so of dry stone boundary wall with its hooped iron ladders as stiles, knew this. The finest spread of antlers proves no impediment to a stag wishing to thread himself between two fence wires. Chin up and ears back, he slips gracefully through, with an admirable disdain for such modern innovations.

Repair of the boundary wall was nearing completion in 1978, but deer came and went freely between park and forest before this—to establish the only wild herd in the county outside. The original stock was the spotted form of fallow deer from the New Forest, but black bucks were introduced later and account for the large number of dark brown individuals to be seen now.

The steep, remoter bracken areas make ideal cover for does with fawns and the bucks spend more of their time out of the woodland than in when their antlers are in velvet, because these bleed easily at this time if inadvertently knocked on branches. Some carry their antlers on into May, but most have shed them by then, to grow new ones for the rut in October and November.

A great deal of lime must be cycled from the soil, through the plants into the antlers, but the deer seem not to eat them after casting them, to get some of it back for re-use, as do deer in poorer mountain habitats. Nevertheless, modern antlers are not as big as those of the ancient stock

47. Fallow deer

excavated from the Margam foreshore in 1974. Small rodents utilise some of the lime store, gnawing at the discarded antlers as they lie among the bracken.

The lowland spinneys at Margam are deer-dominated and open-floored, but enclosure of some in time for the 1978 growing season presaged a change. Until then trees showed a browse line at the ultimate reach of a standing deer, but if there was a wall or trunk for the animal to rear up against, this kinked significantly upwards. Marginal shrubs, even rhododendrons, may be neatly hedged by chomping incisors, and seedlings which seek to grow beneath their elders are doomed from the start.

One of the park's old established badger setts is out in the open and severely windswept until the bracken fronds unfurl in May. The tunnels go down between the rock strata, exploiting softer bands of marl, and the spoil heap at the mouth of one is sprinkled with sparkling coal fragments where the furred miner has excavated a coal seam. Badgers were in occupation in 1978, with dwarf swards of toad rush and *Polytrichum* moss on the bared ground round about and new dung pits excavated in a nearby gravel working. There must be a good population, between here and the sett in the valley below, as 15 badgers were caught in fox traps during the 1973-74 winter—and released.

Foxes share the setts on occasion, as well as constructing their own earths or lying up in old mine entrances. They range widely over the hill face and their numbers are augmented by neighbours from Margam Forest. No less than 63 foxes were killed between October 1973 and Summer 1974 in the interests of game preservation, the population here, as elsewhere in the Coalfield, being much larger than the occasional sightings would indicate.

The central badger sett has been in use during recent years, with fresh bedding trailing away from the entrances, but the annexe is occupied by long-eared, bob-tailed squatters. Rabbits are somewhat localised, with a particularly thriving population in an eastern marl pit. Hares are thought to be on the increase and quantities of neatly nibbled pine cones show where grey squirrels have been harvesting a crop which takes three years to develop from the fleshy red flowering phase.

Small tunnels leading into mossy woodland banks could be the work of either bank voles or wood mice, but there is no mistaking the oval, yellow-green dung pellets of short-tailed field voles in the open. These are most often seen in the purple moor grass areas, where there is a good felt of leaves over the ground surface in which burrows can be nibbled out with no recourse to digging. The voles tuck their tennis ball sized nests of finely shredded grass well up in the moor grass stools, where they are likely to be safe from winter flooding—and where they are blatantly exposed by light grass fires on occasion.

Moles, hedgehogs, common shrews and pygmy shrews help to keep the invertebrates in check. Long-eared bats and pipistrelles live under the roof of Twyn-y-Llydd House at Margam, swooping out on mild nights with private sonar systems working at maximum efficency. Arthur Morgan, who located these, also found a small colony of noctules in the Goytre Valley nearby, roosting in a very similar habitat in an old woodpecker hole. Bats, possibly of this species, fly over the park and there is no shortage of potential roosts in decrepit trees and ancient buildings.

There was a good adder population on the rough hill land, which the park authorities, regrettably, have thought fit to wage war against in the supposed public interest, although well aware that walking in adder country is much less dangerous than bicycle riding or other permitted pastimes. One can only attribute man's unreasoning fear of these shy and self-effacing creatures to the distance which he has strayed from his natural, whole environment.

The beautiful sinuous motion of a grass snake swimming in lake or pool, is a sight not easily forgotten, and both slow worms and lizards can be spotted by the keen-eyed. A tightly coiled grass snake may inflate itself with an audible intake of breath when startled, to become loosely coiled and seemingly more horrifically large, in an attempt to fool the disturber into thinking that it is capable of inflicting harm. A load of musty hay dumped near the abbey a few years ago provided an admirable compost heap situation which tempted a grass snake to lay her eggs —the pencil-thin young emerging according to plan from ruptured eggshells. Frogs and toads are domiciled in the boggier zones.

Buzzards nest in two of the estate's spinneys and can be seen soaring in thermals which they share with the herons. They often rest on the cliff below the Pulpit. Kestrels quarter the air on the lookout for voles, finding prey-spotting easiest over the short greensward of the upland fields reclaimed from the sea of bracken. These are kept in trim by chain harrowing and provide sweeter grazing for the deer.

Merlins have nested during the seventies, and possibly still do. Though small, they are exciting hawks to watch as they shoot, meteor-like, through the sky or indulge in skilful aerial chase of some hapless pipit or lark. The archives tell us that a white-tailed eagle was shot here in 1831 and a hobby in 1923—the usual fate in those days of anything rare or interesting, when men lived by maxims such as 'If it moves, shoot it: if it doesn't, chop it down'.

The parkland, with its mixture of plentiful cover and open flying space, is ideal for sparrow hawks, and these can sometimes be seen with the draggled remains of a finch in their talons. In one pair's territory a pigeon was found dismembered on its nest, with feathers spilling down the trunk, but kills are usually taken to a favourite plucking post.

Wood pigeons are larger than life, as always, and collared doves nest around the abbey and orangery, encouraged no doubt in the first instance by corn put out for domestic fowl. Turtle doves, though a more traditional part of the avifauna, are rarer, but visit in summer and may sometimes breed. Stock doves pass through occasionally.

Pheasants and partridges were formerly reared for shooting and are holding their own now, unaided. The five rectangular plots of conifers on the backing hillside, which stand out like a handful of sore thumbs as the park's main marker from afar off, were probably planted thus as pheasant coverts. The guns waited at the edges for birds to break cover to escape the beaters and make for the next. Woodcock may still be breeding and are seen quite regularly in Margam Forest above.

This is nightjar country and nightjars are rarities now, so this is country to be treasured. Ravens fly cronking across their traditional haunts in Cwm Maelog and armies of jackdaws come chacking through at intervals from holey old trees of the remnant oakwood near the headwaters of Cwm Phillip. Greater spotted and green woodpeckers set up house in other hollow trees, along with nuthatch and tree creeper, and there may be magpies, jays or carrion crows in the branches. The estate rookery is by the old vicarage near the west entrance.

Goldcrests, long-tailed tits and the four hole-nesting tits are on the list of breeding birds, with other holes occupied by the inevitable starlings and sparrows. Some may harbour pied flycatchers, which are around all summer and may rear the occasional family. Redstarts, although resident only in the deciduous woods, fly up to the conifer-clad plateau to feed, as do whinchat and stonechat. Whinchats can be watched on the gaunt skeletons of time-battered pines, making flycatcher-like sorties into hovering swarms of gnats. More usually they are down on the bracken tops with the stonechats. Wrens scurry through the bracken stalks below, mouse-like in movement, but far from mouse-like in voice.

Larks trill their way up to sunlit heights (and rainy ones, too, on occasion) while chirruping meadow pipits erupt skywards at intervals during their busy pottering. Tree pipits favour isolated trees—spreading pines and shapely rowans—for their swooping song flights. That unmistakable harbinger of summer, the cuckoo, is active in May, seeking out the nests of penalised pipits or luckless larks as fostering sites for its demanding young.

Great flocks of fieldfares descend from the skies in winter with modest numbers of redwings, and mistle thrushes can build up into big flocks by August. In spring they are more solitary, using the sentinel trees as staging posts in churring flights from the woods.

Warblers arriving in spring and probably breeding include blackcap, whitethroat, and lesser whitethroat, chiff chaff, willow warbler and wood warbler, while the dancing feeding flights of the spotted fly-catchers can be watched interminably when there are hungry chicks to be fed. The gentle trilling of grasshopper warblers is a rare but exciting sound and the friendly twittering of passing flocks of linnets is always evocative of these wide open spaces. Clinking wheatears pass through in spring on their way to the Coalfield hills and the odd couple may be tempted to stay and breed.

Five finch species nest regularly in the park—linnet, chaffinch, green-finch, bullfinch and goldfinch, but the resident yellow hammers, redpolls and reed buntings have not yet been proved to do so. Tree sparrows come in this last category: bramblings are winter visitors.

Add to these the ubiquitous blackbirds and song thrushes, robins and dunnocks, owls and water fowl and we have an impressive list—indica-tive of the commendable habitat diversity within the bounds of the park. A list compiled by Arthur Morgan just prior to the opening as a country park in 1977 contained no less than ninety-two species, plus three more by then extinct. There is little doubt that the building up of so rich an avifauna has been greatly helped by the lack of disturbance during the many decades of private ownership. It will be an achievement of the first order if these numbers are maintained now that there is free public access to the greater part.

20 STREAMS AND LAKES OF MARGAM COUNTRY PARK

Flora and fauna of Cwm Philip and the old mill leat, the three lakes and Coal Brook

BOUNDING merrily from rock to rock, splashing over obstacles and gurgling through bottlenecks, Nant Philip hurries down a V-shaped declivity in the hillside which looks far too big for it. 'Constant dripping weareth away a stone' and this typical Coalfield stream has been doing a great deal more than dripping over past aeons.

Speckled brook trout lie in deep pools and battle sturdily with the rapids, whilst flattened stonefly larvae escape the full force of the current by hiding under stones. Willow warblers trill from leafy stream-side willows and common sandpipers drop in for fleeting visits on spring and autumn passage.

Flood water replenishes marginal quagmires in times of spate, causing the purple moor grass to reach upwards in steep-sided tussocks. Bog violets nestle into feather-soft cushions of *Sphagnum* between them and golden saxifrage within splash range of the little falls is hung with silver droplets. Delicate wood sorrel flowers peep from the skirts of drier tummocks and sparsely blooming honeysuckle trails over their summits.

Orange-headed drumsticks of the amphibious fungus, *Mitrula paludosa,* rise from sodden holly leaves in wayside pools, over-shadowed by tufts of hard fern and wavy hair grass sprouting from toppled trees. Sometimes deposits of bog iron ore are almost as bright where springs ooze from the rocks laden with iron, which becomes oxidised to rusty ferric hydroxide as it bubbles free. Iron-consuming bacteria give the accumulations a mucilaginous feel—like concentrated tomato soup.

High up on the southern valley flank, where the bordering birches have given way to scattered hawthorns, runs the old mill leat, construc-ted many decades ago to lead unsullied mountain water down to the buildings. This is kept clear and contains feathery growths of stone-wort, *Nitella flexilis,* in the shade of marginal bosses of tussock sedge.

Water crowfoot flowers throughout the summer with big white-petalled cups among circular leaves which float above an underwater mesh of finely branched ones. It is interrupted by bronze patches of broad-leaved pondweed and the spear leaves and bobble flower heads of unbranched bur reed. Very occasionally a little flowering rush can be found pushing up from dark thickets of narrow-leaved pondweed. In spring the marginal yellows and mauves are supplied by lesser spearwort and lady's smock; in summer by greater bird's-foot trefoil and water mint.

Life is easier for many aquatic animals in the leat than in the turbul-ence of the stream and tube-dwelling caddis larvae are particularly numerous on the muddy bed. Their makeshift homes are built on three main patterns. Some are made of blackened fragments of birch leaves, hinged along one side to appear like a slightly opened folder with smaller fragments connecting the two edges, so that the sectional view is a grossly flattened triangle. The maker is probably a species of *Phaco-pteryx.*

Others are of short, longitudinally placed stem fragments built around a scaffolding of four or five one and half inch lengths of water crowfoot stems—the work of *Glyphotaelius* or *Stenophylax.* Yet others are of sand grains built into a framework of twiglets, at least one of which is twice as long as the tube. By this ploy the builder, *Anabolia nervosa,* makes an uncomfortable mouthful for any fish intent on swallowing it.

The golden-winged 'sedge flies' which emerge eventually from the tubes are like gossamer moths with incredibly long antennae. They fly more freely than the alder flies (*Sialis lutaria*), which fold strongly veined wings over their backs and sit around on the bordering spike rush (*Eleocharis*) and meadowsweet. Long-bodied water striders or pond skaters are joined by their shorter-bodied nymphs in summer and share the surface film with water crickets and whirligig beetles.

By June the dragonflies are breaking free from their ugly aquatic nymphs. Most handsome and characteristic of soft hill waters such as these is the golden-ringed dragonfly, *Cordulegaster boltoni.* This is a species which favours running water, in which it may spend as much as five years developing into the superb adult that we see on the wing for a brief month or so. Most have disappeared by August and no British species overwinter as adults. Green dragonflies of this area are probably *Gomphus vulgatissimus.*

The predominantly blue southern Aeshna, *Aeshna cyanea,* is larger and stronger on the wing than either, bringing itself insistently to notice by pounding back and forth along its waterside beat and routing all comers. Specimens of this ilk may be still around in October. The crimson male and mustard coloured female common sympetrums, (*Sympetrum striolatum*) are less closely tied to the leat, ranging far out over the bordering slopes. They like to sit and bask on stones, with transparent wings spread to the sun.

The lower part of Cwm Philip is occupied by high forest with beech, oak, ash, lime, plane and sycamore. A fallen specimen of sweet chestnut shows the timber to be bright yellow. Pebble-floored tributaries flow from sedgy hollows occupied by yellow flags and branched bur-reed to augment the water from the mountain. Angelica and hemlock water dropwort break into a froth of flowers alongside, overshadowing their humbler relatives, the lesser water parsnip and fool's watercress of the stream proper.

The brown trout are larger here, shoaling in pools three to four feet deep in the meanders, while pied wagtails poke for prizes on the shingle banks. Grey wagtails are here too, looping daintily back and forth, upstream and down, primrose breasts like an animated dappling of sunlight through the foliage. These two are always around; yellow wagtails come only in summer and are more likely to be seen out in the open by the lakes. They enjoy chasing the yellow dung flies associated with the dung of larger herbivores. Perhaps the country park will supply foraging for the flocks displaced from the fields alongside Eglwys Nunydd Reservoir by the coming of the motorway.

Plate 16   MARINE LIFE ON KENFIG BEACH—*Author*

77. Neat sand grain tube of burrowing worm, *Pectinaria koreni,* with cockle shells
78. Stranded jellyfish (*Chrysaora hyoscella*)
79. Female shore crab 'in berry' (carrying egg mass)
80. A shore crab swells enormously after backing out of its old skin during ecdysis (the skin change which permits growth)
81. 'Sea grapes', the eggs of squid (*Sepia officinalis*)
82. Egg collars of predatory necklace shells (*Natica alderi*) and shells of their victims

83

84

85

Plate 17   KENFIG FLOWERS
AND
BUTTERFLIES—*Author*

83. Flowers of burnet rose
84. Black hips of burnet rose
85. Brimstone butterfly on thistle head
86. Wall brown butterflies mating
87. Small copper butterflies mating

86

87

The stream ends in an eight feet wide rush of water over the tall weir which takes it into Fish Pond Lake and dumps its load of silt on the expanding headwater marsh. This is colourful in July and August with one of West Glamorgan's specialities, the inch-wide flowers of greater spearwort, seen at their best here in the contrasting company of purple loosestrife, hemp agrimony and great willow herb. Blue trumpets of greater skullcap push out among the rushes beneath white sprays of greater water plantain, and the whole is redolent with the scent of water mint.

Trees crowd thickly about the lake shore, their substance reflected in the deep green depths, and rhododendrons climb the hill to the ruined chapel far above. Foresters, rightly, regard this evergreen as an enemy of more legitimate forest trees, but it is undeniably beautiful when flowering. June journeys along the A48 can be made memorable by the rosy expanse of the old sea cliff sweeping skywards above the road beneath its load of blossoms.

Where its sombre foliage lines the shore, lightened by alder buckthorn, alder and sallow, there is no room for waterside herbs but, as the shade thins, both great and small reedmace grow, with gipsywort and woody nightshade squeezed among great tufts of tussock sedge and bur-reed. Fine clumps of water lilies thrust waxy white flowers above underwater thickets of alternate-flowered water milfoil and narrow-leaved pondweed. Bright wefts of filamentous green algae indicate eutrophication, the fertility stemming very likely from the weft of decaying leaves on the silty bed.

Two islets near the upper end provide seclusion for nesting waterfowl. Moorhens take advantage of the haven to bring off batches of wispy black chicks, and coot are often to be seen, but hirundines tend to favour the more open lakes.

Cwm Philip waters enjoy a brief respite here before racing off again over a series of weirs and south to the River Kenfig, from where some spend another sedentary spell in Eglwys Nunydd, before being sucked into the great steelworks and spewed out again into Port Talbot Harbour. The rectangular pond of the old water garden above the Orangery is almost dry now, but there is still a golden drift of kingscups in spring, followed by a paler one of yellow flags.

Margins of the Middle Lake were very overgrown in 1974, but have been opened out with the coming of the country park to give freer access to the sedgy shoreline. When not flowering, the medley of sword-leaved plants here resemble each other in a quite bewildering fashion, but each can be sorted out with a little practice.

Very like the smooth blue-grey leaves of the yellow flag (*Iris*) are the transversely wrinkled, yellow-green ones of the sweet flag (*Acorus*), but these smell evocatively of tangerines when crushed—hence their

257

popularity as a floor covering in mediaeval times. The leaves of both splay sideways in a flattened fan, a form which at once distinguishes them from those of the bur-reeds (*Sparganium*), which curve away from each other face to face, so that they have an upper and a lower side, as the others have not.

Bur-reed leaves are, in addition, folded into a shallow V-shape with a keel all along the back, whereas the midrib of the brighter green sweet flag leaf sticks out on both surfaces. The central vein of the iris leaf is not the true midrib but is compounded of two side veins with the midrib along one edge. This is brought about by the lengthwise folding of the leaf and the fusing of the inner face to itself except at the base, where it opens out to accommodate the younger leaves forming inside.

Reedmace or bulrush leaves (*Typha*) resemble those of iris only in colour. They are longer, with parallel sides and blunt tips, and spiral gently upwards from a flanged, cylindrical base. The pond sedges (*Carex*) have folded leaves in three ranks, each fitting snugly against two sides of the triangular stem.

Sweet reed grass (*Glyceria maxima*) is the only one of the tall water-side grasses at all common, there being little or none of the more familiar true reed or reed canary grass. Stems and leaves are striped with purple in some years, the colour given by the spores of a smut fungus, *Ustilago longissima*. Sweet reed grass shares dominance with branched bur-reed and the usually rare sweet flag, which is a plant of South-east England and the Border Counties, growing at the west of its geographical range here. It belongs to the arum family, but has little in common with its relatives apart from the chunky spadix or spike of tiny massed flowers. No doubt planted in the first instance, it has held its own among the native flora and proved sufficiently aggressive to push many of the more familiar species aside. Hefty underwater stems can be seen spreading out across the mud into deeper water, diamond-patterned with the scars of leaves of former years.

For plants crowded together in the narrow belt of shallow water there is little room to spread 'ordinary-shaped' leaves sideways, and the best way to obtain enough light is to reach upwards for it. Waterside representatives of many different families have found the same solution to the same problem during the course of evolution, but their reproductive structure did not undergo the same confusing convergence. By August there are usually enough flowers and fruits about to show how very different these apparently so similar plants actually are, and 'By their fruits ye shall know them'.

Refreshingly different are the water lilies and only the yellow 'brandy bottles' are here. Underwater leaves are delicately transparent, frilly-edged and broader than long: floating ones are firmly rigid, waxy-coated and longer than broad. The first kind are regarded as the

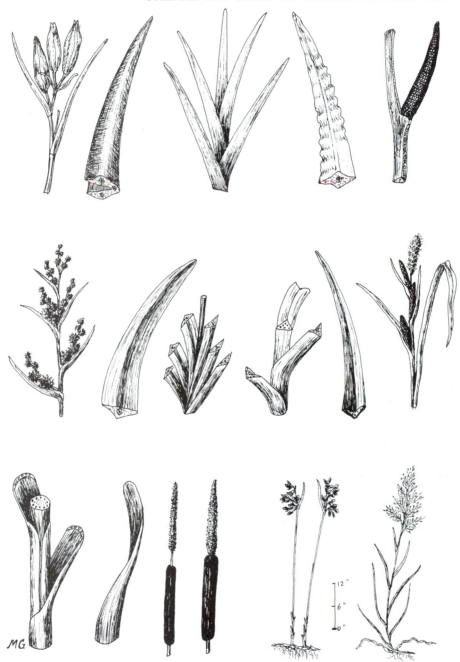

48. Recognition characters of sedge-like plants. Top: Iris fruits and leaf; leaf arrangement in iris and sweet flag; sweet flag leaf and fruit spike. Middle: Branched bur-reed flowers, leaf and leaf arrangement; great pond sedge leaf arrangement, leaf and flowers. Bottom: Reedmace or cat-tail leaf arrangment and leaf tip; lesser and greater reedmace flower spikes; bulrush or clubrush and sweet reed grass

259

juvenile form and only this sort is produced in the deep shade of over-arching sallows, suggesting that light starvation prevents advance to maturity. Deeply shaded stands usually fail to produce flowers, but the penetration of bright sunlight through clear water can sometimes boost food production by these submerged leaves so that flowering can occur prematurely. Excess food is passed back into the cumbersome horizontal stem, so that flowering can be achieved on stored products in later years, but not all that chunky substance is a nutrient reserve. Anyone who has tried to plant a water lily and found it floating repeatedly to the surface, will know how much air is stored there too.

Water forget-me-not (*Myosotis scorpioides*) and marsh bedstraw flower quite willingly in the shadows. Submerged leaves of water milfoil and narrow pondweed solve the difficulties of gaseous exchange under water by having their flimsy substance dissected into narrow segments which present a maximum surface area for dissolved gases to pass in and out. It is the narrow-leaved water starwort (*Callitriche platycarpa*) in the deeper water, the firmer-leaved *Callitriche stagnalis* on the seasonally dry fringes.

Most striking of all is American skunk cabbage (*Lysichiton americanus*), another member of the arum family. Broad yellow spathes reach to ten inches and more in May but can still be overtopped by the fleshy yellow flower spikes within. Come August, the leaves which conceal the monstrous fruit spikes may be as much as four feet long and eighteen inches across. With such dimensions it readily exceeds acceptable limits and has periodically to be cleared, handsome though it undoubtedly is.

Lake plants give an impression of lush fertility and this is reflected in the animal life. May sees the shallows wriggling with tadpoles and both frogs and toads are to be found ashore. Lesser water boatmen scud among scraggy wefts of Canadian pondweed and mayfly nymphs grow to maturity on mud stabilised by water plantain. *Limnephilus vittatus* caddis larvae in neatly tapered tubes of fine silt fragments move quite rapidly across the bottom deposits. Pond skaters skate and alder flies fly—but usually no further than to a handy leaf where they can settle and sun themselves.

Although not part of the Nature Reserve, this Middle Lake is usually regarded as the best of the three for water fowl. Dumpy little grebes produce featherweight, golf ball sized offspring which maintain a discrete silence while mother is underwater searching for provender, but set up an excited 'yacking' as soon as she reappears. It is likely that great crested grebes were discouraged in the past because of their liking for fish. 1963 yielded the rare excitement of a bittern.

Mottled mallard lead broods of fluffy ducklings from secret nests among the sedges in spring to face the joys and hazards of their big new

49. Six plants whose fruits are relished by water fowl. Top: Bulrush or clubrush, lesser bur-reed. Middle: Narrow-leaved pondweed, water milfoil. Bottom: Curled dock, water pepper

world. Teal, too, are to be seen summer and winter, sometimes topping the hundred mark between November and February. Garganey were last recorded in 1922, but gadwall turn up in modest flocks of twenty to thirty in winter and the evocative whistling of wigeon can be heard during the colder months. Tufted duck are around most of the time, a

July adult with as many as nine ducklings in tow or a December flock of fifty or so. Pochard and shoveler sail the lake in winter.

This is the season when a high-stepping water rail may be stalking furtively around the sedge beds. Lapwings lollop loosely through the lower air, seemingly so much more indeterminate than the purposeful arrow flights of the snipe. Both may be well away from the open water and a few pairs of either may stay on in summer to breed. The odd jack snipe comes to the tussock grassland east of the lake in winter. Long-legged redshank sometimes fly in during the bleak months between the autumn and spring passing of the common sandpipers.

Swallows and house martins are part and parcel of the summer scene, but not sand martins. Their swoopings may be accompanied by the scratchy songs of sedge warblers from the verdant lake fringes, but dippers and kingfishers are birds of the rockier of the two outlets streams which hurries the overflow waters westwards to Eglwys Nunydd.

Furzemill Lake, the third and oldest, was emptied about 1977 for the curing of a leak, but is fast getting back to normal. A pair of mute swans was in residence again by 1978—wasteful feeders, biting off far more than they can chew. Their leftovers accumulate as a thick driftline of severed shoreweed leaves, sprinkled with harsher lengths of water horsetail. Orange beaks get muddied as they dig holes in the earth banks to get at plant roots.

They resented the intrusion of a pair of Canada geese which commuted between Margam, Kenfig and Eglwys Nunydd in 1978. During May, when territorial instincts were at their height, the geese were being constantly harried, and there was no doubt as to which birds were dominant. The swans sailed majestically around the pool, with wings at half mast, like animated mantelpiece ornaments, chivvying the geese into flapping flights which took them to a temporary respite on the other side. Smaller fry in the form of tufted duck and mallard were ignored, as was the pair of lesser black-backed gulls which watched with interest from the little cluster of islets which they had appropriated.

Oak boughs sweeping low over the water provide admirable preening posts for moorhens. These birds perch incongruously among the branches with no problems of balance, poking, tweaking and combing recalcitrant feathers into a watertight sheath in readiness for the next swim. Odd though they seem thus tree-borne, they are less odd than the grey herons which swap a superb airborne grace for gawky ganglings when they alight in the Scots pines of the old heronry. Notwithstanding, equilibrium once established, a sentinel heron in a pine top can be as statuesque as Nelson on his column.

This is an ancient heronry, formerly one of only three in the old county of Glamorgan, with Penrice and Hensol, and containing about twenty nesting couples around 1870. Those who competed with them for fish, however, made life difficult and they were reduced to very few soon after, while in some years the site is deserted. During the late 1960s and early 1970s as many as twenty two birds might be perched in the trees alongside some half dozen nests. Broken eggshells below showed that there was desultory breeding, but few young have been brought off successfully during recent decades.

The ancestral site is still used as a roost and fine big crop pellets can be picked up under the trees. These meal-leftovers, which are gulped up the long route through sinuous neck and dagger bill, are not always of fish bones, but sometimes of fur. Unwary water voles are as acceptable as basking frogs or newts, but the toads are more likely to be rejected, as 'nasty tasting.' Sometimes chitinous large-eyed heads of water boatmen peer out from the furry matrix, as though the ever energetic owners had swum their way to the periphery of the contracting mass in a vain attempt to escape. These seem very small prey for so large a predator, but the sometimes so stately herons are opportunists and take whatever comes their way, perhaps as a peppercorn relish.

Alongside the pellets are discarded feathers—superb works of art in grey and black, fluffily plumose towards the base of the quill and sometimes dusted with traces of powder down. This last emanates from special groups of feathers on breast and thighs and is found among British birds only in the heron, which uses it to help mop up after messy meals. (All the Margam lakes contain eels, which are slimier than most other fish.)

No doubt the lakes have been stocked with other kinds and there are certainly two species of stickleback at Furzemill. Water boatmen are so thick in some seasons, chasing after the myriad water fleas and *Cyclops,* that the herons could scarcely avoid them. Pond skaters live on top, *Tinodes* caddis larvae on the bottom, in irregular galleries of mud particles snaking across the stones. Mayflies emerge in May to join the clouds of St. Mark's flies gyrating over the lake margins.

Dragonflies and damselflies are busy laying eggs in July and August— carelessly or carefully as their makeup dictates. Common sympetrums are among the most slapdash. Flying in tandem, the bright red male whips his yellow-bodied partner down towards the water at intervals, so that the fertilised eggs are washed off her tail. Sometimes he misjudges the distance and any eggs that drop will fall on the surface film to float away and, as likely as not, be eaten by a passing pond skater. She supplies her share of the motive power and their passage is slow enough for the beating wings of both to be visible as they course back and forth over the surface.

Common coenagrion damselflies take more trouble with this all important operation. The powder blue male allows his drabber mate to settle on floating vegetation and curve her tail round to deposit her eggs

263

carefully on a downward facing surface. Usually he holds his abdomen erect, with thorax bent forward at a right angle and wings beating vigorously. Sometimes, however, he takes a respite—poised obliquely with wings folded over his back as though suspended by an invisible thread. Only the rigidity of his body, from tail claspers to head, holds him in place on his wife's shoulders and he is off again to another nursery area as soon as she is ready. Maybe it is she who takes the initiative, pushing him ahead in a 'get off my back' gesture. It is difficult to be sure, so expertly are they tuned to work in harmony.

Not so the common ischnura, where the variegated female has no help from her blue-banded black mate once she has collected his sperm. Common blue damselflies (*Enallagma*) keep together, laying their eggs on plants well below water level. One or both may completely submerge in the doing, crawling down a stem to offset their natural buoyancy, but sometimes he jibs and lets go, to await his partner's reappearance.

All species seem to prefer sunny shorelines at Furzemill, where the fine-leaved water starwort of more shaded stretches gives way to a fringe of rushes above the water horsetail sward with its bottle sedge, spike rush and intermittent grey clumps of seaside bulrush.

Furzemill water seems to be mostly quite acid and poor in nutrients, with much of the bed unvegetated or bearing early successional phases such as the finely dissected *Nitella* stonewort, with a close mat of shore-weed rosettes in the shallows. Alternate-flowered water milfoil and wispy hornwort, lacking the usual crust of lime, are suspended in the water with hair-leaved water crowfoot and narrow-leaved pondweed.

Before the emptying of the lake, exclusion of the deer, falling of the big trees and clearing of the undergrowth in 1977 there were some fascinating differences between one part and another which can no longer be detected. Where deer waded in over grassy shallows to drink they stirred up sufficient rich silt to smother the poverty-loving shore-weed and deposited sufficient dung to fertilise a whole new range of plants, including large-flowered forget-me-not, water pepper, gipsy-wort and the two bur-reeds. Rare marsh speedwell (*Veronica scutellata*) mingled with ragged robin and woodland loosestrife, whilst liverworts such as *Chiloscyphus* and *Pellia* nestled between the rush stems.

Where heron and deer combined to add fertility the difference was even more marked. Here water purslane (*Peplis*), marsh St. John's wort and marsh pennywort, all small species typical of soft water moorland pools, were crowded out by rank growths of greater water plantain and yellow iris, knitted together with great bindweed. Moulted feathers got caught among the emergent pink spikes of water bistort and the excess nutrients nurtured a fine scum of green algae, peppered with duckweed fronds.

Plate XIII   CORVIDS OF THE WOODS—*Keri Williams*

47. Top: Raven with half grown chicks
48. Bottom: Jay with newly hatched chicks

49

51

50

Plate XIV   VEGETATION OF DIMINISHING ALLUVIAL FLATS—*Author*

49. Top left: Meadow cranesbill flowers are more than an inch across

50. Middle: Comfrey flowers come in white, mauve and purple

51. Top right: View inland across a remnant of the Baglan Canal within the Petrochemical Works, in 1980—a site threatened by motorway construction

52. Bottom: 'Turkish towelling' flowers of Bog-bean

52

Pre-1977 ground vegetation under the heronry was qualitatively and quantitatively different from that of the main woodland floor, its lushness attracting deer which added their quota of dung to the white guano splashing down onto the bracken fronds. There was a local influx of red campion, chickweed, nettle and elder saplings, with a little bittersweet and persicaria. All were larger than average and all are species associated with gulls and auks on offshore islands.

Deer are now fenced out and herons visit in smaller numbers, so it is unlikely that these animal-induced differences in the flora will persist or reappear. The 1978 paucity of lake vegetation—about a quarter of the fifty species recorded in 1974—is probably due to the enforced dry spell with things likely to return to normal in a year or so.

The dipper stream heading westwards from Furzemill follows a steeper gradient than the gently flowing Coal Brook leading off to the south. It is boulder-floored, with accumulations of rotting leaves in slack water, and contains caddis flies and mayflies, water crickets and wandering snails, but in far smaller numbers than the quieter stream.

Coal Brook runs through open fields to Twyn-yr-Hydd, a wooded section of the Nature Reserve, and has to be cleaned at intervals to rescue the flow from the choking embrace of the skunk cabbage. Animals were more crowded in May 1978 than in any other of the park's waters. The inevitable sticklebacks were in full breeding regalia and tadpoles hung like notes of music on the tenuous stems of water crowfoot.

Scarlet water mites rowed erratic courses through thickets of floating scirpus (*Eleogiton fluitans*), so vividly conspicuous that they must surely be inedible, and the 'red for danger' a warning to predators. Large pond snails lumbered across bronzed leaves of broad pondweed and wandering snails were everywhere.

Two very different kinds of caddis tubes were being dragged through the wriggling hosts of midge larvae on the silty bed. *Limnephilus flavicornis* utilised short lengths of hollow rush stems, placed irregularly crosswise. The much smaller curved tubes of neatly packed silt grains had probably been made by *Sericostoma personatum*.

Water beetles came in several sizes and in both adult and larval form. The only species certainly identifiable was the great diving beetle. Vicious hunters at all stages of the life history, these were making successful grabs at mayfly nymphs on the bottom, but faring less well with the fleet-footed Corixid water boatmen, which rowed hither and thither at high speed. One of these *Dytiscus marginalis* beetle larvae was battling with the current pouring through the culvert from the lake, swimming vigorously upstream, but getting nowhere.

Equally fierce and much uglier were the stumpy nymphs of broad-bodied libellulid dragonflies, hidden away among the marsh bedstraw.

Some of them were half buried in silt, emerging fluffy with minute algae and diatoms, which afforded splendid camouflage. Any prey animal might be excused for failing to perceive the lurking monster in the pale green coat—excused, but not spared. The ability to bury itself can be vital to this dragonfly of soft waters, as it can survive weeks of drought by this means.

One placed temporarily in a jar tried constantly to climb out of the water, so may have been ready to emerge, as the adults can be seen on the wing at any time from May to August. If so, it would have spent two years crawling in the mud. The dark-bodied female will lay her eggs with no help from the male, hovering over the water and dipping her abdomen below a surface occupied here by whirligig beetles, pond skaters and water crickets. Mid-July 1979 saw a veritable swarm of dashing, powder blue libellulids with side spangles of gold, darting back and forth across Furzemill Lake.

Sight may play a more important role than scent in the location of water surfaces. A shiny green groundsheet spread for a picnic well away from any water by the eastern entrance to the Park fooled a number of insects with its reflective surface.

Red damselflies (*Pyrrhosoma nymphula*), flying singly or in tandem, came repeatedly to alight on it, weightlessly and with an enviable grace. Far from weightless were the air-borne water beetles seeking new territory. These blundered in at an angle calculated to take them straight to cool green depths and, as often as not, turned an unrehearsed somersault on impact. The crash landing was followed by an agitated swim across the slippery fabric, the beetle rowing frantically with flattened oar-legs in a vain attempt to submerge. Some managed to get air-borne again, others fell off the edge and scuttled thankfully down among the grass. All had a long fly ahead if they were to reach a habitat of their choosing.

Beetles, pugnacious or ponderous, are among the comedians of the insect world. It is the dragonflies which epitomise the range of interest in West Glamorgan's new country park. For these who enjoy poking in obscure corners for the bizarre and ugly, there are the alga-coated nymphs: for those who seek beauty there are the gossamer-winged adults: for those who want only relaxation there are the lakes and streams which house the young and the airy parkland that is the hunting ground of the old.

Part Six

The Rolling Sandhills of Kenfig Burrows Nature Reserve

Kestrel

Long before man began to roam the Earth insects were well established. They adapted themselves in a fantastic variety of ways to the problems of gaining a livelihood and of perpetuating themselves, and many species were so successful in this that they have remained unchanged for millions of years. They found a satisfactory way of life and stuck to it.

L. Hugh Newman in "Man and Insects."

21 EVER-CHANGING DUNESCAPE, RIVER AND SHORELINE

The coming of the sands: changes of river course and fish population: Castle Wood, Marsh and Reedswamp: sandy saltmarsh and fossil peat beds of a changing coast.

KENFIG Burrows cover 1,580 acres and form the biggest dune system in the dune-rich counties of West and Mid Glamorgan. They are regarded by the Nature Conservancy Council as one of the most important Sites of Special Scientific Interest in Wales and support an incredibly rich flora and fauna containing a number of British rarities. These depend on the calcareous nature of the sand and the high water table, which makes gumboots a must for a thorough exploration at almost any season. Underneath are the Keuper Marls of the Triassic New Red Sandstone series, with glacial drift above and Carboniferous Limestone below.

The ancient borough of Kenfig was a seaport in Norman times, but its sand-choked ruins are now one and a quarter miles from the coast. It was not necessarily on the open shore when served by sea-going vessels, because the name, from 'Cefn y Ffig nen' implies 'The ridge standing out of the marsh', suggesting a site like that of the Isle of Ely rising from the Fens. Today's wealth of dune slacks and marshes around Kenfig Pool, which, at 70-80 acres, is the largest natural body of fresh-water in Glamorgan, is probably an interim phase in the drying out, as undulating deposits of blown sand lift the surface above the water table. The sequence has been reversed, however, since the late sixties, with a general rise in water level and enlargement of the areas of standing water. This seems to be due to the cessation of pumping in nearby coal mines, now disused, so that the excess water is accumulating underground.

Evidence of ancient settlement has been found near the mouth of the River Kenfig in the form of Bronze Age and Romano-British artefacts, and the present B4283 road across the north-east corner of the dunes follows an old Roman highway, for long believed to be part of the *Via Julia Maritima*.

The ancient borough of Kenfig was given a church by Morgan Mwynfawr in 520AD, but town and castle were pillaged by the Danes in 893AD. Later, in 1147, when Robert Fitzhammon added it to Glamorgan lowlands conquered from 1080 onwards, he deemed it so

270

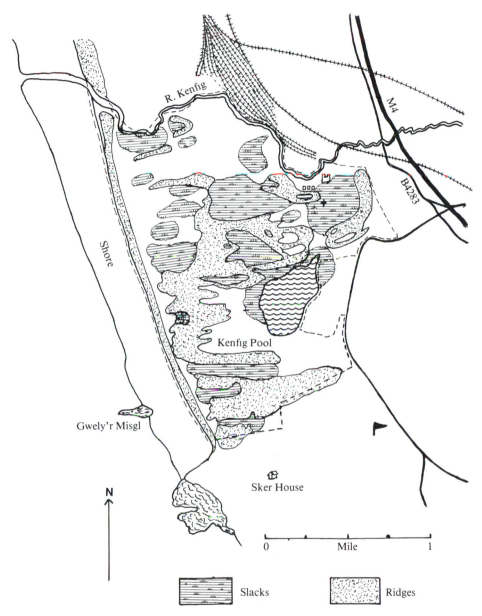

50. Sketch map of main dune ridges and slacks at Kenfig Burrows (adapted from Nature Reserve Management Plan). Reserve boundary marked with broken line, Kenfig Pool with scalloped hatching. Buried borough of Kenfig indicated by castle, church and house symbols near Castle Marsh south of the railway marshalling yards

271

fertile a manor that he kept it for himself and his heirs. His acquisition was fiercely disputed by the native Welsh, whose 1980 aversion to English holiday homes is nothing new. They burned Kenfig Castle and town twice in the twelfth century and twice in the thirteenth! The last castle, isolated fragments of which still appear above the sands at times, was an 1170 version built by William Earl of Gloucester and probably demolished by Glyndwr about 1405.

Already the sands had begun to take their toll. In a letter of 1384, Richard II described 'An unprecedented high tide, swollen and infuriated by a great wind, devastating the shore, carrying away lands and houses and leaving in their place nothing but sandhills'. These became populated by hordes of rabbits, which were poor compensation for those who had lost fertile acres.

Leland wrote of the sand creeping landwards to bury town and farmland in 1540 'Almost shokid and devourid with the sandes that the Severn Sea there casteth'. The burial reached the point of no return in the great storm of 1607, which brought like disaster to nearby Newton. A pamphlet of the time described these as 'the great South Wales floods'. 'Huge and mighty hills of water tumbling one over the other into the marshes and valleys. Several churches were engulfed or washed away, 500 people drowned.' Yet Kenfig, completely buried a couple of hundred years before, continued to be represented in parliament until 1832!

Grass planting was started after the seventeenth century disaster to prevent further inroads of the sand, and the leases of local farms contained clauses ensuring that the tenants gave a few days a year to the maintenance of these plantings. Species names quoted in Evans *'Tir Iarll'* (1912) are somewhat ambiguous: 'arundo arenaria (sand reed) and ammophila arundinacea (sea sedge)'. The Latin is a mix of several species in modern terminology and the vernacular implies two water plants which would scarcely be used on a town site unless flooded. Plants referred to were probably marram grass and, possibly, sand sedge.

Bradley, in *Glamorgan and Gower* (1908), was not enamoured of the dunes, to which he refers as 'A tremendous waste of bare sand, tortured by the gales of centuries into every conceivable shape that such shifting substance will cling to. Far as the eye can follow and much further towards Port Talbot and the smoke wreaths of the busy hives behind it, curling up the mountains, stretches the heaped up driftage of unnumbered gales'.

Today, vegetation has closed over much of Bradley's 'desert', which is a popular holiday spot for occupants of 'the busy hives behind', but there have been other hazards. The building of a power station was mooted at one time, the low rocks of Sker Point offering handy proximity to unlimited cooling water offshore. A big railway marshalling yard had nibbled 178 acres from the back of the Burrows by 1960, but the pipeline installed in the pool to provide the Steel Company with fresh water in an emergency was never used. The seven mile haul road along the shore, which enabled building stone to be taken from the South Cornelly Quarries to Port Talbot's deep water harbour, threatened to lead holidaymakers into sanctuary areas, but its ends were blocked in the early seventies and the broad expanse of tarmac broken up in 1977 when it was realised that the increments of sand blew off its smooth surface as easily as they blew on. This was part of the conservation policy of the Kenfig Corporation Property Trust, whose ownership was finally proved in a 12 year long wrangle, when records from as far back as William the Conquerer were used in evidence. The unique area was deservedly scheduled as a local nature reserve in 1978, around the time when yet more was being nibbled away north-east of the pool during construction of the M4 motorway.

The River Kenfig (Afon Cynffig), once navigable up to Kenfig Borough, has five main sources along the partially wooded edge of the Coalfield, and loops south past modern Pyle to the ancient pile of Kenfig Castle and on across the burrows. Planning of the marshalling yard in 1958, as described in the June *Railway Gazette* of the year, involved the diversion of the river where it debouches onto the dunes. The weir impounding water to be led off to the Margam Steelworks had to be re-sited, and the needs of the migratory fish passing upstream were discussed, but still no fish pass had been installed, 20 years later.

Sewin or sea trout have started coming up the river again since 1977, after a lull brought about by pollution. They run best after heavy rain in spring, when it is possible to get over the weir with no fish pass. But the whole can dry out below the weir for days at a time, as during the 1976 drought. Sewin attained weights of 4 pounds at Pyle before the river was diverted. They were breeding in the headwaters at that time and may well be induced to do so again.

Bullheads, stone loach, minnows and three-spined sticklebacks occur in the river and rudd in Castle Marsh. Ten-spined sticklebacks are usually seen only in the ditches. According to Greg Jones, dace (*Leuciscus leuciscus*) like small, silvery roach, may live in freshwater stretches. He has seen river lampreys (*Lampetra fluviatilis*) above the weir, clamped head downwards onto stones (or an old tobacco tin) by their suckers, and sea lamprey (*Petromyzon marinus*) below the weir. The last are much the larger, one in the loop of river around Castle Marsh reaching a foot long. Sea bass and grey mullet may also move up river at high water, together with the inevitable eels.

Brown trout sometimes come down from the upland reaches, undeterred by iron pollution from the mines. Dr. Ann Edington has shown that the basic nature of the water (around pH 7) enables these and their invertebrate prey to withstand as much as 5 milligrammes per litre of iron in the water—an amount which would not be tolerable in more acid waters such as the River Afan.

The old river course now by-passed by the new in the vicinity of the castle is deep and still, offering different conditions from the rest. Gently swaying fronds of Canadian and narrow-leaved pondweeds rise from a layer of black peat as much as 5 feet down. *Riccia fluitans,* an aquatic liverwort, crowds along the margins in summer, its bifurcating fronds blanching when forced above water level by mutual pressure. Freely floating fronds are long, narrow and bronzed, those climbing the banks are chunkier, and a lighter green.

Fonseca identified 64 species of Diptera or two-winged flies at Kenfig during his visits of 1952, among them three soldier flies, the small, wasp-like *Oxycera trilineata, Nemotelus notatus* and *Odontomyia viridula,* all frequenters of waterside habitats. Their eggs are laid on the water surface and their larvae are aquatic, sometimes hanging head downwards from the surface and retaining the larval skin as a float when they pupate. *O. viridula,* its abdominal colour varying from green through white to yellow and orange, is an essentially southern species, and can be very abundant in June, July and August.

The river near the castle is edged with purple loosestrife, yellow iris and wispy marsh horsetail, with greater water plantain and branching bur-reed advancing into the water. Behind are alders, sparsely laced with willows and behind these again are bays of marshland dominated by sweet reed grass with tumps of tussock sedge. Castle Pool presents a broad stretch of open water in winter, but is occupied in summer by meadowsweet with reedmace, greater willow herb, marsh woundwort and hard rush. The surrounding cover makes this a favourite haunt of bird watchers and wildfowlers. Both pool and marsh have enlarged recently as part of the general rise in the water table.

Herons come to Castle Marsh to fish and it is still a favoured haunt of redshank, but the ruff which used to feed here when at peak numbers in early spring do so no longer. Teal and mallard breed and are joined by other duck in winter. Garganey have been seen in summer on occasion and marsh harriers are not unknown. Bitterns were seen in March 1972—the month that produced the first county record of a serin, here at Castle Marsh—and bittern sightings have been increasing over recent years.

A water pipit turned up in January 1972, possibly the one seen at Eglwys Nunydd in March, while aquatic warblers visited in August 1975 and again in 1976 and 1979. Reed buntings favour the area and king-fishers are often to be seen, hovering over the water before taking the plunge, like the pied kingfishers of Africa, as well as fishing in the traditional way from a waterside perch. Two or three of Kenfig's ten pairs of reed warblers home in on Castle Marsh in summer, along with swifts and hirundines. Wood pigeon's 'coos' and green woodpecker's 'yaffles' can be heard at most times of the year.

Yellow shell moths flutter over waterside docks on which they fed as caterpillars, their bright wings ornamented with wavy lines. Black and green striped emperor moth caterpillars chew the bramble leaves: tiger-striped cinnabar caterpillars munch their way through the waterside ragwort, and dark green fritillaries, meadow browns, small heaths and skippers grace the sultry summer days.

Below Castle Marsh the river flows through wet dune woodland dominated by alder. Firm stretches of bank support remote sedge, mint, brooklime, forget-me-not and bittersweet; marshy stretches hairy sedge, greater skullcap and golden kingcup. Moschatel and marsh valerian appear in spring.

The pill bugs, *Armadillidium vulgare*, wear an armoured cuticle heavily suffused with lime and can roll themselves into an impregnable ball to escape predators (though not playful pusses). They have none of the problems of water retention experienced by two of the local wood-lice, *Oniscus asellus* and *Philoscia muscorum,* which spend most of their daylight hours skulking under logs.

Snails collected from under a board near the alderwood by the warden, Steve Moon, in 1978 include rounded snails (*Discus rotundatus*) and the long narrow 'cornets' of two-toothed door snails (*Clausilia bidentata*). Garlic glass snails (*Oxychilus alliarius*) emit the smell for which they are named when agitated. The thin translucent shells of silky snails (*Ashfordia granulata*) are furnished with oblique rows of bulbous-based hairs which are best observed with a hand lens.

This wet oak-alder wood on deep sand is probably unique in Glamorgan—where other dune woodlands are planted or drier or at an earlier successional phase of birch and sallow. The increased water-logging is causing some of the wind-trimmed oaks to die, but the alders are incommoded not at all, and are spreading out across the sands. There is usually little grazing except by rabbits, in strong contrast to the spinney between river and railway where ponies are pastured and the alders are leggy with a marked browse line at top pony-stretch and little or no under-storey.

The river flows from Castle Wood into a reedswamp, the reed canary grass fading out as the sea is approached, leaving the true reed undis-puted king. Reeds, like alders, are advancing out across the dunes with the rising water table. Although blown sand is accumulating among their bases and building up the level, reeds, once established, are difficult to dislodge, the younger surface rhizomes being sustained with water by older ones at greater depth, now sanded over.

Towards the coast the river moves into a broad dune hollow. It is sandy-floored and fast-flowing, with little plant life on the yellow bed. Only where it has scoured down to the underlying gravel as it breaks through the seaward ridge of dunes, is the bed stable enough to support short fronds of *Enteromorpha,* which become coated with diatoms in winter. Even the reeds are rooted on top of the vertical banks, with little but dark velvety carpets of another green alga, *Vaucheria,* among their bases.

The river was used to mark the parish boundary, which has been the county boundary between West and Mid Glamorgan since 1974—but the old course when this was delimited and the new one which it follows now are greatly at variance. The sands have given way on the outside of each bend, so that the modern river zig zags across the less sinuous line which it once followed as soon as it breaks free of the stabilising bank vegetation in the wood.

The seaward dune ridge has deflected the mouth northwards since it was mapped in the 1940s and the stormy winter of 1977-78 saw its course across the beach pushed back to the south. The accompanying photograph of the river mouth was taken in 1972: it is very different now! Fresh water diffuses out over the sands where infant dabs lie in the shadows of ripple marks and flustered flounders shuffle down among the moist particles until they are quite invisible. These are small fry for herons, but no less than 9 of these gangling fishers were together at the river mouth on 1st August 1979, a month when 10 mallard took up quarters here.

It is not just coincidence that gulls gather on this stretch of the beach. Like us, they prefer fresh water for drinking and washing, so resting and preening flocks like to stand and splash in the spreading river. On 3rd October 1979 as many as 57 greater black-backs were gathered, although there were only 3 of the usually commoner lesser black-backs, some of which may have moved away south. Already 27 common gulls had arrived, the river mouth flock building up to 67 by late November and 122 by Christmas. Herring gulls were most abundant, with 267 at

51. *Lycoperdon caelatum* and *Lycoperdon ericetorum* puffballs in winter

276

the river mouth on 3rd October and almost as many more at a little distance, their ablutions completed. 87 of the 90 black-headed gulls were at the river mouth on this date, with 110 a week later. A pair nested on the marsh in 1977, for the first time in 40 years, but were unsuccessful and have not tried since.

Sea water floods back into the looped river course at high tide to create mini-saltings, surrounded by brackish marsh covered with sea sedge. Summer provides lavishly for the hosts of seed-eating birds which flock to the coast from the frozen hinterland in hard weather. By November broad driftlines of fruits and nutlets snake across the ground, more being pushed up river by each tide as they ripen and fall from the drying heads. Most conspicuous are the shiny triangular brown nutlets of sea sedge and the paler elongated segments of the six-partite arrow grass fruitlets. The capsules of sea rush and mud rush shed inumerable seeds too small to be distinguished with the naked eye. Those from the lidded capsules of sea plantain are coated with mucilage which absorbs water, making them appear like tiny, half-sucked toffees. Deep mats of red fescue produce grain which is not nipped off by grazing animals and so adds to the harvest. Aster heads become covered with a fluff of white parachutes, offering additional attraction for foraging birds.

Tidal influence extends up river almost to the line of dunes bordering the inland side of the sandy basin where several tributaries join. Some big, sea-bleached tree trunks have been stranded in the north of the basin during past storms. This area is seldom inundated in normal weather, however, and sea mayweed flowers on into November in a tall ungrazed sward of sea rush and red fescue. The maritime variety of curled dock forms untidy clumps and narrow-leaved vetch struggles through the melée, producing rounded juvenile leaflets at first, then narrowly pointed adult ones.

Cord grass extends upstream almost to the reedswamp bordering the inner dunes, displacing some of the now sparse glasswort. It is salutary to realise how little salt water this aggressive newcomer needs to get established—and how little mud. It occurs in two main types of situation here: narrow creeks up which salt water creeps at high tide and shallow depressions further inland, where salt water penetrates only at spring tides, but evaporates slowly during the subsequent fortnight if not diluted by rain.

Although of hybrid origin, the *Spartina* fruits freely and is visited by foraging finches. Its chief associates are sea aster, both the purple rayed and yellow discoid forms, and scurvy grass, which produces extensive swards of seedlings in early winter.

The whole community is something of a jumble, with salt and brackish water species together and plants of the higher, drier zones growing alongside those of lower, wetter ones in the freely draining sands. Common sea lavender, salt-marsh grass and sea milkwort from the marsh grade into rock sea lavender, long-bracted sedge and sea sandwort from the dunes.

It is here, at the forefront of the battle between land and sea, that the most rapid topographical changes occur. During stormy periods an eroding sand cliff behind the beach shows that the sea is winning; but a recognition of the old storm beach ridge of sea-rounded pebbles under a discontinuous skin of sand only 100 yards south of Kenfig Pool, shows that the land is the long term gainer. Further inland—at the foot of Newton Down near Porthcawl—is another old beach deposit, lying along the base of what was once a cliff-line bounding a marine-cut platform created earlier in the Pleistocene.

Walk on the beach in the calm of midsummer and uninterrupted sand lies underfoot, with little foredune ridges building up behind: but visit during the winter gales and there is little evidence that this is an accreting and not an eroding shoreline. Hungry waves licking at the foot of the crumbling cliff cause major collapses and many tons of sand get swept away on a single tide.

On 29th January, 1978, when snow covered the Coalfield and two trains were 'lost' near Inverness, the bitter Kenfig wind, armed with fierce rain squalls, seemed to have lifted most of the sand from the beach. There has been less, anyway, since the Sker gravel digging enterprise took so much, but the winter foreshore was now of stones, some elevated on little cones as the matrix of softer material was scoured from round about. Overall loss of sand is also expedited by changes of currents with construction of the Margam breakwater and offshore dredging.

Such sand as remained was sifted by the wind, the finer particles lifted in a knee-deep haze of swirling white, the bigger shelly flakes, dampened by rain, staying put as a yellow film. The blown sand was settling out on the pebble ridge upshore, where ringed plovers lay their eggs in May, thus reversing the usual intertidal trend from pebbles at the top to sand at the bottom. Such winds are quite capable of lifting a moving landrover onto its side.

Downshore the hull of an old wreck protruded starkly from the stones, its timbers held together with one inch diameter wooden pegs. This had appeared from beneath the surface once before and then been sanded over again. Other, more ancient, features entombed until the early 1970s were the peat beds, exposed at all levels on that January foreshore but most obviously at the top and bottom. The peat was the colour and texture of chocolate fudge, stained by orange ferric iron patches but containing few recognisable plant remains. It had been laid down in beds 3-4 inches thick, which dipped slightly to the south, along the coast. Arthur Morgan had recently found a fossil deer antler near the river mouth, a little north of the main peat exposures.

These old terrestrial deposits, which are matched at Margam and Swansea, are evidence of a period when the sea was the invader and the land in retreat. Today's accretion has not yet reclaimed the lost acres, which went under during a period of rise in sea level. It seems that the beds are more intact here than at Margam, where their earlier reappearance was also expedited by the commercial taking of sand. Peat was at least 2 feet thick in 1979, when no underlying estuarine clay was visible, although a bed of pale clay occurs under the upper sand cliff south of Sker Point. A fossil tree stump was exposed by the tides of 18th and 19th August 1978.

Since the storms of November 1977 the sea has been nibbling away at the sand cliff which stretches south from the river mouth almost to Sker Point. It has exposed up to four successive driftlines of wood, one above the other, with 1-2 feet of sand between each: driftlines containing none of the usual polythene of modern deposits and probably quite old. Each represents a former surface which has been covered over as the dune built up, pushing the waves back.

The main longshore drift at present is from north-west to south-east, the direction of the January 1978 sandblow, which had resulted in embryo dune formation at the southern corner of the beach where sand failed to lift over Sker Point. Sand couch had begun its work of stabilisation, but this was no neat foredune ridge, as sometimes at Crymlin, the whole assemblage of little sandhills seeming in a state of flux, like the Baglan foreshore. Sedimentologists tell us that the gradient of the sea bed offshore is steepening—so that the excess water is accumulating underground.

22 FLORIFEROUS SANDSCAPE OF DUNES AND POOLS

Flowers of wet and dry habitats; special rarities; Kenfig Pool. Effects of trampling on the soil fauna of mites, ticks and springtails.

SINCE mediaeval times, plants of many kinds have been making valiant attempts to prevent the wind-borne sands from taking off again. On the whole they have been successful, their present efforts aided by the almost virtual absence of the farm livestock which has checked their growth during periods when the commoners' grazing rights were exercised. Rabbit populations wax and wane, with a major decline after the incidence of myxomatosis in the mid 1950s, so that by 1958 the vegetation had thickened up to a state where returning rabbits found much of it coarse and unpalatable.

Sometimes the elements get the upper hand—as witnessed by great dune blowouts bounded by knife-edged sand crests. The sheer bulk and spread of underground marram stems exposed on these newly scoured faces is a revelation. Reaching up from as much as 20 feet below the surface, they pin-point the vital role of this grass in building up the level and binding the freely-flowing sand grains. Only the most seaward of the ridges which they form and hold is parallel to the coast: most others, some of which reach 50 feet high, are at right angles to it.

Blowouts may occur at any stage in the plant succession, and the leeward, uncut slopes of the sharp-edged ridges can be swarded with a late phase of dewberry and burnet rose thicket. Sometimes the entire summit is lost and replaced by a sand crater in which swirling sand grains can be an abrasive deterrent to tender seedlings. During quiet spells marram seeds germinate and tiny mounds of sand begin to collect round the young but wiry leaves, while a few pioneering plants of yellow stonecrop, sea spurge and cat's ear appear between. Hardy runners of sand sedge move in from the edges in ordered ranks, their evenly spaced shoots like toy soldiers on parade.

On the seaward ridge, where the same type of community is growing in a primary succession instead of a second or third attempt to cover the sand, the rare sea stock appeared in 1975. A judicious scattering of the copiously produced seeds by the wardens enabled it to get a good hold by 1980—in more senses than one, the stout taproots beneath the modest first year rosettes penetrating very deeply except where it had advanced over the haul road. Sea convolvulus and sea holly occur with it, but dune pansies seem to be retreating inland and the sea kale growing by the river mouth in 1843 has been extinct long since.

Pearly everlasting has established in places and there are showy eruptions of viper's bugloss and hound's tongue, great mullein and evening primrose. Pink swards of rest harrow and thyme are interrupted by mignonette, foetid iris and yellow rattle, while lady's bedstraw and various of the yellow peas give pleasing splashes of colour. 1978 was a good year for autumn felwort (*Gentianella a amarella*), which is scattered through about 30 sites, and for the rarer yellow bird's nest (*Monotropa hypopitys* ssp. *hypophegea*), which is growing very near the south-western edge of its geographical range. Other local species are fennel, wild columbine and the little rock hutchinsia, which flowers with the whitlow grass and rue-leaved saxifrage of early spring. An exciting 'find' in 1980 was maiden pink (*Dianthus deltoides*).

Green-winged orchids are among the first to bloom, in mid-March, and among the most abundant of the dry place orchids, with twayblade and common spotted orchids—all of which vary greatly in size, depending on how much cover they have to battle with. The dune habitat produces an attractive, stumpy form of early purple orchids. Most of the orchids grow in slacks, but bee and pyramidal orchids favour less waterlogged sites.

Leaves of the bee orchids show as translucent green rosettes in the sere swards of January, well before most have pushed up from the underground tubers—hence the frost-blackening of their tips so often observed when they bring themselves more especially to notice during their June flowering. By May some will be affected by an orange rust fungus: others may be dead.

1980 produced a spring which saw a mass killing of bee orchids throughout the country—the 7-week drought of April and May proving more than most could take. The blackening of leaves this time was due to wilting and shrivelling as the water supply gave out, and few rosettes survived to flower. Bee orchids have always been regarded as notoriously temperamental—here one year and gone the next. Evidently it is not the orchids which are to blame, but the vagaries of the British climate, which can nip them in the bud. A smut fungus (*Ustilago tragopogonis-pratensis*) sometimes attacks the goatsbeard—that yellow 'Jack-go-to-bed-at-noon' daisy which burgeons into outsize 'dandelion clocks' at fruiting time.

There are puffballs in plenty, including the cute, slender stalked *Tulostoma brumale,* which is so much commoner on Glamorgan's

52. *Lycoperdon perlatum* puffballs in winter

dunes than in the rest of Britain. White cricket balls of *Lycoperdon caelatum* live on as papery brown basins up to 3 inches across after their myriad spores are shed. *L. ericetorum* and *L. excipuliforme* are smaller and commoner. Edible morels, including the rare *Verpa conica,* and black earth tongues appear in early summer and there are usually traces of fairy ring champignons (*Marasmius oreades*).

Much of the mature dune grassland becomes brackenland when the fronds push up in June. Other ferns tend to shun the drier sands, but polypody is represented by the tetraploid version with rounded spore clusters and the hexaploid one with these elongated at right angles to the midrib. The rare moonwort fern is most often found in the short turf of paths—growing pale and leggy in the shaggier growth alongside. Adder's tongue, its nearest kin, is much commoner, but is a plant of the slacks, where it may form veritable swards.

Dune slacks cover a large proportion of the 1,580 acres of sand and help to stablilise it, because wet sand does not blow like dry. Some hold quite deep water in winter and never dry out completely in summer. In most the water table sinks below the surface in summer but the thick vegetation maintains a high humidity at ground level. Some are sandy-floored, with centaury and yellow-wort; some peaty, with bog pimpernel and water starwort in deep moss carpets.

The wettest give sanctuary to hornwort, water milfoil and water crowfoot. Some retain a low-growing vegetation of brookweed and marsh pennywort, where short-lived summer crops of fairy flax can reach to 12 inches high instead of the usual 1 to 2 of drier sites. Other extensive marshy tracts are crowded with marsh speedwell, greater skullcap, ragged robin, great water dock and giant horsetail. A rather striking form of hogweed with narrowly dissected leaves is *Heracleum sphondylium* var. *angustisecta.*

Creeping willow is more characteristic of slacks than is any other plant. Often in low thickets, the male catkins thrust forth their pollen-packed stamens at the time when the associated cowslips are in full bloom, the combination giving a close haze of yellow. The twiggy growths arrest the passage of sand escaping from the ridges round about and build up to form the 6-7 feet high, steep-sided 'hedgehogs' for which Kenfig and other western dune systems are so noted.

June brings a fine colour contrast when the reddish early marsh orchids, purplish southern marsh orchids and their sometimes massive hybrid progeny push up from mats of kidney vetch and bird's-foot tre-foil. Marsh helleborine orchids cover large areas and there are a few patches of *Epipactis palustris* var. *ochroleuca* which lack the maroon pigment of the common kind and are peculiar to Kenfig and Whiteford. Musk orchid *(Herminium monorchis)* was found here by Gordon Goodman in 1960. This is a rare plant of south-east England's chalkland and is more likely to be encountered on the dunes of Holland.

The broad-leaved fen orchid (*Liparis loeselii* var. *ovata*) is commoner at Kenfig than anywhere else. Arthur Morgan counted 1,500 plants in just two slacks in 1978 and the number had doubled by 1980: but it was confined in Britain until recently to the dunes of South Wales. It has now turned up at Braunton Burrows in North Devon. In Glamorgan it is also at Whiteford, Oxwich and Crymlin Burrows: in Carmarthenshire at Towyn and Laugharne. The flowers are a cryptic green, but by mid-September the leaves turn yellow and the plants become more conspicuous. Broad-leaved helleborine flowers vary from yellowish-green to reddish-purple and appear under cover or in the open. Last to flower are the little autumn lady's tresses orchids, their stems and leaves downy with white hair and the white florets produced spirally around felted spikes. There are fewer now than when livestock was pastured on the burrows; many evidently choking to death among the ungrazed herbage.

Another rarity which is on the up and up is round-leaved wintergreen (*Pyrola rotundifolia* var. *maritima*), until recently known only in Kenfig Burrows, Flintshire and Lancashire. It was advancing rapidly when first discovered at Kenfig in 1939 and has been spreading steadily since. By 1953 it had migrated west to Crymlin Burrows, by 1965 east to Merthyr Mawr and by 1968 to Oxwich. Braunton Burrows across the Channel and Towyn Burrows were reached in 1964 and Laugharne in 1972. It likes the same conditions as felwort and both are late flowerers, the white cups and purple bells making an attractive partnership. Like most of the special plants (and the best of the spinneys) they prefer the permanently moist soils of the slacks.

The biggest 'slack' with the most diverse flora is Kenfig Pool, which varies from 70 to 80 acres in extent and 12-14 feet deep in the centre. Originally part of a spreading marsh fed by the River Kenfig, this is now independent of the river. Esconced in a hollow of the Carboniferous Limestone, which lies unconformably below the Triassic rocks, the pool is fed by springs bubbling from cracks beneath its bed. These are said to flow the faster when pressure above is diminished at times of low water, and they certainly found a new vigour when the Steel Company partially emptied the pool to insert its pipeline in 1955.

No water was extracted from the pool by this route, as Eglwys Nunydd Reservoir was fully operational before the next drought called for emergency supplies. The old black pipe now makes a handy footpath through splashy quagmires and is appreciated as a super anvil by the song thrushes for breaking snail shells in a wilderness of sand and silt. The proposed carbide works was granted water from Kenfig Pool in 1940-41 and the Porthcawl Golf Course has its own pumping station and pipeline, but there are neither power boats nor sailing craft at present.

Water level in the pool, like that in the wells of Newton Nottage, is said to be affected by Bristol Channel tides, but movement is small and difficult to detect. Although very low during the long drought of 1976, the pool *can* be fuller in summer than winter, so its springs must be tapping a considerable underground reservoir. The late Dr. F. J. North attributed the low levels in autumn to a depletion of the reserves in the limestone from which the feeder springs bubble up. It was full in July 1961, when besnorkelled zoologists from University College, Swansea, were catching mute swans for ringing by diving beneath them and grabbing them by the legs. Level was much lower during the horizontally driven snows of February 1963, when frozen lapwing and curlew corpses were strewn across the dunes. Possibly the springs were locked by ice, way back along the supply channel in that exceptional freeze-up.

At that time the land form of shoreweed (*Littorella*) which greened the ice-encrusted shallows, bore the direct brunt of frost above the slushy break of wind-lashed wavelets rimmed with vagrant vegetation, torn from the depths and cast ashore in tangled rolls. There was a record 'high' in 1968: then, eight years later, at the end of the 1976 summer, water was down to the lowest remembered level—that of half a century before in 1926—having retreated forty yards in places.

The pool started to refill in September, but again the shoreweed was exposed to the bitter January frosts of 1977; quite unabashed and producing daughter leaf rosettes at the ends of radiating runners nurtured only by autumn rains instead of deep submergence. The leaves retained their flattened form and terrestrial solidity with few air spaces between their tightly packed cells. Figure 53 contrasts these January 1977 plants with the normal winter form from deeper water, where the leaves are cylindrical and erect instead of closely pressed to Mother Earth for protection. The internal tissues of these are separated by large air spaces holding the oxygen necessary to their well being. In such less crucial circumstances the number of daughters is usually fewer—as with more affluent man—and their growth has less of the sinewy tautness of the tough little rosettes exposed to the elements—and to winter-hungry rabbits, hares and voles.

The water advanced 12 feet during the last two weeks of January 1977, but was still well short of high water mark. Ten-spined sticklebacks lost no time before exploring their new territory, nosing into the shoreline as it advanced. The level rose faster than the plants could respond in the prevailing low temperatures and the first four whooper swans to arrive from their northern breeding grounds were forced to vacate the pool and browse on the surrounding grassland for a fortnight, being unable to reach down to anything worth eating. When the

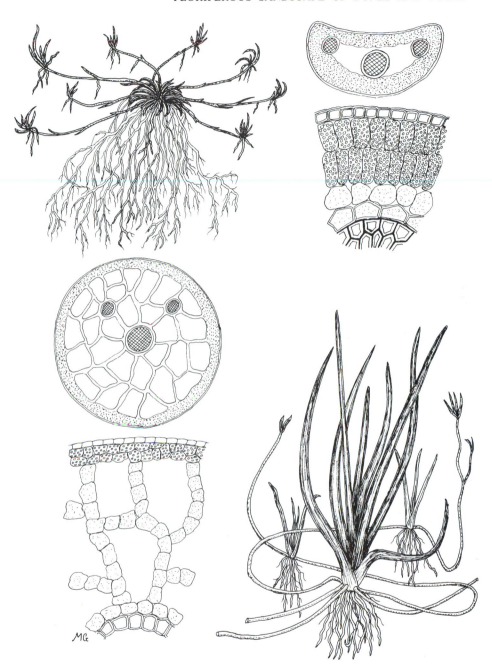

53. Shoreweed in January. Top: Small land form producing daughter plants on runners; Bottom: Normal, larger, aquatic form. Both with diagrammatic and detailed cross-section of the leaf to show the absence or presence of air spaces

285

swelling waters began to lap around the western sedge swamp, the plants, resuscitated by so much heavy rain, were readier to respond and the swans were able to return.

Vegetation is much lusher round this western half of the pool, where reedbeds pass back into closed willow carr and there are ample hiding places for beast and bird. This is the windward side, where wave action is slight and the generous plant cover entraps sand blowing across the dunes to build up the level. This has not always been the case and the dynamism of the changing landscape is easier to pinpoint here than among the repetitive expanse of dunes, where it is so easy to get lost.

Fifty years ago there was a tradition that the pool had moved inland —away from the western shore—a quarter of a mile in a century. Around 1600 it probably extended as far to windward as the high dunes, from which blown sand spilled over to push the water margin back whenever the wind was strong enough to bear it aloft. When Colonel Morrey Salmon started bird watching here in 1908, the whole of the western shore was open sand, a third of that now occupied by scrub being still under water. He used to row a boat round a willow-crowned island well out from the shore, but this has long since been incorporated into it.

By 1930-35 straggly bits of vegetation had got established, but had small effect in staying the encroaching sand and were insufficient to smother the low swards of mudwort many of which have faded into obscurity by now. It was not until the 1939-45 war that reedbeds and willow scrub began to appear. 35-40 years later this tentative beginning has built up to give the densest growth anywhere about the pool. Any sand coming across now is likely to be entrapped long before it reaches the open water, and the shore is stabilising rather than advancing.

This advance of sand in the west has been counterbalanced by an advance of water in the east, where wind-driven wavelets have cut back beyond the sand to form a low earth cliff in the marginal boulder clay, leaving displaced pebbles on the beach below. The extent of the migrtion of the pool to leeward is hinted at by the fact that the old boathouse, where cormorants spread draggled wings to dry, is now completely surrounded by water. Although probably built upon the shore, mid-nineteenth century maps show that already a causeway was necessary to reach this. It will be interesting to see if the pool gets bigger now that wave-cutting to leeward is no longer matched by unhindered sanding to windward.

Little grows on the receding side, but this is not entirely the fault of the waves. Inmates of the nearby caravan site spill down on summer days to disport themselves in and out of the water. The open sand is an attraction in itself, and harbours few insects, so human pressure in the

54

55

53

Plate XV FAMILIAR WATER
BIRDS—*Keri Williams*

53. Left: Kingfisher on lookout post
54. Top right: Grey heron in nesting tree
55. Bottom right: Black-headed gull in winter plumage

287

Plate XVI   MISCELLANY FROM KENFIG NATURE RESERVE—*Author*

56.   Top left: Rigid sand tubes of the worm, *Pectinaria koreni* and flexible tubes of the sand mason worm *(Lanice conchilega)* with incorporated shell fragments

57.   Top right: Foetid iris   **59.**   Bottom left: Henbane

58.   Mid left: Sea fern grass   **60.**   Bottom right: Black bindweed

288

growing season suppresses growth. The surface geology map (Figure 69) shows that dune sand borders the pool only to north and south. The boulder clay of the eastern fields has not been sanded over and the marshy scrubland to the west occupies a deposit of sandy alluvium.

In winter a froth of wind-driven suds accumulates along the lee shore, with strands of spiked water milfoil many yards long threaded between the bubbles. Shaggy shoots of stonewort (*Chara aspera*) and hornwort (*Ceratophyllum demersum*) resembling sweeps' brushes, collect in windrows along the edge. Their whorled branches and leaves are crusted with lime taken up from waters which, for non-saline ones, are unusually alkaline, with a pH averaging 8.2 and ranging from 7.9 to 8.6. The severed shoreweed leaves drifted in below have probably been pulled up by swans, which are notoriously wasteful feeders, or by other underwater grazers among the waterfowl.

Two beautiful pondweeds with broad, translucent leaves are the bronzed perfoliate *Potamogeton perfoliatus* and the shining *Potamogeton lucens*. These, and their commoner floating and submerged relatives, contribute a generous crop of nutlets to the diet of wintering waterfowl.

Another rare beauty is the lesser water plantain, with delicate three-petalled flowers, borne usually in a single umbel, but sometimes duplicated in the robust plants of subsidiary pools alongside, and showier than the common water plantain. Figure 58 shows how variable this species can be; and how confusing in winter, when the subulate leaves may bear no blade and are distinguishable from those of rushes only by the diaphragms showing through their transparent substance.

Underwater leaves of lesser spearwort, on the other hand, are heart-shaped and broader than those of flowering shoots. Nevertheless, the fruits of the two resemble each other quite closely and the primitive Monocotyledonous water plantain (*Baldellia ranunculoides*) is named after the primitive Dicotyledonous spearwort (*Ranunculus flammula*) and could well have evolved from the same ancestral stock before divergence of flowering plants into the two groups of Monocotyledons and Dicotyledons. Greater spearwort, unnoticed in recent decades, turned up in 1980—confirming an old record.

Contributing to the riot of flowers in the poolside mires are tubular water dropwort (*Oenanthe fistulosa*) and marsh speedwell (*Veronica scutellata*); bulrush and greater bird's-foot trefoil and, of course, orchids and irises and purple and yellow loosestrifes.

How fortunate for the naturalist who likes to stand knee deep in water mint and gipsywort listening to the rattle of dragonfly wings and the hum of nectar-seeking bees, that most people prefer the empty sands of the further shore—and how fortunate for the birds and bees. All, inevitably, have an impact on the ecosystem by sheer weight of numbers and, on these friable soils, by weight of individuals.

The effect of walkers, horse riders and particularly motor cyclists, on the vegetation of the sands is manifested in bare yellow strips insinuated between the rough herbage. Seedlings germinate on these in quiet periods, but little ones, like thyme-leaved sandwort, can easily get smothered if there is a sand blow. Groundsel and sow thistle do better, but plants most likely to establish with a fall in the amount of traffic are those which creep in from the margins, like thyme and red fescue. Rest harrow is very sensitive to treading but others, such as bird's-foot trefoil and lady's bedstraw prefer a certain amount, as this saves them from being overrun by uninhibited grass growth. The nitrogen-fixing lichen, *Peltigera* and many mosses, can grow only in such low swards, but are vulnerable to pressure and do better if the closeness is achieved by rabbit grazing.

The composition of the sward on paths inevitably affects the distribution of animals able to live there and those beneath the surface will be influenced by soil compaction as well. The animals of marram dunes are most susceptible to treading, because of the greater displacement and grinding action of the sand: those of creeping willow slacks are least disturbed.

In dune grassland, Andrew Brown encountered only half as many harvestmen (Opiliones) and wolf spiders (Lycosidae) in trampled areas as in untrampled ones, but other surface-living animals were less affected.

He took soil cores 12 inches deep and 2½ inches across from path centres, path edges and untrodden areas and examined these for small animal life, finding a ten to fifteenfold reduction in compacted sites. Globular-bodied ticks and mites (Acari) were much the most abundant animals, springtails (Collembola) comprising most of the rest.

Very low counts were made on the marram dunes, where the main species was a Cryptostigmatid mite, *Oppia nova*. This is an external parasite requiring three large meals from three different hosts and able to withstand long periods of starvation in between, but not of desiccation—hence not many survive in loose sand. Of 403 animals recorded in untrampled sand, 7/8 were ticks and mites, and practically all the rest springtails: of 42 on the path, 2/3 were ticks and mites.

In the dune grassland there were 20 times more mites in untrodden parts. *Oppia nova* was again the commonest, and was one of three species living under the path as well as one of the six away from it. The ratio of Acari (ticks and mites) on path centre, path edge and adjacent zones in brackenland was 59:267:1275 or 1:4½:21½; that for springtails was 15:183:98 or 1:12:6½. The predominance of these in lightly

54. Three rare flowers to be found at Kenfig: round-leaved wintergreen, yellow bird's-nest and autumn felwort

trodden sites was attributed to the greater wetness there. Beetles showed a similar trend at a much lower level (ratio 3:12:9 or 1:4:3). Centipedes, millipedes and flies, the other groups recorded, were too few to indicate preferences.

Dune slacks occupied by creeping willow revealed a different picture, with three times as many animals in the lightly trampled sand as where undisturbed, and even the heavily trampled path centre showing marginally more. Acari, overwhelmingly dominant again, gave a ratio of 743:1464:437 or around 2:4:1; springtails 16:22:36 or 4:5½:9. Beetles preferred the trampled sand (20:14:7 or 3:2:1); flies the untrampled (0:12:65 or 0:1:5).

The Phthiracarus mite which was particularly abundant in path centres, is a burrowing species, so is not dependent on the pore space between the sand grains, as the non-burrowers are and is hence less inhibited by compaction. It lives on dead wood, probably creeping willow roots, which are likely to get more damaged and moribund on the paths, and their decomposition to edible consistency is likely to proceed better in the drier routes followed by these than in waterlogged, anaerobic zones alongside.

291

These tiny creatures may seem too insignificant to affect us in any way, but they are part and parcel of the 'living soil', which is an incredibly complex community in miniature, and it is on this living soil that all creatures ultimately depend. If excessive disturbance and compression, particularly by the motor bikes which shatter the weekend peace for other users, can be diverted to less sensitive areas, it will inevitably be for the long term good.

23 INTRODUCTION TO THE ANIMAL LEGIONS OF KENFIG

Range of sites; gall formers; woodlice, centipedes and millipedes; snails, slugs and spiders; wasps, flies and beetles; bugs, grasshoppers and dragonflies

WITH so admirable a diversity of plant life, it follows, as the night the day, that the dependent animal life shall be equally diverse. Kenfig Pool has always been a winter Mecca for ornithologists, but specialists in other fields home in on the Burrows in the sure knowledge that it will be well worth their while. Since the appointment of the wardens in 1976, certain animal groups have been documented on a day to day basis, in a way formerly impossible. Eventual collation of the data should yield a mine of information relating to Kenfig's spacious terrain of shifting sand and standing water.

Some of the plant/animal associations are very close. Chloropid flies, *Lipara lucens,* cause cigar galls on reed stems and gall wasps, *Diplolepis rosae,* are responsible for the attractive red bedeguars or robin's pincushions on the wild roses. The closely-related *Diplolepis eglanteriae* induces the formation of smooth, scarlet pea galls on the leaves of burnet rose.

Another parasitic wasp, *Diastrophus rubi,* produces distorted elbows on dewberry twigs, these becoming pin-pricked with holes when the young wasps emerge. Dark red, woody stem galls on twigs of willow are caused by a fly called *Hexomyza schineri*. Caterpillars of a moth, *Stigmella* (formerly *Nepticula*) *aurella,* chew serpentine galleries in bramble leaves, these getting wider as the makers wax fatter. Brown blotches on the shiny leaves of wintergreen are probably the work of *Coleophora* moth caterpillars.

Beach fauna and dune fauna overlap in the sandhopper territory of the driftline, and it is here that the special south-westerly beetle, *Nebria complanata,* described and illustrated in 'The Natural History of Gower' can be found. These are voracious hunters, guerilla squadrons emerging at dusk to prey on sandhoppers and other tasty morsels.

Sandhopper relatives in the shape of pill bugs and woodlice occur on the forward dunes. The woodlouse, *Porcellio scaber,* unlike the drought-resistant pill bug, is very vulnerable to moisture loss, although commonly found on dry dunes. It hides by day and emerges to feed after sundown. The rare white woodlouse, *Platyarthrus hoffmanseggi,* which is usually associated with ants, is found here, sheltering in the cavities of vesiculate industrial slag used as hard core for the haul road. ('A hole's a hole for a' that'.)

Centipedes are some of the principal predators on smaller life on the drier sands, where, with herbivorous millipedes, they turn up much more frequently than in the slacks. Andrew Brown set pitfall traps for invertebrates on 150 nights in dry dunescape and 200 nights in slacks and got neither centipedes nor millipedes in the latter. He caught more than twice as many centipedes as millipedes in the former, but this does not necessarily imply that more are present—simply that they scamper farther and faster and are more likely to topple in.

Most eye-catching of the creepy-crawlies on the sands are the snails. On calcareous dunes like Kenfig these are very numerous and big deposits of empty, sub-fossil shells may be exposed in dune blow-outs. Sometimes living snails are no more lively looking, because the periostracum, or outermost layer which supplies the shine, becomes abraded by wind-blown grains. This applies particularly to the brown-lipped and white-lipped hedge snails (*Cepaea nemoralis* and *C. hortensis*), which are polymorphic, or 'many-formed'. Shells of these may be plain yellow, brown or pink or variously striped with from 1-5 dark bands. These colour patterns are inherited and some of all kinds appear as fragments at the 'anvils' of song thrushes. The sound of a thrush tapping a snail on a rock or path to break the shell and get at the contents is familiar in gardens. On the dunes, except by the haul road and the pipeline, the only things offering themselves as anvils in the desert of soft sand may be old tins and bottles. A tiny scrap of broken glass can be utilised over and over again, until lost to sight in the pile of shells it has been instrumental in smashing.

Professor Cain has suggested that shell colour can provide immunity from thrushes if they camouflage the wearers, but the presence of all colour types in all habitats sheds some doubt on this. Plain yellow ones probably win out on bare sand, purple and yellow striped ones among the reddish marram bases and pink and brown ones in willow thickets, but why have none evolved a green shell? Snails of the grey dune will be in greatest trouble during the wet weather which tempts them out of hiding by day, because their former habitat of whitish lichen and wispy-tipped moss will then be an olive green one of expanded *Tortula ruraliformis* moss cushions and rain-sodden foliage. Seasonable colour changes of habitat which cannot be matched by the snails will also negate any camouflage patterns.

Thrushes prefer a big juicy beakful and garden snails (*Helix aspersa*) are as popular with them as is *Cepaea*. The very numerous but smaller snails formerly known as *Helicella* are seldom bothered. Common on open sand at Kenfig are wrinkled snails (*Candidula intersecta*), banded snails (*Cernuella virgata*) and cone-shaped pointed snails (*Cochlicella acuta*).

Sandhill snails (*Theba pisana*) are the specialities here and are sometimes referred to as white snails, although variously banded in brown and white with pink inside the mouth. This is a Mediterranean species, particularly abundant along the North African coast, and is at the northern edge of its range here. It has long been known at Tenby in Pembrokeshire and two attempts were made to establish it on the Swansea Golflinks at Blackpill—by Jeffries in 1862, with 'a basketful' on each occasion. This population thrived for many years, but the only record from there this century is of sub-fossil (possibly 65 year old) shells found by Dr. Quick in 1927, and it is probably now extinct.

In 1969 the sandhill snail was found by Chatfield, Dance and Pickrell at Merthyr Mawr beyond Porthcawl, which is as far east as it gets, and it has since turned up at Kenfig, where it was feeding contentedly among the sea stock in 1979, in a meeting of rarities. Nevertheless, this Lusitanian species is thought to be a true British native only in Cornwall and the Channel Islands, so someone else may have had a go at introducing it here.

On sunny days *Theba* climbs up plant stems to get away from the hot sand surface, but it feeds only when the plants have been moistened by rain or dew. Some have been watched laying their white egg masses in September, 1½ inches below the surface in damp sand, which they press down with their fleshy foot.

Of the two slippery moss snails, only *Cochlicopa lubricella* is able to live in the drier areas, *C. lubrica* cleaving to moister ones, where pellucid snails (*Vitrina pellucida*) are particularly common. A dozen more species have been identified in damp mossy turf bordering slacks,

55. Gelatinous lichen, *Leptogium lichenoides,* with large shells of marsh snails, *Lymnaea palustris,* and small ones of wrinkled snails, *Candidula intersecta,* in winter

among them moss bladder snails (*Aplecta hypnorum*), ribbed grass snails (*Vallonia costata, V. pulchella* and *V. excentrica*), flat valve snails (*Valvata cristata*) and pygmy snails (*Punctum pygmaeum*).

Large black, orange and hedgehog slugs emerge from hiding after rain, along with grey field slugs (*Agriolimax reticulatus*) and marsh slugs (*Agriolimax laevis*). The dwarf pond snail (*Lymnaea truncatula*) and fragile amber snail (*Succinea pfeifferi*) are all-purpose, amphibious species, as at home under water as in the dried up slacks of summer. Figure 55 shows shells of the larger marsh snail (*Lymnaea palustris*) among fronds of a charming gelatinous lichen (*Leptogium lichenoides*), fluted and frilled, with the fawn colour and texture of fungus.

It is surprising that so many 'wet footed' molluscs can live on dry dunes, but there are far more in the slacks, where there is not only less danger of drying out, but where food is more succulent. Spiders, particularly wolf spiders, are also commoner in slacks: less, perhaps, because of their inability to withstand drought, than because of the greater choice of prey animals to be found there.

Various money spiders of the group Linyphiidae scurry among the bracken of the older dunes and Clubionids, *Cheiracanthium erraticum,* guard silken egg sacs hidden in the foliage. These are the most handsome of their group, the dorsal red stripe bordered by greenish yellow patches on a green background. Delicately patterned brown crab spiders (*Xysticus cristatus*) lurk among the foliage ready to leap on anything appetising from the size of a bluebottle to that of an ant. Bristowe (1958) describes how the male of this species binds his spouse with silken threads before attempting to mate, so that he can make a safe getaway while she is unravelling herself. Not all male spiders avoid getting eaten at this stage, but even predacious females do not have things all their own way.

Clubiona phragmitis is one which emerges at night from its cobweb hideout in the reeds to search slowly and methodically for prey, but may

295

itself fall prey to the leaden spider wasp (*Pompilus plumbeus*). In this case both hunter and hunted are furnished with venom, but the spider almost always loses to the wasp. This last constructs a nest for its young by burrowing in loose sand and the paralysed spider is placed inside to supply food for the growing wasp grub. Fonseca and Cowley, working at Kenfig in 1952, were the first to record a Clubionid spider as the victim of a British leaden spider wasp, although these are commonly taken in Southern Europe. In the north the wasp more often goes for wolf spiders such as *Arctosa perita*, which blend so exactly with the sand as to be invisible until they move.

Another wolf spider, *Arctosa leopardus,* which was a first for Glamorgan when found at Kenfig by Cowley, falls prey to another spider hunting wasp, *Anoplius infuscatus,* which again uses it to provision her young in the nesting burrow. Such wasps are often referred to as parasites, but they are more strictly predators and 'parasitoid' is a better term. The silvery spiny digger wasp (*Oxybelus argentatus*) seeks out two-winged flies, *Thereva annulata,* when on the prowl. No less than 25 of the 64 species of fly identified by Fonseca at Kenfig in July 1952, were new records for Glamorgan, this reflecting the paucity of competent dipterists able to tackle so complicated a group, rather than their intrinsic rarity.

One of the better known Asilidae flies, *Philonicus albiceps,* is, itself, capable of taking prey as large as *Ischnura* damselflies. Big hunting wasps, too, may be seen flying past with blue damselflies (*Enallagma*) drooping limply from their jaws, but large dragonflies are capable of catching airborne wasps. The male of one of the Empid flies, *Hilara lundbecki,* has swellings on the first pair of legs which house spinning glands. With these he wraps up a tempting bit of prey to be passed to the female in flight, just prior to mating. Not only birds and humans indulge in courtship feeding. Through June, July and August these male flies swarm close above the water of the more permanent slacks.

Another Dipteran of interest here is the smallest of the bee flies, *Phthiria pulicaria,* which frequents the flowers of cat's ear and mouse ear hawkweed in June and July. Green larvae of Syrphid hover flies can be seen wriggling around the bases of plants, where their elders sip nectar—'dressed to kill' in the black and yellow livery of a wasp, but in fact merely sheep in wolves' clothing!

Picture-winged flies or Trypetids are elegant little creatures with a dark patterning on wings which are waggled enticingly during court-ship. They are gall formers. *Urophora cardui* forms hard swellings in the stems of thistles; *Urophora jaceana,* which is found with it in dry grassland dominated by rat's tail fescue (*Vulpia membranacea*), feeds on knapweed in its larval phase.

Although there are marginally more beetle larvae in slacks than on dunes, only 2/3 as many adults favoured these wetter areas in Brown's study. These often bask on the sand surface when the sun is shining and tend to get blown together into hollows, from which they find difficulty in escaping. A wake of loose sand grains slips away behind as they try valiantly to struggle up the sides.

The most obvious of the beetles is usually a slack dweller—the scarlet poplar leaf beetle which feeds, sometimes ten or a dozen together, on the shoots of creeping willow. Other Chryosmelid leaf beetles of the slacks, *Aphthona nonstriata,* are smaller and a metallic blue—feeding exclusively on the leaves of yellow iris.

More widespread than the poplar leaf beetles in the drier areas are the sulphur beetles (*Cteniopus sulphureus*), which seem to be flying and settling everywhere on midsummer days. Normally very conspicuous in their primrose yellow uniforms, they merge invisibly with their favourite flowers, the wild mignonette, where they congregate to gorge themselves with pollen—spurning almost every other as food. As Tenebrionids, these are related to those whose grubs supply the mealworms for pet keepers. Even commoner in 1976, and brighter, were seven spot ladybirds, but this was a peak year, some would say a plague year, for these, which are usually far fewer.

Another colourful Coleopteran hop, skipping and jumping along the paths is the green tiger beetle (*Cicindela campestris*) with daffodil yellow spots on pea green wing coverts. Its larvae are less agile and spend their time lurking in little colonies of vertical burrows whose entrances resemble those of burrowing bees. Because they rely on food passing by, they are much slower to mature than most beetle grubs.

White and maggot-like, they have three pairs of legs at the front for climbing up to the burrow mouth and a pair of hooks at the back for anchoring themselves when they get there. The head and jaws are well armoured for tackling ants and others which come too close to their booby trap. A grass stem waggled above them will be grabbed instantly in hope, and dropped in disappointment.

Methocha ichneumonides, the wasp which parasitises them, employs cunning to get at the vulnerable white segments behind the 'crash helmet'. She is smaller than the male and black and red to resemble a prey ant quite closely. Her head, too, is strongly armoured, so that she can allow herself to be grabbed and dragged into the burrow, where she paralyses her captor and lays her egg inside it. Only she has evolved the thick head which enables her to survive this treatment unscathed. Males are soft-headed. Having done what she must to ensure the continuance of her race, she escapes and plugs the burrow mouth (formerly occupied by her assailant's head and jaws) with a small pebble.

The wasp grub feeds on the insensible beetle grub for two or three weeks, growing rapidly, then hibernates to emerge as an adult in summer at the appropriate time for mating and seeking out another

297

young tiger beetle. Potential host grubs which are not discovered spend two years instead of two weeks reaching full size, then build themselves branch chambers off the bottom of their burrows and pupate, to emerge as speckly green beetles in spring.

Predacious Carabids or ground beetles come in many shapes and sizes, from the tiny *Bembidion pallidipenne* to the more conspicuous *Harpalus melancholicus* and violet ground beetles. Many, such as *Agonum micans,* and the familiar dor beetle have a lustrous sheen. A 'longhorn' with shorter horns than most is the wasp beetle (*Clytus arietus*). This is a master of mimicry, the 'wasp image' of black and yellow stripes, accentuated by the jerky progress with antennae waving to a meaningful buzzing accompaniment.

Plant sucking bugs are legion and the Mirid or Capsid bug, *Pilophorus clavatus,* is one of the more notable. Oval black negro bugs (*Thyreocorus scarabaeoides*) can speckle violets and buttercups quite thickly and both sexes stridulate.

Assassin bugs such as the heath assassin (*Coranus subapterus*) are carnivores, mostly blood suckers, with young as well as adults able to stridulate. The slender yellowish field damsel bugs (*Nabis ferus*) prey on plant bugs, aphids, leaf hoppers and small caterpillars. They are closely related to the assassins and, like them, grab their food with the front legs and spear them with the 'beak'. *Dolichonabis lineatus* is one of Kenfig's marsh damsel bugs.

Those idyllic lazy, hazy days of summer, which only 1976 produced in profusion, are best typified by the rasping drone and spurting exuberance of grasshoppers. Although some continue to spurt into the chill of autumn, the group as a whole conjures up an aura of sultry heat, from which it is but a small step to the cicadas and crickets of more tropical zones.

They are primitive insects, little hoppers growing into big hoppers by gradual stages, with none of the cataclysmic metamorphosis from earth-bound caterpillars to high-flying butterfly that we see in more advanced groups. These undergo no inert pupal or chrysalis phase, nor does the growing nymph which replaces this occupy a habitat which is alien to the adult, as does the aquatic nymph of the dragonfly. The growing hopper undergoes about eight instars or skin changes and at each change the wing buds, the body and the hopping capabilities get a little longer.

A youngster about to moult loses its bounce and becomes quiescent while its old cuticle or exoskeleton is gradually dissolved from within by enzymes produced from the insect inside, which is rapidly growing a soft new coat. When all is ready, the creature inflates itself with air and the pumping of its deep breathing splits the old coat so that the hopper can wriggle free. Once liberated, it swells with satisfaction before hardening up and 'tanning its hide'—the brown tannin imparting water-proofing properties as well as a darkening of colour. As they near maturity the sexes are easier to distinguish, both by the noisier chirruping of the male (which can be heard 200 yards away), and by the rapier-like ovipositor or egg laying organ projecting from the female's rear.

Most noble of the infantry battalions of grasshoppers, ground-hoppers and bush crickets at Kenfig is the long-horned great green bush cricket (*Tettigonia viridissima*). This is widespread and can be encountered anywhere from the intermittent ground cover around the pools left by the sand dredgers at Margam to the lush vegetation by Kenfig Pool.

When the tension is suddenly released in those impressive thigh muscles and the hind legs straighten, the insect shoots away with less than the expected verve. In spite of those well-developed wings, which span nearly three inches, the 'great green' prefers to crawl or, if excited, to run, and nothing approaching the flight of some of its Mediterranean relatives is ever attempted. Like those more nimble creatures, however, this sonorous songster enjoys sunshine and is commonest in Britain along southern coasts, as here, and absent north of the Midlands and the Wash.

Male crickets like to climb when adult and can be spotted on the tops of evening primrose and thistle heads. Adult females seek crevices or soft patches of sand where they can poke the long ovipositor to bury eggs which will not hatch until things have warmed up sufficiently in May or June of the following year. Grasshoppers are omnivorous from the start, dietary items progressing from aphids and ants to butterflies and beetles as they grow, the proteins laced with vegetable matter. Cannibalism is part of their accepted code of conduct. It behoves them to go into hiding for the moult, for it is then that they are most vulnerable to drying out or getting eaten—perhaps by a brother who is functioning on a different time cycle.

Dark bush crickets (*Pholidoptera griseoaptera*) are most likely to be seen on the edges of thickets although ranging through all types of habitat. Brown and spider-like, they lack wings, but will drop considerable distances to elude capture. Like those of the 'great green', their orchestrations usually begin late in the day and continue well into the night and, like them, they feed on both plants and animals. Some plants put up a resistance and the fuzz of hairs and acridity of sap in the leaves of Yorkshire fog grass prove an effective deterrent to hungry young *Chorthippus* grasshoppers.

Nineteen or over a third of Britain's forty three species of dragonflies and damselflies have been found on the dunes at Kenfig and Margam and some are quite numerous. Damselflies can breed in abbreviated slacks while the bigger dragonflies wander far from the waters of their youth, so they can be encountered anywhere, but the environs of Kenfig

Pool provide the most spectacular gatherings in July, when egg laying is in full swing.

The green lestes (*Lestes sponsa*) is most beautiful of the damselflies, with the large red (*Pyrrhosoma nymphula*) so common in the spinneys at Margam, running it a close second. Both sexes of lestes have a superb lustre, the green male clasping his bronzed partner firmly by the scruff of her neck while she inserts her eggs in the stems of plants below the water surface.

The common blue (*Enallagma cyathigerum*), like the red, appears in early May, two months before the green. In common with the slightly less blue *Coenagrion puella* and mostly black *Ischnura elegans,* this hovers close to upstanding marsh vegetation, nipping in at intervals to snatch a midge or gnat from a stem. *Coenagrion pulchellum* was added to the Kenfig list in 1980.

This much rarer damselfly, which breeds here, is declining in Britain as a whole and another handsome newcomer in 1980 and 1981 is the demoiselle agrion, *Agrion virgo*. Green-bodied, like *Lestes,* this is distinguished by the dark metallic blue iridescence of the male's wings and the sheeny brown of the female's.

The emperor (*Anax imperator*) is well named and one of the largest British insects, with 4 inch wing span and 3½ inch body, though a midget by fossil dragonfly standards. A blue-eyed monster, it terrorizes smaller dragonflies, which it out-manoevres and grabs in flight, and it is equally fierce during its two years as a nymph, when a younger brother makes as good eating as a tadpole or froglet. Plenty of invertebrates can kill a vertebrate by more subtle means, but few are as capable of consuming one whole. Emperors are predominantly south-easterly and Kenfig is near the western edge of this auspicious hawker's range, although several have turned up in Pembrokeshire.

Orthetrum cancellatum is a beautiful darter, the male blue-bodied and dark at both ends, the female yellow and black. Both lack the brown wing bases of the rather similarly coloured broad-bodied libellulid (*Libellula depressa*) which haunts the Margam slacks and has recently been confirmed at Kenfig Pool. Four-spotted libellulids (*L. quadrimaculata*) are the largest of the darters. True to form, they dart repeatedly flycatcher fashion, from a favourite perch to intercept their prey.

Sympetrum dragonflies emerging from the water are slenderer than most of their fellow darters—almost half way to damselflies, except that they alight with wings spread, instead of folding them neatly over their backs in the manner of most demoiselles. The common species is *Sympetrum striolatum*. After hatching, the spiny nymphs adopt a colour to suit their environment and crawl around preying on lesser creatures for about a year, before maturing as superbly efficient flying machines.

300

The ruddy sympetrum (*S. sanguineum*), found on Kenfig by Fonseca in 1952 and again by Roy Perry in 1979, was a first record for Glamorgan. It is distinguished by the club-shaped end of the crimson male's body, but young males and females are not easy to recognise so the species may get overlooked. It is, however, spasmodic in its occurrence, waves of immigrants sometimes arriving from the continent and turning up in quite new areas. As a breeder it is normally found only in South and East England, but Castle Marsh should offer adequate facilities with its wealth of lowland water plants. It tends not to wander so far from the water as its commoner counterpart, and has an altogether weaker more fluttering flight. *S. scoticum* was first spotted in 1981. It is smaller and darker than the others and a female was photographed laying eggs over open water near the pool's edge.

Another rather magnificent and rare species photographed by Arthur Morgan in 1978 and found again by Perry in 1979 is *Aeshna mixta*. This is smaller than the generally commoner *Aeshna juncea,* which is the main species of the usually more acid water of Western and Northern Britain, although outnumbered by *Aeshna cyanea* at Kenfig Pool, and it lacks the golden leading edges to the wings. Yet another turned up in 1981 as the wardens became more dragonfly conscious and quicker at spotting strangers. This was the hairy dragonfly, *Brachytron pratense,* which flies from mid-May until July and is getting scarcer in Britain. The golden-ringed dragonfly, *Cordulegaster boltonii,* so common along the hill streams of the Coalfield, is by no means so in the lowlands, but has been seen at Kenfig.

How well justified are the admirable efforts put into the establishment and development of the reserve by the Mid Glamorgan County Council!

24 WOOLLY BEARS AND SILK COCOONS

Butterflies and moths of the Kenfig Sandhills

KENFIG is as good a place as any in Glamorgan to seek out that most popular group of insects, the butterflies. Almost all the county's species have been seen here at one time or another. A notable exception is the marbled white—which occurs in the Ely Valley near Cardiff and

Wentwood in Gwent to the east, Gower (Whiteford) and Pembrey to the west and the Somerset cliffs to the south, so may turn up at any time: a prize to be watched for.

One of the most dashing, and one well fitted to battle against the powerful winds which sweep in from the sea, is the dark green fritillary. Bright orange, with wings patterned in black, silver and an elusive green and spanning 2½ inches, these powerful fliers sail effortlessly on the fickle breezes of late summer and autumn, laying their eggs singly on dog violets in early August.

Once hatched, the infant caterpillars eat their vacated eggshells, then curl up to sleep the months away until April tempts them forth with tender young growths. Some call it hibernation, some diapause, but this remarkable ability to enter a state of suspended animation not only solves the winter food and heat energy problem, but synchronises the life cycle, so that laggards can catch up and all be ready for mating at the same season.

Butterflies such as the painted lady, which are not physiologically adapted in this way, usually perish at the first frosts, whatever stage of the life cycle they happen to be at. Kenfig must await the coming of migrants from Europe and North Africa each June before there is any chance of seeing their spiky black caterpillars huddled in silken tents on thistle or nettle leaves—or munching their way to an early maturity before winter overtakes them and forces the survivors back south. One cannot but wonder why they come so far for so small a profit, but they are always welcome.

Another with a similar life cycle is the clouded yellow, which reaches Kenfig in good numbers some years, but is never predictable. The colourful spreads of dune legumes supply the nectar that others of their kind reaching southern Britain usually get from clover and lucerne fields.

A much humbler migrant, liable to arrive almost any time but usually seen in late summer is the rush veneer moth (*Nomophila noctuella*), which is dark brown and parallel-sided when at rest. The tiny caterpillars feed among clover or knotgrass and squirm dementedly if poked. This must be very off-putting for would-be predators, and many live on to spin tough little cocoons in which to spend the winter. Some, at least, will outlive the painted ladies and supply some home-produced moths in spring. The violent wriggling is characteristic of all the Pyralid caterpillars, another of which on Kenfig is the speckled, oatmeal *Scoparia pyralella*.

'Woolly bear' caterpillars are much the most conspicuous to be met marching purposefully about their business on the sands, and these come in many patterns. The true woolly bear is the young of the garden tiger moth (*Arctia caja*), in which the fuzz of black and ginger hairs is

302

relieved by white speckling. The brilliant design on the moth's under-wings flashed in the face of an enemy is sufficiently alarming to frighten most marauders away, but warning colouration is ineffective as a deterrent by night. Tiger moths have surmounted this deficiency by emitting ultrasonic squeaks—too high pitched for human ears—but quite audible to foraging bats, which pick up the moving forms in their radar systems. These soon learn to associate the sound with the nasty taste and leave the night-flying tigers alone.

The cream spot tiger (*Arctia villica*), which has even more striking colours, is quite local in the south and east and found only as far north as East Anglia. It is on the wing in July and August, but the shaggy black caterpillars feed on into October, on plants such as ground ivy and groundsel, before hibernating. They wake in spring with a good appetite to satisfy before spinning their cocoon of greyish silk.

Ruby tigers (*Phragmatobia fuliginosa*) are more distantly related and altogether duller, but produce similarly hirsute larvae. The first crop of these is about in May and June, the second from July until spring.

Two collected in August 1979 continued to feed until October, when they settled down for the winter, but were by no means fully comatose. Each time their outdoor jar flooded, they climbed up the vegetation stalks—returning to the better cover below when the rainwater was tipped out. One became bloated and died in February: the other survived to feed up a little and fabricate an oval cocoon in which to pupate.

Related to the tigers in the Arctiidae are the footmen moths, of which the white ermine (*Spilosoma lubricipeda*) is the best known. This, too, has furry caterpillars, black ones, which hatch from neat batches of eggs on dandelion or dock leaves. These grow to overwinter in cocoons woven of pale silk and dark hair and hidden in the ground litter. Attractively black-flecked, velvety white moths emerge to fly by night from mid-May into July.

Southern oak eggar moths (*Lasiocampa quercus*) produce equally hairy caterpillars cross-banded in brown and black. These are always encountered singly, having no gregarious infancy, their mothers dropping eggs at random as they fly, so that they are on their own from the moment of hatching in August or September. They enter diapause half grown, consuming more bramble, dewberry or hawthorn leaves in the spring before turning to purple chrysalides in yellow cocoons which are guyed to the ground with strands of silk. It is the acorn shape of these which gives the name of oak eggar: and at no stage do they feed on oak. The less common grass eggar (*Lasiocampa trifolii*) caterpillars do not emerge from the eggs until February or March. Their smooth black skin is lost beneath a haze of golden bristles when fully grown in June and ready to produce the brittle brown cocoons.

56. Fox moth caterpillar: growth stages and emergence of pupae of parasitic wasps

Fox moths (*Macrothylacia rubi*) and drinkers (*Philudoria potatoria*) are closely related to the eggars and comprise more of Kenfig's shaggy bears. Drinker caterpillars are seen regularly between late April and mid July, white blotches showing through the dark hairs. They feed on grass and reeds until ready to spin the long, narrow cocoon from which a dapper yellow or orange, night flying moth will emerge in July. The name of drinker is said to arise from the caterpillar's liking for dew.

Fox moth caterpillars were particularly abundant in 1978 and are unmistakable in the early stages when their soft blackness is banded with yellow (though more narrowly than in the common, tiger-striped cinnabars of the ragwort patches). Figure 56 shows the shrinking of the yellow circles to arcs with successive skin changes and their final disappearance in the whiskery overwintering stage, after which no more nutriment is taken before pupation in the spring.

It also shows adherent pupae of parasitic wasps emerging from a larval phase spent in the caterpillar's body where the eggs were laid. Vital organs are left till last or spared, so the moth caterpillar lives on until its grisly burden has no more use for it. An otherwise healthy looking caterpillar with two parasite cocoons attached was picked up on 15th September 1978. During the next three days more parasites were extruded, giving daily counts of 2, 5, 8 and 10. During this period the host became sluggish and ate nothing, but voraciously devoured one square inch of bramble leaf introduced on the 6th day and nearly as much on the 7th. It continued to live, with desultory feeding for another week, although shrunken to half its former size, but was obviously in no state to overwinter, the fat reserves which should have sustained it having passed into the substance of the ten wasplets.

There seems no end to the woolly bears of Kenfig. The vapourer (*Orgyia antiqua*) is another, though quite unrelated and of different

Plate 18   PLANTS AND ANIMALS AT KENFIG
—89 Keri Williams, 91 Jack Evans, rest Author

88. Cowslips among coarse grass
89. Leveret in its form
90. Henbane appeared after construction of the carpark in 1980
91. Grey dagger caterpillar
92. Young, striped phase of fox moth caterpillar
93. Autumn felwort
94. Tiger-striped cinnabar caterpillars on ragwort leaves

95

98

Plate 19   DRAGONFLIES AROUND KENFIG POOL
—95, 96, 97 Jack Evans, rest Author

95. Mating pair of *Coenagrion puella* damsel flies, the female buff
96. Male blue damsel fly, *Coenagrion puella*
97. Male *Aeschna cyanea* dragonfly
98. Red damsel fly, *Pyrrhosoma nymphula*
99. Female broad-bodied libellulid
100. Male broad-bodied libellulid, *Libellula depressa*

99

form. This is one of the tussock moths and the whiskers form paste-brush tussocks along the back, with a big bush of longer ones at either end. The pupa and moth are also hairy, the adult male with furry legs and white blazes on the scribbled orange wings. The female is wingless and scarcely ventures away from her vacated cocoon. Here she is mated and on its deflated substance she lays her eggs to tick over gently until the following spring.

Bristles of this caterpillar, some of which are built into the cocoon, can cause a rash on sensitive skins. Those of tiger moths act similarly and it is possible to see the irritant fluid seeping from the hairs of a disgruntled tiger caterpillar. Fox moth larvae are a less reprehensible handful, but few birds apart from the cuckoo will take any of them.

Superficially similar to the ermine but much bigger is the puss moth (*Cerura vinula*), but the bizarre caterpillar, which feeds in willow thickets, has little in common with any other. Arthur Morgan captured a mating pair in May 1978 and persuaded the female to lay her spherical red eggs in captivity, so visits to the Burrows for the next twelve months included a peep into the wardens' caravan to see how the family fared. After three weeks a wispy black caterpillar nibbled its way from the top of each egg, which resembled a smaller version of the red sawfly galls so common on willow leaves.

Shaped like a gipsy clothes peg, each tapered from a black facial disc backed by a pair of red-spiked horns, to two slender tail appendages barred with red. The black segmented body was ornamented with yellow saddles. Although so minute as to be best viewed through a hand lens, each wrigglesome scrap showed the correct puss reactions. When provoked it held on amidships, rearing head and tail over its arched back and waving them from side to side. Further provocation caused a red whiplash filament to shoot from each tail segment and swish forwards just as the tiny black 'kitten' spurted a lethal jet of formic acid from a gland under its mouth.

Not all grew at the same rate, but they gradually changed through their various instars to become green with a white-bordered black saddle cloth and red and yellow face mask. Just before pupating they turned a deep wine red, then set about spinning themselves cocoons on the stout branches provided. Scraps of yellow wood were chewed off and incorporated with the silk to render these quite invisible on the broken ends. They needed to be in shade. If a branch was turned to face the sun when a cocoon was half finished, the maker abandoned it and moved to the shady side to start afresh. A cocoon made on the base of the container had no floor and the pupa could be watched wriggling inside, its new wing buds clearly visible as flaps reminiscent of those of a young grasshopper. In this case they would be blown up to full size in one operation: a trick learned by the machinery of evolution over aeons of time.

Liquid pumped into the cocoon during its manufacture rendered it so hard that it was almost impossible to damage with a hammer blow! No ordinary moth could have forced a way out, but the puss is no ordinary moth. When the time was ripe in May, each captive produced a secretion of caustic potash to soften its prison walls and emerged through a hole near one end to stiffen its wings up ready for a maiden flight over the dunes.

Emperor caterpillars (*Saturnia pavonia*) spin less ornamented cocoons with a ring of stout, convergent spines inside the narrow end. These diverge to let the moth out, but thwart trespassers trying to get in! This quite common species is our only British representative of the Saturnidae, which contains the silk moth and some of the world's largest, but the cocoons to be found on Kenfig are of no commercial value to potential silk manufacturers. Their makers are as black and bristly as the woolly bear at first, variously decorated with bright yellow spots, and take on the more familiar green and black banding of the illustrations only when fully grown. The antennae, like the wing buds, are visible through the chrysalis wall, so it is possible to see whether a male or female moth will emerge by their degree of feathering.

Lackey caterpillars (*Malacosoma neustria*) will most probably bring themselves to notice by the communal silken webs which they occupy before perfecting the elegant blue side stripes and crawling off on their own. Magpie moths (*Abraxas grossulariata*), although named for the gooseberries (*Ribes uva-crispa*) on which they sometimes feed, are more likely to be found in the hawthorn and blackthorn bushes with the lackeys, or on spindle trees. The black and white 'magpie' pattern of both broad-winged moth and looper caterpillar are brightened with orange—a warning to birds, which usually avoid them, even during the caterpillar's long winter hibernation low down in the food plant.

One of the first on the wing in spring is the Hebrew character (*Orthosia gothica*), which takes its name from the black 'lettering' on

57. Drinker moth: from left to right: female moth, young and old caterpillars, male moth and pupa

the grey wings. An all over grey moth on the grey background of the grey dune community is the common footman (*Lithosia lurideola*), whose bristly grey caterpillar feeds on lichens. Camouflage of a different hue is adopted by the brown patterned mother shipton (*Euclidimera mi*), which is an active day-flying species nurtured among grass and clover. Dark arches (*Apamea monoglypha*) occupies a similar niche, but is a night flier. Most of its caterpillars grow slowly and overwinter, but some feed up ravenously from July onwards to produce a second generation of moths in the autumn.

The clay moth (*Leucania lythagyria*) is a denizen of marshy grassland, both caterpillars and moths coming to life at night and hiding by day. Treble bars (*Anaitis plagiata*) must be sought among the St. John's wort where their caterpillars feed. Also barred are the variable common heath moths (*Ematurga atomaria*), which often frequent more acid sites than this and patronise legumes rather than heathers on Kenfig. Another quite typical of heathland is the knot grass (*Apatele rumicis*), whose striking red, white and black caterpillars do as well on haw, birch, sallow, bramble, dock, sorrel or plantain as on the heathers and bilberry which they may favour on the uplands.

The shiny red caterpillar of the goat moth (*Cossus cossus*) is unconventional in eating wood instead of foliage—mostly willow in dry dune slacks. This is a practice not to be recommended, and it takes them no less than three years to reach pupation stage, during which time they are said to smell of Billy goats. The snout (*Hypena proboscidalis*) is notable for the sensory palps which protrude, snoutlike, from the head. Caterpillars are likely to be found on milkwort.

The garden carpet (*Xanthorhoë fluctuata*) is a Geometer, its looper caterpillar describing geometric antics in its passage around the Crucifers which nourish two generations a year of this common triangular black, yellow and grey moth. Stripey brown and white common carpets (*Epirrhoë alternata*), whose two generations are brought up on bedstraw, are seen even more often. Red twin spot carpets (*Xanthorhoë ferrugata*) are rather more rufous and can be found on bedstraw as well as other lowly plants.

Many other species were recorded by the wardens, Steve Moon and Wilf Nelson, during 1979-80, these ranging from the elephant hawk to the mouse, the common emerald to the common crimson, the yellow belle to the garden pebble. Their names are as evocative of summer nights as is the chirruping of crickets—cream wave, clouded border, straw dot and smoky wainscot; bordered pug, latticed heath, rivulet and silver hook. Many specimens were attracted to a light trap and released after identification. The impressive legions caught must be equalled or surpassed by those uncaught, and indicate the wealth of insect life on Kenfig which can only be touched upon in two brief chapters.

Part Seven

More Animals of Kenfig's Dunes and Pools

Rudd and hornwort

A new breed of traveller is intent on making the most of the natural amenities of the coast, and is finding that it has more to offer than a bracing walk along the front, a saucer of cockles and a peep at 'what the butler saw'.

In "AA Book of the Seaside."

25 COLD BLOODED CREATURES IN AND AROUND THE POOL

Aquatic invertebrates and plankton: fish, frogs, toads, newts and reptiles.

STANDING water creates sanctuaries by deterring the public and many non-aquatic inhabitants of the poolside quagmires are there for this reason. Such are the lacewings, scorpion flies, earwigs and the orange tip and green-veined white butterflies which sip from the milkmaid blooms. More venturesome individuals fly out to feast on pollen served in white water crowfoot cups.

Commas, brimstones, peacocks and red admirals among waterside flowers are unable to join the pollen eaters, their coiled tongues functioning only as drinking straws, but they have no cause to fret. Flower nectar, once thought to be pure sugar solution, is now known to contain amino acids and lipids and to provide a complete diet. Flowers which rely on butterflies and moths for pollination, unable to tempt them with excess pollen, have evolved the inducement of high nectar levels—to the satisfaction of all.

Most unusual of the Lepidopterous community at Kenfig Pool are the two species of china mark moths. Even less conventional than the wood eating goat moth caterpillar, these live under water, wrapping themselves in flattened tubes of leaf fragments, caddis fashion, and browsing on submerged foliage. In June or July a brown and white moth emerges from each of the silken webs spun just above water level, feeding by night, but often disturbed by day to flutter low over the pool surface.

Others which emerge on gossamer wings from limpid shallows are mayflies, which are unconventional in having two flying stages in their life history instead of one. They surface first as sub-imagos, the fishermen's 'duns', fly briefly for a day and then settle to split their skins once more and emerge as 'spinners', which take no food and survive for three to four days at the most.

Quantities of shed mayfly skins adhere to poolside posts in July, particularly to their shady sides, but their almost virtual absence within a bird's reach of the top and the guano splashes on the plants below, show that perching birds take their toll before the insects break free for their ephemeral mating flight. Mayflies breeding in the pool include the elegant *Ephemerella ignita* and squatter *Caenis moesta* and *C. robusta*.

312

Plate XVII   BEETLES OF KENFIG BURROWS—*Author*

61. Top left: Seven spot ladybirds *(Coccinella septempunctata),* two larvae (centre) and two pupae, on wild clematis leaf

62. Top right: Scarlet poplar leaf beetle *(Chrysomela populi)* departs after laying a batch of ginger eggs on the back of a creeping willow leaf

63. Mid right: Brown willow leaf beetles *(Galerucella lineola);* two pairs and batch of white eggs (right) on nibbled grey sallow leaf

64. Bottom left: Oil beetle *(Melöe violaceus)* among grass

65. Bottom right: Bee chafer beetle *(Trichius fasciatus)* on hemlock water dropwort head

313

Plate XVIII   MOTH CATERPILLARS—*Author*

66/69. Top and mid: Four stages in the development of lackey moth caterpillars from communal life on the home web to solitary wandering

70. Bottom left: Gold tail or yellow tail caterpillar on bramble

71. Bottom right: Drinker caterpillar on nettle

Damselfly nymphs nose above the water on summer afternoons, rupture their ugly skins and emerge, a soft pastel shade at first, changing gradually to the brighter hues of adulthood after the limp wings have crisped up for flight. Viewed early in the morning they may be beaded with dewdrops—a sparkling burden which is shed by vigorous shaking, like a spaniel emerging from a swim. There follows a pumping of wings to generate the necessary heat energy to fly off into the dawn light.

The miraculous 'birth' of dragonflies is seldom witnessed, because it happens at night. Active hunting occupies the first half of the day; later, when replete, they rest. A dragonfly relaxes with wingtips tilted forwards: when aierted the wings flip back at right angles to the body, ready for instant take-off.

Summer days see caddis flies of the Leptoceridae breaking free from their watery prison, wriggling first from the curved, horn-shaped tubes of fine sand grains, and then from their skins, to spread golden, moth-like wings and join the shimmering hordes above the water. One which is striped or silver rather than gold, with iridescent steely blue on the wings is *Mystacides,* a small caddis called 'silver longhorn' by fishermen because of the long black and white antennae.

It is odd that these free-flying creatures, mayfly, damsel, dragon and caddis, breathe through gills in their larval stage and have no need to surface for air, while beetles and bugs, which spend their adult as well as their larval life in water, need gaseous air to breathe. These are for ever popping up and down to replenish their air bubble, into which a certain amount of oxygen can diffuse from the water, but which finishes up as almost pure nitrogen and of no more use to its owner.

The water scorpion (*Nepa cinerea*) employs other tactics when in the shallows or high on underwater plants, tilting the long breathing tube at its rear up to the surface. This and the broad claw-like arms which snap closed at the 'elbow' like a jack knife to grasp the prey, are responsible for the name of water scorpion, but there is no sting in that tubular tail. When mildly agitated, *Nepa* rows gently away from trouble with the remaining unmodified legs: when more seriously disturbed, it opens its wing cases to flash the red-patterned abdomen and startle its antagonist into retreat.

Saucer bugs (*Ilyocoris cimicoides*) are among the most dashing water bugs in the pool—and the most lethal. A puncture from their broad sucking proboscis has been likened to the sting of a hornet and they are capable of killing dragonfly nymphs three to four times their own size. Their well developed wings are furnished with such weak muscles that flight is impossible. Three lesser water boatmen present are *Corixa panzeri, Arctocorisa carinata* and *A. germari.* Like the larger, back-swimming water boatmen, these water bugs have hairy legs to use as

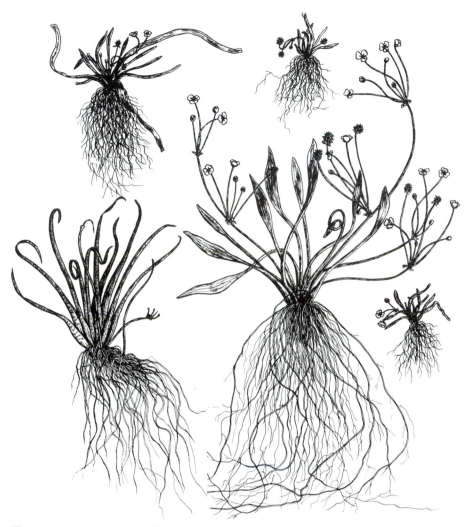

58. Lesser water plantain, different habitat forms. Bottom left: Over-wintering plant with bladeless leaves and old flower stem. Others: Summer plants, the small ones dwarfed by water shortage and rabbit grazing

oars. During the backward stroke the hairs are rigidly spread to increase the pushing power; on the recovery stroke they collapse.

Water beetles are similarly endowed, even the whirligig beetles which stick to the surface and have their eyes halved horizontally, so that they can see adequately both above and below the surface film. Their silver glint is due to wax, which makes their upper surface unwettable but is lacking below, the beetles having the buoyancy of a lifeboat, which prevents them from overturning.

316

The *Gerris* pond skaters, bugs again, are also coated with water-repellent wax, so that they remain unwetted by the splashiest wavelets. The four hind legs merely dimple the surface film as they row across it, with the shorter front ones held at the ready for grabbing prey.

Bugs and beetles become very concentrated in the shrinking pans beyond the main pool as the water dries up—a veritable feast for waterside birds, a few of which get taken by the local sparrow hawks while their attention is diverted by the unaccustomed riches. Although able to fly to more permanent waters, the insects seem not to do so until the pressure of bodies builds up to quite unnatural densities. Not all the life can fly away. Some will bury itself in the mud, the rest is doomed to die—as surely as the snails in the grass fires of March.

Sixteen species of midges and nine species of worm were found by A. T. Jones during an investigation for the Welsh Water Authority in 1977 and 1978. Larvae of the *Chironomus* midges, four species of which were found, are known as 'blood worms', the gyrating swarms of adults as 'dance midges'. Like the two *Tubifex* worm species found, they oscillate from mini volcanoes of mud on the pool bed, imbibing oxygen and food. *Tubifex* writhes into a coil when agitated, and it is coils of hundreds such, knotted together, which are sold as food for pet fish. *Lumbriculus variegatus,* which is like a small red earthworm, is a master of the art of fragmentation, each piece growing a new head and tail, and it seems to indulge not at all in sexual relationships.

Another, well able to regenerate lost parts, is the unrelated two-horned flatworm, *Polycelis nigra,* which undulates through the bright green suspension of algal soup and feathery stonewort (*Nitella*) which drifts against leeward shores in autumn. This and *Polycelis tenuis* are black; *Dendrocoelum lacteum* is a milky white. Although able to swim, this crawls by means of tiny hairs or cilia—as effectively along the ceiling of the surface film as along the floor and furnishings of its watery world!

Of the leeches found by Jones, *Glossiphonia heteroclita* and *Helobdella stagnalis* feed in approved leech fashion by plunging their proboscis into the prey and sucking out the juices and soft flesh. Both feed on water snails, sometimes taking refuge in shells from which they have siphoned out the owner, *Helobdella* also sucking insect larvae dry. *Erpobdella octoculata* is a more traditional carnivore, swallowing worms and insect larvae whole. A less common leech, which feeds ghoulishly in the nostrils and throats of ducks and swans is *Theromyzon tessulatum.*

Water hog lice (*Asellus aquaticus*) tend to spend the winter in couples, the male clasping the female to his underside. The smaller, paler *Asellus meridianus* is not known to pair up in this way, possibly, it has been suggested, because there are far more males than females. All the more reason, one would think, to grab a partner and hang onto her!

Pea mussels and orb mussels (*Pisidium nitidum, P. henslowanum* and *Sphaerium corneum*) have been identified by Peter Dance and Jones found six species of whirligig snail (*Planorbis*) in the pool. Wandering snails and Jenkins's spire shells forage over the bed and *Bithynia tentaculata* deposits honeycombs of egg capsules in regular rows. Short-toothed herald snails (*Carychium minimum*) and smooth grass snails (*Vallonia pulchella*) enjoy the rotting, mushy leaf mould at the pool's edge and marsh, striated and common whorl snails (*Vertigo antivertigo, V. substriata* and *V. pygmaea*) burrow into sodden plant litter.

Except in the shrinking pools of summer, the small animals of the zooplankton are quite sparse, not approaching the dense suspensions of water fleas in the Margam pools. Water fleas are present (*Daphnia pulex* and *D. curvirostris*) along with *Cyclops,* in which the female's pair of pendulous egg sacs is clearly visible to the naked eye. These zoom around like little dynamos, actively grabbing at food particles, unlike the long-feelered Calanoida which sieve their substance from the water in passing. Two members of this group present in summer are *Diaptomus vulgaris* and *D. gracilis,* which carry only one egg sac apiece. A special member of the pool's lesser animal life is the creeping Bryozoan or moss animal, *Cristatella mucedo.*

The plant and animal plankton at the base of the 'pyramid of numbers' has been investigated by Jones, who named ten diatoms, half as many rotifers and two each of the blue-green threads, *Anabaena* and *Oscillatoria.* The only 'blanket weed' filaments among the green algae are *Spirogyra:* the pea green water blooms drifting at the mercy of autumn breezes consist mainly of feathery tufts of *Gloeotrichium.* A drop of water under a microscope can be full of interest. Hollow balls of *Volvox aureus* bowl around the field of vision among quadrupled cells of *Scenedesmus,* slender sickles of *Ankistrodesmus,* microdots of *Chlorella,* highly mobile *Chlamydomonas* and many another. In fact the plankton is quite sparse and it is the larger plants on which most of the smaller animals and ultimately the fish depend.

At the top of the food chain among the wholly aquatic inhabitants is the pike (*Esox lucius*). Like all 'top dogs,' this can get into serious trouble when young—not least by migrating too widely through peripheral backwaters and getting cut off with the advance of summer. Many three inch long pikelets had to be rescued from shrinking puddles in September 1978 and replaced in the pool, where they seemed loath to swim away over the empty sand floor after the torrid jostle of bodies in the labyrinthine marsh beyond. Lean, pop-eyed and long-snouted, like marine pipe fish, they invariably headed for the nearest thicket of algae when they finally plucked up courage to move.

In their former prisons they had burrowed into the surface mud, but they are less able to survive dry spells in this way than are the tubbier

318

tench, which are blessed with the binomial of *Tinca tinca*. The mean length of five pike caught in the north-west of the pool during a survey of 1977 was 2 feet 7 inches, but most were smaller: the mean of five tench from the south-west was just under 1 foot 10 inches.

Netting operations undertaken by Piers Langhelt and the Welsh Water Authority have revealed good populations of both these species, but more by far of rudd (*Scardinius erythrophthalmus*). The hot summer of 1976 provided exceptionally good conditions for the survival of rudd fry and by the end of summer in 1977 20,000 second year rudd were hauled out in one netting, 7,000 in others, giving an estimated population of between 100,000 and half a million, depending on the number of shoals of similar magnitude. No bigger ones were caught, however, so this population explosion may be a flash in the pan and it is not yet possible to assess their growth rate under average conditions.

Rudd were already abundant by 1961 and more were subsequently introduced from Oxwich, but they breed when quite small and seem never to have grown large. Tench, on the other hand, commonly reach to 6-7 pounds and pike are said to go up to 20 pounds—fattened on their younger brethren and on tench. Colonel Morrey Salmon, fishing from a boat with father and friend in 1908, landed 5 pike between 15 and 18½ pounds in a few hours. It used to be said that Margam Estate, annoyed by people fishing in the pool without permission, put the pike in to reduce the numbers of other fish!

Nevertheless, rumour also has it that there were only pike, eels and sticklebacks before 1958, when fish were rescued and brought to the pool from a drying stretch of the Tennant Canal. Ten-spined sticklebacks are commoner than three-spined, yet some authors, including T. B. Bagenal in the Hulton Group key *Identification of British Fishes*, aver that ten-spined sticklebacks are unknown in Wales. In fact, they occur regularly, from Penrice Lakes on Gower, through Port Talbot, Margam, Kenfig and Cosmeston Lakes near Cardiff to the Marshfield dykes beyond.

Eels of 2-3 feet long are occasionally seen wriggling away from the pool along damp gullies en route for the Sargasso Sea, but it must be a very determined eel that crosses that vast expanse of uncharted dune between pool and sea—even with a dozen respites in slacks passed along the way. Travel through wet grass on a dewy night is well within their capabilities, but they could easily be overtaken by daylight when far from open water. It would be interesting to know if elvers manage to get into the pool under their own steam, or whether migrating eels come later in life. Elvers have tremendous staying powers and need smaller amounts of water to achieve their slippery passage, but are less well equipped with muscle than their elders. The blind instinct which drives them on through such adversities is one of the larger of the small miracles which Kenfig has to show us.

Fish are around all winter; amphibians hibernate, but may remain out of circulation for as little as five or six weeks. Their spring emergence varies from year to year and is closely geared to temperature. Frogs were still active on 27th November in 1979, matriarchs and patriarchs backing down into loose moss swards when disturbed, but they were abroad again by the end of January in 1980. Toads, which usually emerge quite a bit later, were already out of hiding by 25th January in 1977. In the frigid winter of 1978-79, on the other hand, no toads were seen until the beginning of April, while in 1980, when the cold snap did not come until March, frog tadpoles had already hatched by 18th February, a week or so ahead of those in the Glamorgan uplands.

Winters were longer and colder at the beginning of the century when autumn colours were associated with September rather than November, as now. A. Loveridge, in the *Glamorgan County History* of 1936, reports his latest frog sighting as 27th September (in 1913) and his earliest as 13th April (in 1905), although stating spawn to be deposited about mid-March. Frogs were more widely distributed then than now, but they have suffered less drastically from the loss of wetland habitats here than in much of England. Housewives in The Valleys still complain occasionally to the press about 'plagues of frogs' and the Kenfig warden apprehended boys with buckets full of toads in late February and early March 1980, in each case 31 to a bucket (and persuaded them to replace their booty in the pool!).

The first thought of both frogs and toads on waking is to get into the spring scramble to indulge their sexual urges, but the physiological process has started long before that. A stroll round Kenfig Pool on 27th November 1979 revealed dead as well as living frogs, their oviducts lying separately from the mauled carcases, like hollow white worms. More significantly, speckled grey objects resembling miniature owl pellets lay alongside. Viewed under a hand lens these proved to be balls of firm white jelly packed with spherical specks, mostly black but a few 'blind' or white. Eggs, then, had already been formed in autumn, to ensure a rapid response as soon as winter withdrew its icy grip.

It is scarcely surprising that so important a food source as that in the eggs should be laid down during a period of active feeding, rather than imposing an added burden on nutrients stored to sustain the low key of metabolic activity during hibernation. Daffodils use the same ploy, fabricating perfect little flower buds within the bulbs before the winter quiescence.

Further material may be added to the frogs' eggs before laying —as in the sequence of different sized yolks which we find in the oviducts of table poultry. The main expansion, however, is due to water absorption externally and already some of the displaced 'pellets' had swollen into sizable jelly blobs.

59. Four rare flowers to be found around Porthcawl: spring beauty, blue-eyed grass, meadow saffron and spring squill

It is this property of swelling when moistened that is probably the chief deterrent to ingestion by predators, and the reason why the gelatinous masses—often passed over as fungal—are so common on the dunes when the amphibians are abroad again in February and March. Commenting on these remains, Loveridge suggested that the predators, mostly magpies and crows, eviscerate the animals in order to eat the spawn, implying that they were disturbed before being able to do so. Evidence gathered at Kenfig through the seventies indicates that they do this in order to eat everything *but* the spawn, and, in the case of toads, the skin.

This last is furnished with secretory glands which appear as pinpricks on the outside but as pink swellings on the insides of the many skins turned inside out and left like crumpled scraps of rag. Toads seem to be less distasteful to the Kenfig predators than previously believed, certainly at the 'hungry' end of the winter; foxes, the smaller Mustelids, buzzards and even herons being likely candidates, along with the Corvids, for having found out how to avoid the nasty flavour by skilful manipulation.

The prominent parotid glands exude toxin which is highly unpalatable to mammals, causing dogs to froth at the mouth when it comes into contact with the mucous membrane, although harmless to paws and hands. If a toad is going to use this defensive mechanism when handled, the irritant is usually secreted as it is picked up, probably in response to fright, after which it will sit quietly in the palm of the hand.

Frogs have no such armoury and in consequence are more preyed upon and more secretive. Often the first evidence of their emergence is the unheralded appearance of football sized dollops of 'tapioca' spawn, with no sign of the donors. They come and go by night and the mating process is over in three days. Toads can go about the whole affair in a more protracted fashion with less to fear, but their antagonists are learning and evolution may be currently working to nurture a race of toads which is quicker off the mark.

At present they can scarcely be missed. In the demented race to get their own genes immortalised in the ongoing population, all are triggered off together, lest crucial opportunities be missed, and they stay together. When the hordes start to head for the pool or their chosen slack (and only a few are used) there seem to be toads everywhere. Females are never enough to go round: one recent study has shown them to be outnumbered five to one: and the randy males get quite hysterical in their search.

There are toads in tandem, toads in tiers and toads clutching hopefully at other males, to be cast off, disappointed. Only the males croak, so, if it makes a noise when mounted, it is not a suitable partner! Reed stems emit no sound, and may be clutched lovingly to a masculine chest and fought over, but produce no threads of spawn to unwind among the other water plants.

As in any such gregarious activity, there is a peck order. Larger males have gruffer voices, and only males already in possession of a female use them if another tries to unseat them. Experiments in Oxford have shown that size alone is no deterrent to the attacking would-be suitor, but that he will desist if the croak engendered by his advances is throatier than his own—helped by vigorous kicking of the dominant male. Females at the bottom of balls of twenty or so struggling males can be asphyxiated and produce no spawn for any of them!

These carryings on can last a month—from about 11th February to 11th March in an average year. After ejection of some 3,000 eggs in small batches at half-hourly intervals, the female is considerably deflated and of no further interest to the opposite sex. She is dropped, for a spell of recuperation in the pool, before making off to her own nook or cranny where she will cogitate the year away until her growing load of eggs brings her back to meet with her own kind again.

Tadpoles, which hatch in about a month, absorb their egg yolk, but not the jelly surround, then feed on algae, changing to animal life or carrion later. Toad tadpoles, like adults, are distasteful, even to newts, and more likely to survive to maturity than the frog tadpoles, which are relished by dragonfly nymphs and great diving beetle larvae as well as grown amphibia, fish and water fowl.

He frogs are no more sensitive to the niceties of love making than he toads and on 24th February 1977 a misguided male frog was seen

101

02

103

104

Plate 20   KENFIG POOL AND ITS PLANTS—*Author*

101. Kenfig Pool beyond the pillars of the motorway, at haytime
102. Perfoliate pondweed
103. Lesser water plantain in the bordering marsh
104. Yellow loosestrife

323

105

106

10

108

Plate 21   KENFIG POOL AND
                   TOADS—*Author*

105. Accreting, seaward side of Kenfig Pool
106. Mating toads
107. Predated toad with oviducts exposed
108. Spume builds up on the leeward shore of Kenfig
         Pool in an Autumn gale

mating with a long suffering female toad—as a prelude to what might be a spherical tangle of jellied egg strands. . . . Closer scrutiny of the fly-sized objects hopping round the pool in June and July will reveal these, not as the anticipated insects, but as froglets and toadlets, their tadpole tail almost absorbed into the squatter body of the adult.

In mid-September 1978 one inch long froglets were skipping through every damp hollow. This was a propitious year for them, as cub scouts had helped earlier in the season by collecting stranded masses of frog spawn laid on flooded footpaths and carrying them to the pool. Such miscalculations of water permanence during 'February-fill-dyke' is a major source of population loss.

Adults are predatory, frogs snapping up prey in their jaws more often than toads, which prefer to flick out their long tongues, chameleon fashion. Insects, woodlice, slugs, snails and worms figure in their diet, and toads may eject little pellets containing iridescent scraps of beetle wing cases and the armoured chitin of heads, jaws and legs. Both are mainly crepuscular, feeding at dusk and dawn, with frogs, as the more palatable, the more unobtrusively nocturnal.

Smooth newts are common at Kenfig, and may appear earlier than the other amphibians, although usually spawning later. No less than twelve were swimming in a small deep pool on the snowy 21st February in 1965 and newts appeared in late January in 1977. Hibernation is brief: spring and early summer are spent in the water: late summer and autumn on land.

Mating involves less mass hysteria and fertilisation of the eggs is internal, as in birds and mammals. Unlike her frog and toad counterparts, the female newt has freedom of choice. It is not his wrestling ability which wins the male his partner, but his charms. He indulges in a complicated courtship ritual of tail swishing and more evocative wiggles, during which a powerful scent is given off. Having enticed the female of his choice to follow, he deposits his little white sperm sac on the bed of the slack, leads her on and then halts her in such a position that she is standing above it and can suck it up into her cloacal orifice. Fertilised eggs are laid in little sets on submerged plants or litter and the tadpoles lose their gills (but not their tails) and come ashore in July, or later in a cold season. Adults also come ashore then, losing their dorsal crest, which is continuous along the body and tail, not divided amidships as in the great crested newt.

This last, with body crest fringed, dragon style, is known to be present in only two of the slacks and lays its eggs later, from May to July. Each is deposited singly and stuck to a leaf whose edges are sealed with mucilage to enclose it. Only about a hundred are needed, because they are too well camouflaged to be easily discovered by predators. The whole life cycle is slower and tadpoles, which eat water fleas and their ilk, may need to overwinter, even where the feeding is good. Altern- atively they can hatch a month after egg laying, produce legs three months later and lose their gills to become land-bound by September—not returning to the water to breed for three years.

Palmate newts, which are commonest on the upland moors, have not been found in the reserve, but are known to occupy pools nearby. Food of all adult newts consists of small animal life.

Grass snakes and viviparous lizards are Kenfig's two reptiles, both present in fair numbers. A sloughed snake skin found in 1977 measured 4 feet 8 inches and the wearers are likely to be seen in the pools, swim- ming with head rasied well out of the water. As with amphibians, fertilisation in reptiles can be internal or external. Grass snakes lay eggs in the warmth of fermenting vegetable debris—lizards give birth to live young, as their scientific name, *Lacerta vivipara,* indicates.

26 KENFIG'S BIRDS

Rarities, water fowl, marsh birds, night roosts, winter visitors, passage migrants, summer visitors and residents.

As the largest natural body of fresh water in Glamorgan, Kenfig has, for centuries, been a gathering ground for water birds. During the past five decades, since before the Second World War, these have been subjected to growing pressure from the vastly increased local popula- tion—and its dogs. Indiscriminate shooting was allowed during the 1950s and sailing during the 1960s, but guns are now controlled and yachts banned, while Eglwys Nunydd Reservoir provides a retreat during periods of heavy use by holidaymakers. The coming of the wardens and the daily watch for both birds and potential vandals has marked a turning point. At last the swans and great crested grebes are able to bring their families up unmolested in summer and the duck flocks are no longer showered with shot in winter.

White-tailed eagles have not been recorded since 1816, but the first Glamorgan record of a goshawk was made at Kenfig in 1962 and the third and fourth records of red-footed falcons in 1972 and 1973. Stone curlews have not been seen since 1939, but spotted crakes were here in 1969 and 1970, corncrakes in 1965 and 1971 and quail in 1969 and 1971. Nightjar and corn bunting no longer breed, but reed warblers have started to do so and Glamorgan's first serin turned up here in 1972. Montagu's harriers are sighted increasingly often in May, June and July, aquatic warblers in August and September and firecrests in Autumn. Kenfig's first woodchat shrike turned up in May 1981, the fourth to be seen in Glamorgan.

Always first to meet the eye as the pool is approached are the mute swans, but these have had a chequered history. Only since 1978 have their eggs and chicks escaped vandalism: prior to that the families present had been transferred from the Porthcawl pools, where cygnets are still likely to have their necks broken by hooligans! First and second clutches of eggs were invariably stolen until the wardens mounted a 24 hour guard. Three of 1978's five cygnets were taken in July and August, possibly by a fox: five of 1979's six survived, but the cob died in December. . . . from pride or exhaustion? A second pair by the river mouth had deserted by 19th May of this year. Small parties of adults and juveniles fly in from elsewhere in winter, some commuting regularly in 1979-80 between Barry and Kenfig, but these are bullied and sometimes chased off by the residents.

Wintering whooper and bewick swans also get harried by the strongly territorial mutes and shuttle to and from the pool and the Steelworks reservoir. They tend to arrive by night, to become targets by dawn and

60. Whooper swans and great crested grebe

to be gone by nine o'clock. The fourteen bewicks visiting in 1977 were chivvied by the whoopers, which had moved in earlier and annexed the winter feeding rights.

Bewicks wintering at Slimbridge were marked in the Spring of 1978 before they dispersed and were recorded as far away as Germany, before they met foul weather and turned back. One of several subsequently found in Britain, pitched down at Kenfig—for just a quarter of an hour before being seen off by the locals!

Teal, mallard and tufted ducks breed, but the tufted ducklings disappeared in 1977 and 1978, probably gulped down by the pike, which like to temper their fish diet with fowl. Mallard failed altogether in 1978, doing better on the Newton Pools at Porthcawl.

All three are common in winter, teal flocks building up to 120 in January 1979, tufted to 55 and mallard to 23. Gadwall and pochard topped 50 in this month and wigeon were up to 130. Shoveler and goldeneye were present in more modest numbers, equalled, momentarily, by the 15 goosanders, which stayed only a few minutes. Long-tailed ducks and pintails come singly, and two mergansers called in February.

Scaup and ruddy duck are also rare, and an interesting visitor in the 1978-79 winter was a North American ruddy duck, skulking, small and dark, in the reeds. A few of these which escaped from Slimbridge some years earlier, have been breeding up in Somerset and Gloucestershire, so that a hundred or so were now looking for accommodation in Britain, like the gone-wild Canada geese before them. An American wigeon sampled Kenfig's hospitality in October and November 1975 and a ferruginous duck in August 1976, but smew have not been seen for some years now.

Geese come seldom, but 25 passed over in January 1978. Whitefronts are the most likely, grey lag, bean and barnacle much rarer. Pink-footed were last recorded in 1911, but Canada geese have started to visit recently. Brent geese are creatures of the seashore and rest around Sker Point when they pass this way. The snow goose of May 1978 was undoubtedly an escape, like the Chilean flamingo of summer and autumn 1976 and the red-crested pochard of September 1978.

A breath of Hebridean lochs is brought by the great northern, blackthroated and red-throated divers when the shallows are crusted with ice and the sand powdered with snow, the last the rarest of the three. Rednecked phalaropes have only been recorded three times, the 1956 bird being a first for Glamorgan, and grey phalaropes get blown in by great winds on occasion. Red-necked grebes, too, have only been seen three times, Slavonian grebes not much more often, and the black-necked grebe of 1921 was a Glamorgan first which has been followed by others.

Little grebes are almost always around in winter and sometimes pair up in May, but then disappear for the summer. Great-crested grebes are

72

74

75

73

76

Plate XIX   FLOWERS AND MOTHS OF KENFIG—*Author*

72. Top left: Golden oat grass
73. Bottom left: Rue-leaved saxifrage
74. Top right: Dotted border moth
75. Mid right: Poplar hawk moth
76. Bottom right: Swallow-tailed moth

329

Plate XX BUTTERFLIES OF THE DUNES—*Author*

77. Top left: Grayling
78. Top right: Small pearl-bordered fritillary
79. Mid left: Large white
80. Mid right: Small white (and bee)
81. Bottom left: Common blue
82. Bottom right: Holly blue

more regular, with 12 present to greet the New Year in 1979. Since 1977 these have been breeding successfully for the first time since the 1950s, with one chick reared in that year. Two pairs each brought off a single chick in 1978, when a third pair built a too obvious nest in the iris-bogbean pool to leeward and had its eggs stolen. Grebes invariably seem to lose their first egg to crows, as they lay early in March, when there is little cover, but are able to lay three clutches if earlier ones fail. Chicks were not seen until July after the late spring of 1978 and the parents carried them on their backs for unusually long—a full fortnight—thus thwarting the pike. By September they were about half grown, having escaped the vandals which killed the Eglwys Nunydd grebe chicks.

Water rails stalk through secret places and almost certainly breed, as they are active the year through. The homely moorhen, too, can be counted among the residents, along with a few pairs of coot, whose kind rises to a cronking crescendo in winter, when slaty black hordes converge from overseas. Their flight is weak and flappy, their landings gauche and splashy and their take-offs achieved only after much puttering along the surface, but none of these shortcomings deter their influx. Expert divers, they yet prefer to feed ashore in winter and scrunch landwards through crackling ice, hundreds at a time, to graze the frost-laced turf of the pool fields.

Flocks swelled from 700 at the beginning of January 1979 to 930 at the end, staying at about this level for a month before dropping to 500 in late February and gradually to 130 on the wardens' weekly counts to the end of March. April saw a continued gentle fall to 35, with 19 non-breeders still present in late May. Crimson-pated chicks were bobbing round the pool by 3rd June, some of the broods showing considerable size discrepancies between members, and the non breeding (or failed breeding) flock had increased to 28 by the end of June and 122 by the end of July. From August 1979 on the monthly maxima were 256, 490, 498, 550 and 536, so the 'Winter flocks' are with us for more than just the winter.

All these, the swans, ducks, divers, grebes and gallinules, keep the water open during hard weather and even February 1978, 'the month of the lost lambs', when the dunescape took on the appearance of a snow-bound Alaskan hillscape, saw only the periphery of the pool frozen. At such times the kingfishers have to hover to look for fish far from their usual poolside perches—or resort to the salt water pools at Sker. Herons are also at a disadvantage when the open water is too deep for their accommodating length of leg.

Kenfig's first purple heron visited in April 1978, blown in by strong south-easterlies, and was content to sample the new environment for a fortnight before moving on. As at Crymlin Bog, bitterns have been causing some excitement during recent years. Derek Wells, in his account of Kenfig's birds in 1972, was already able to report this avian oddity skulking in the western reedbeds, and its unlikely booming may yet become commonplace. The little bittern of October 1977 was Kenfig's second.

Traditional waders are more a feature of Sker than Kenfig. Even the common sandpiper of inland waters is but a passage migrant at the pool, like the rarer green sandpipers and wood sandpipers. Jack snipe drop in on passage or spend part of the winter alongside the healthy population of resident common snipe, while woodcock may be flushed in the colder months from the snipe-frequented slacks. The collared pratincole of May 1962 made Glamorgan history as a first.

Terns on passage may be tempted in from the seashore in rough weather to the sheltered fishing of the pool, and for some of the rarer ones freshwater is their chosen habitat at all times. Such are the marsh terns, which hawk insects over the water—the 'lake swallows' of the 'sea swallow' tribe. Black terns are fairly regular, with 22 at the pool in mid May, 1979, white-winged black terns less so. November 1979's juvenile royal tern was the fifth record of this species for the whole of Great Britain and Ireland. The leg band revealed it to have been ringed in its native America earlier in the year. The arctic skua zooming over the pool in September 1974 must have caused some consternation among the regulars. More usually these, with the equally rare pomarine and great skuas, are seen from Sker Point.

Sand martins call only in passing—the sands at Kenfig are too mobile and too public for their nesting needs—but swallows, house martins and swifts linger longer. Swifts had already appeared by 25th April in 1979, only a week or two behind the swallows and martins. By mid May no less than a thousand were swirling along aerial highways above the pool—with swallows peaking at only three hundred and house martins not exceeding twenty. The June maximum was four hundred swifts, with only twenty or so of the other two. The July drop as the residents moved away south was followed by a big movement through from the north in August, with three hundred together at times.

Swallows and martins are in no such hurry to leave and reached their 1979 maxima in the reedbed roost by the pool in August, with five hundred swallows near the beginning of the month and four hundred house martins near the end. Migration is on a broad front through the Glamorgan lowlands, with few much-frequented flyways, but the pool inevitably attracts travelling hirundines, and they can still be counted in hundreds in September. The last swallows of 1977/78 and 79 were seen on 24th, 12th and 21st October respectively, the last house martins on 6th, 28th and 6th October, with sand martins seldom seen after September.

Not only hirundines assemble in the reeds in autumn—starlings do so in a much bigger way where reeds and sallows grow together. The flock, composed mostly of young birds, amounted to five or six hundred in July and August 1978 but was greatly swollen in 1979. Already by 6th June in that year, several hundred birds had begun to congregate in night roosts by the pool and these had built up to several thousands by the end of the month, continuing through July and August, but falling off to very few in September. Five counts made during August varied from fifteen hundred to ten thousand with a mean of nearly five thousand. October saw them back again, several thousands strong, in northern dune scrub: 19th December saw a flock totalling a minimum of eight thousand birds circling over the pool before cascading in a chattering mob into the rustling reeds alongside. Five thousand or so were thronging in the reeds on the occasion of the Glamorgan Naturalists' Trust's 19th AGM, in the new Kenfig Centre on 1st November 1980.

It scarcely needs saying that so vociferous (and edible) a concourse does not go unnoticed by the local sparrow hawks, but the sorry little piles of starling feathers make little difference to the pulsating life of the nightly gatherings. Sparrow hawks, like kestrels and buzzards, are around most of the time, other birds of prey are more exceptional. The osprey of May 1978 was Kenfig's first, the marsh harrier of that same month Kenfig's second (and Glamorgan's fifteenth). Hen harriers have appeared several times during winter since 1976 and hobbies were

61. Golden plover

spotted four to five times during the seventies. Merlins are fairly regular in winter and peregrines can sometimes be seen making spectacular stoops on some luckless wader or juvenile gull.

Reed beds can be full of surprises and have welcomed their share of Glamorgan's bearded tits during years of population explosion since 1970, although there was a decade without prior to this. Eleven years elapsed between the first aquatic warbler in 1962 and the second in 1973, but several have turned up since. A similar gap exists between Glamorgan's first water pipit near Cardiff in 1961 and no less than fifteen sightings between 1968 and 1974, twelve of these at Kenfig and two at Eglwys Nunydd, with others subsequently. Such an agreement of 'non-records' hints at a period of dimmed awareness among bird watchers rather than absence of rarities, as it is only the bright, brave or brash who would claim their 'little brown bird' as aquatic warbler or water pipit.

Some of the other unexpecteds are more convincing—hoopoe, golden oriole, great grey shrike and bluethroat (a Glamorgan first). The blossom-headed parakeet of 1976 and green parrot of 1977 had obviously slipped their fetters and were out on a spree. Less exotic but still exciting are woodlark and ring ouzel, lesser spotted woodpecker and Lapland bunting (the two in September 1977 comprising Glamorgan's second record).

Not all the winter visitors frequent the pool, but owls, like harriers, tend to forage over the wet areas. The slow, purposeful flight of day hunting short-eared owls is always a joy to watch and these have often been present three at a time during the late seventies, going to ground in rough weather. Little owls are resident near Mawdlam Church but barn owls are no longer in Sker House, and the lack of suitable nesting places limits the sightings of tawny owls.

Fieldfares and redwings come in force to help distribute the unwanted but gaily orange fruits of the sea buckthorn. Bramblings merge into the chaffinch flocks and a few redpolls and siskins join the linnets in birch and alder. Reed buntings stay throughout the year, probably outnumbering greenfinch, goldfinch and bullfinch, and are by no means confined to the reed beds.

Resident meadow pipits and skylarks are much in evidence, both summer and winter. The cheery song of the lark can brighten the dullest of February days and territorial display may begin in earnest from the middle of the month. Dunnocks and linnets, too, may be singing before the end of February, a promise of things to come on those mild damp days when the wintry sun entices an uncertain haze of steam from sodden leaf mould. The perky little stonechat seems often incapable of song, but was holding territory by the end of January in 1979. This wisp of a bird, which outlives the bitter winter gales to brighten the flowering gorse-tips with the yellowhammer, has been chosen as the reserve emblem.

So characteristic is the laughing call of the widely ranging green woodpecker, that this was the first suggestion for this honour, but Afan Argoed Country Park had already earmarked it. Greater spotted woodpeckers are usually about but, necessarily, confined to the vicinity of trees.

As much a symbol of the tenacity of bird life in the face of adversity as the robin, is the wren, whose habit of delving deep into vegetation and making discrete flights among the bracken stalks, may render it immune from the cruellest winds. Arthur Morgan watched one on New Year's Day, 1979, burrowing into the breeze-whisked tops of snow-covered tussocks, using wings and feet to get through the snow layer and disappearing beneath. A few minutes later it would explode in a flurry of snow, pausing briefly to fluff out red-brown feathers and shake off the snow before bustling off to the next tump. It was very likely seeking the newly dispersed spiders which had been trailing long silken strands across the plants during the previous ten days.

Spring is heralded by the passing of migrants headed for northern Britain or Europe. Such are the little flocks of pied, white and yellow wagtails, the blue-headed form of the last turning up once in a while. Grey wagtails, like pied flycatchers, seem to pass this way only in autumn.

Wheatears and chiff chaffs are among the first to arrive, but both are likely to pass on through. During periods of heavy grazing, wheatears have stayed to breed, but their method of ground feeding needs short turf to be effective and today's shaggy swards do not appeal to them. Strangely, it is through winter rather than summer that chiff chaffs may be tempted to stay, as in 1979-80.

Redstarts, goldcrests, wood warblers and lesser whitethroats are usually passage migrants, but a pair of the last probably bred in 1977. The other common warblers are all summer residents, mostly in reedbeds or scrub: reed warbler, sedge warbler and grasshopper warbler; whitethroat, blackcap and willow warbler, but flocks of 20 or so pass through in April for more distant parts.

Warbler trapping at the pool lagoon for ringing and measuring was carried out in September 1979 and Glamorgan's first ever barred warbler was caught, along with garden warbler and blackcap on the 11th. Spotted flycatchers perform their own inimitable brand of gamin pirouette in the procuring of flies for their young.

Where there are stonechats the habitat seems right for whinchats, but these two complementary species seem to divide the county between them, the first filling the coastal niches and the second the upland ones, so whinchats are only seen at Kenfig as they pass through.

Blue, great and long-tailed tits are almost always around, making big inroads into the caterpillar populations, but marsh tits breed only occasionally, as in 1977. Willow tits and coal tits feed their way through the spinneys rarely in autumn and winter.

Of the six Corvids only magpies and carrion crows breed at Kenfig, the first being seen up to eight at a time in winter and the crows not usually many more together. Jackdaws are essentially gregarious and, like ravens, can be seen over the dunes at almost any time. Rooks stray across from adjacent arable land much less often, but two were watched detaching themselves from a flock of twenty to mob a short-eared owl just before Christmas, 1979. Jays, as woodland birds, seldom venture onto the dunes.

Tree sparrows have come to Kenfig in their general shift west and probably breed there. House sparrows, with their love of buildings, are not much commoner in this delectable wilderness. Those other garden birds, song thrush, mistle thrush and blackbird are more widespread, bringing themselves particularly to notice when they flock in winter. Even the usually more solitary blackbirds increased from the usual group of about six on the pool fields to fifteen in the cold weather of February, 1979. When the ground is frozen, their mode of food getting by scratching among the surface litter can be much more effective than mere pecking.

In spite of the shortage of high woodland and close turf, Kenfig Burrows harbour a good range of hedgerow and farmland birds, while the richness of freshwater habitats makes them one of Glamorgan's top ranking ornithological sites.

27 WILDLIFE DETECTIVE IN SEARCH OF MAMMALS

Mammal remains in owl pellets and fox droppings; shrews, hedgehog, mole, bats, brown rat, mice, voles, harvest mouse, hare, rabbit, fox, stoat, weasel and badger.

WARM blooded mammals have the greatest appeal of any animal group but are less well known than most. Some damage man's crops or poultry, others are relished as food by his cats and dogs or by man himself, and all lie low when humans are abroad. To learn about mammals first hand one needs to be something of a detective and to have infinite patience. Such a one was Arthur Morgan, county mammal recorder and nature reserve warden, so quite a lot is known about Kenfig's mammals.

Knowledge of local populations comes to most of us through examining what the cat brings home, and it can be a little like this on Kenfig. The first sure record of the presence of water shrews was obtained in the 1979-80 winter from remains in a short-eared owl's pellet.

Rosemary Nelson analysed 40 or so pellets of indigestible bones and fur thrown up from the crops of the overwintering owls during that period. Mostly the remnants were of field mice, bank voles and field voles, but there were also passerine feathers and bones (hollow to lighten the load during flight) and the hard parts of great diving and other beetles.

This was a study to discover what the owls were killing, the discovery of the new mammal coincidental: but food remains are not always of kills. Starling feathers appear in the droppings of foxes, which would be quite incapable of surprising starlings at their roosts and would have been scavenging the sparrow hawks' leftovers. Too often the presence of sheep's wool in their dung leads to foxes being labelled as lamb killers when they are, in fact, eating the remains of still-born lambs.

62. Water shrew, water crowfoot and silverweed

Few ewes are so meek or so stupid as to let a fox help itself to a healthy lamb, and carrion is easier meat by far to so omnivorous a creature.

The sleek, dark-furred water shrew is more secretive than the other two species, whose lighter fur blends with the sand. Nevertheless, common and pygmy shrews are usually spotted only when scooting across a path, to be lost among the coarser vegetation beyond. Occasionally high-pitched squeaks give a clue to the location of an encounter between two of these excitable little insectivores. Such meetings may be so stressful that one of the combatants dies in its tracks, and the corpses, which can be picked up quite frequently, enable the beasts to be identified in the hand.

Hedgehogs, which are classified as insectivores, although taking a much wider range of food, are also most often found as corpses, particularly along the roads and particularly in the autumn when there are a lot of young around. Unfortunately they are slow to learn that curling up in a pricky ball is no defence against cars: the experienced ones are dead! These hedgerow 'urchins' can be seen out in daylight, however, and their slender, pointed faecal pellets are likely to be found anywhere. Usually these are permeated with recognisable parts of beetles and other insects; worms and slugs leaving fewer remains. If the scraps are of small birds or mammals only the expert could distinguish them from those of stoat or weasel. When hedgehogs have been feeding on blackberries and dewberries the pip-studded faeces resemble the crop pellets of certain passerines.

Moles are sustained almost wholly by earthworms, which occur only where sufficient organic matter has accumulated in the sand to supply their needs. On most of the Burrows the high water table ensures that this does not take long and moles are quite abundant. Though the mole hills may be lost in shaggy grass or burnet rose thickets, the roofs of mole tunnels are often thrown up across paths. Sand grains are not easily compacted beyond a mole's ability to push them aside, so the phenomenon of rows of molehills following one side of an uncrossable path is not seen here as in more compressible soils.

Normally the tunnels are quite near the surface but, as the water table drops, so do the worms, and the moles after them. During the long 1976 drought the worms retreated to deeper and deeper levels or shrivelled from lack of moisture, and the mole tunnels were seen to converge on the slacks wherever possible. The water was slow in returning at Kenfig, although wetland sites with more superficial catchment areas were back to normal by September.

At the beginning of February 1977 moles were still in residence among poolside fleabane and flag which are normally waterlogged months before. A molehill of yellow sand thrown up at the base of a pussy willow had reached a diameter of more than a yard and a height of two feet by then and new sand was still being added. During the subsequent weeks the moles were in retreat—following the worms—as both were flooded out of burrows built among succulent water plants. More traditional insectivores suffered little hardship during the drought, entomologists agreeing that insects and spiders generally thrived the better for all the extra sunshine of that not-easily-forgotten season.

Bats were in their element, pirouetting back and forth through gyrating clouds of midges and moths on sultry summer nights. 25-40 appeared during May dusks in 1976 to hunt 50-100 feet above the western side of the pool and out over the moister dunes. They flew fast and straight, with rapid direction changes interspersed with vertical drops. Most were large and long-winged, others had shorter rounded wings and more erratic flight: both were bigger than our commonest bat, the pipistrelle. The shorter-winged ones were still around in October and numbers survived the winter.

Flocks were up to 40 again in May 1977 and were still of two species flitting over reeds and sallows, with a third species foraging along the field hedges in late autumn. On the wing they are too fast for identification and Kenfig lacks the hollow trees, caves and buildings that are used as roosts, so no names can be put to them. There are established colonies of long-eared bats and pipistrelles at Margam House 3 miles to the north, while serotines and possibly high-flying noctules and daubentons hunt over Newton Pool 3 miles to the south, so any of these may visit Kenfig.

A bat of pipistrelle size found an admirable hunting beat in Borg Warner's Motor Transmission Factory on the Kenfig Industrial Estate in 1978. The insects of an area formerly part dune and part poorly drained farmland had been replaced by an indoor population of house flies—a new food source to be exploited, for the benefit of all. The bat was watched regularly by workers on the afternoon shift as it hunted by artificial light, no longer geared to the normal light and dark regime of the great out-of-doors.

The most remarkable feature of this incident is that the bat's sensitive radar system for echo-location of air-borne flies was still effective in the volume of noise emanating from the machine presses. It is unlikely that the artificial light could have helped as bats do not normally hunt by sight, although few nights are totally dark.

Brown rats, although as omnivorous as hedgehogs, have nibbling incisors which put them with the plant-eating rodents. Exploiters of man's wastes throughout the urban areas, these are not generally to be seen on Kenfig, but a small colony appeared by the pool beach during the late summer of 1977, clearing up picnic debris left by visitors.

We should be grateful to them, as a self-appointed sanitary squad, correcting our untidiness. Africa has its vultures, India its crows,

Central Australia its kites. Nature, the benign Mother, sees that nothing goes to waste and that no species shall suffer the harmful build-up of its own effluents (unless that species chooses to exterminate its natural allies). It is unfair to blame the rat for spreading human disease if we supply it with the disease to spread.

That other cleaner-up-of-scraps, the house mouse, has not been recorded and is, indeed, rare now in Glamorgan. The browner wood mice or long-tailed field mice, on the other hand, are everywhere. 1978 was a good year for them and by mid-September, after a summer of continuous breeding, their little burrows were very conspicuous. Although the entrances were only an inch and a half across, there was often as much as a small bucketful of clean yellow sand outside, pushed out with long whiskery noses as well as flung out backwards by scrabbling hind feet. Much less sand can be seen excavated from vole holes, which are more superficial and often entirely above ground in dense vegetation.

At this time of year the dispersing field mice families were digging out extensive winter quarters well below the reach of frosts. There was much coming and going and the overprinted tracks of naked pink feet showed that each had one preferred route into the burrow across the impressionable doormat of loose sand. Later on, when they had settled in, the gnawed remains of black burnet rose hips began to appear in little piles outside the entrance—the red ones of dog rose, too, where these grew in the neighbourhood.

Andrew Brown carried out a live trapping programme on 60 nights in the early seventies, baiting his Longworth traps with cereals, mostly oats. He caught wood mice far and away the most frequently, but the fact that voles are out more by day may have had some bearing on this.

Among sea buckthorn the catch was thirteen mice (which were living on the orange buckthorn fruits) and nothing else; this no doubt reflecting the absence of the ground cover beloved by voles, under the densely prickly bushes. In dune grassland he obtained ten mice and one field vole.

Blackberry bushes and grass tussocks around the carpark proved to be the most highly populated habitat, with eight wood mice, two field voles, five common shrews and one pygmy shrew, which two last should not have been attracted by the vegetarian bait. This environment was littered with tins, paper and picnic scraps, which provided shelter as well as food, but shelter afforded by bottles can prove lethal, creatures entering easily enough, but being unable to climb back up the slippery sides.

It is evident that small mammals are not as susceptible to human pressure and the inept and noisy scrabblings of urban canines as is sometimes believed. Careful lifting of a sheet of corrugated iron, with its illimitable sunwarmed 'runs', may reveal drowsy rodents as well as reptiles. They are around all the time, using our bric-a-brac to their own ends, while the superior beings go blindly about their 'Countryside Appreciation', unaware of the subtleties of the life system into which they intrude.

Another source of mouse fodder is along the tidal driftline where edible refuse from picnics and boats mingles with water-borne nuts and seeds. Predated remains of the unlucky ones are easier to find here. Feeding is by trial and error and the honeycomb of tracks so readily visible in the friable sand, show where tiny feet have pattered up to poisonous or unpalatable plants such as spurge or sea holly and come away, leaving these unscathed. In places there may be selective grazing of a particular species, such as smooth hawk's beard.

When not eating seeds and fruit, they prefer soft foliage and will take the leaves of hawkbit, sandwort and storksbill too if no succulents are available. On the whole they tend not to store food, but to seek it as they go. The caches seen are more often of leftovers, shells and husks. Very small diameter burrows suffice for mice and some of these beach foragers hole up among the marram bases.

The very different poolside habitat also houses a healthy population of wood mice, living alongside the bank voles, which are more restricted to this sort of thick cover and were not found in Brown's trapping programme. The density of the rodent population here can be judged by the fact that 11 of 14 live-traps set overnight in mint and loosestrife in September 1976 held prisoners the next morning and the other three traps had been sprung by creatures which got away. Apart from one shrew, all were mice or bank voles.

Diurnal activity was well shown by a trap set at 9.30 one October morning. A bank vole was removed at 3 o'clock and another an hour later, or perhaps the same one, unable to resist a second nibble at the oats! Bank voles, like mice, tend to shell their seeds and eat daintily, discarding the coarser fractions. Short-tailed field voles can live on more fibrous food, champing their way through stems and roots, and these are more widely spread through the area. Because of their wider food range, they come less readily to baited traps, so it is difficult to assess their abundance relative to the others.

Some grasses are too coarse for their liking but the fine needle leaves of the fescues and broader ones of the meadow grasses (*Poa*) are much enjoyed. This goes for rabbits too, and an area overrun by one seldom holds many of the other. The occasional recurrence of Myxomatosis among the rabbits gives the voles a chance to multiply, allowing the fescue to arch up over their above-ground tunnels to constitute an even more valuable source of cover than of food. This cover is no better than that of the slacks, but is not under water for half the year.

Voles may scratch up roots to eat from the tunnel floors, but mostly they feed on the grass shoots, pulling these down from the severed base, then getting a grip higher up to haul again—so, if not consumed directly, little piles of grass chopped into lengths of ½-1½ inches accumulate at intervals. The strips of grass over the tunnels are thus not only withered but considerably thinned.

It seems that these above-ground voles do not set out deliberately to build a tunnel, but press on with the all important business of feeding and the tunnel just happens—as surely as with soil-swallowing earthworms. It is only possible to appreciate their extent when they are revealed by a light grass fire or by the melting of snow which has lain for a long time.

A finger run along the line of wilted blades to expose the run reveals not only grass caches but little heaps of sausage shaped dung pellets, sometimes only six inches apart; some moist, others disintegrating to yellow 'sawdust'. These are much larger than the minute faecal remains of mice because of the greater amounts of fibre, and it is likely that they are ingested twice, like those of rabbits, to give the intestinal bacteria a second chance to break down the cellulose.

Defaecation can occur immediately inside the entrance, in short side branches or just off the tunnel at a higher level, where the grass is pressed back but not severed. Where *Camptothecium* survives among the grass bases the runs pass over the top of the moss and favour it by thinning the light-excluding layer above. Sometimes enough light gets in for seeds to germinate, particularly among the dung pellets. Self heal is commonest, with moderate amounts of heath violet and less storksbill, thyme-leaved sandwort, mouse-ear chickweed and common chickweed with its roots permeating the fresh dung.

Any of these are likely to have their leaves nipped off. With larger herbs the nodes where the branches diverge may be eaten and the less fleshy internodes discarded: with creeping cinquefoil the leaf stalks may be eaten exclusively. It is not usually difficult to distinguish vole grazing from rabbit grazing, because everything is on a smaller scale.

An incidental feature of the vole passages is their use by other creatures such as woodlice and snails. By October they may contain shrunken woolly bear caterpillars, probably the ones which failed to 'get away' because of the load of parasitic ichneumon wasps which they carried. Discarded coats from normal skin changes are more difficult to find.

Water voles are not uncommon in the lower reaches of the River Kenfig, plopping into the stream with so much air trapped in their water-repellent fur that they look like silvered submarines. They have not, however, been found in the pool, probably because the only steep banks suitable for burrowing there are those where food plants are sparsest and human interference greatest.

In the marsh opposite, a sturdy population of harvest mice was discovered in the seventies. These creatures were associated with corn crops in the past and with rank hedgerows in those days of earlier corn harvests, but not usually with freshwater vegetation. It is here, however, that the most suitable cover occurs. So nimbly do they scamper through the vegetation tops, helped by long, prehensile tails, and so lightweight are they, that they need never fret if the ground beneath is under water. They retreat to drier zones in winter and have been found feeding on the plump seeds of marram grass—their own private corn harvest.

Harvest mice were not known in Glamorgan until 1971: yellow-necked mice have not been seen at all, although present in neighbouring counties, and dormice are extremely rare. They are not confned to Kenfig in this part of Mid Glamorgan, five other colonies having been found within a few miles: north-west of Nottage, on Locks Common at Porthcawl, at Barlas east of Cornelly, Lampha Court near Castle-upon-Alun and near Goitre in the Margam Forest behind Port Talbot. Harvest mice are essentially southern and eastern in their distribution, which fits fairly well with the distribution of cereal-growing districts. The two Pembrokeshire records and one of the two Caernarvonshire

63. Selective baiting for harvest mice (left): vandalised ball and bank voles (right)

ones have been made since 1975. Otherwise all Welsh records are in Glamorgan, with Margam and Kenfig the most westerly.

In order to find the elusive mites, Arthur Morgan set up baiting centres in 1976. He cut circular holes the diameter of a harvest mouse in a number of tennis balls, which he fixed on pegs about a foot above the ground in the poolside tangle of cocksfoot and oat grass. The balls were the size and height of summer nests and were baited with mixed bird seed.

They attracted no attention at first, but on the fifth day word got around among the whiskered ones, whose random searchings had paid off. Venturesome voles and meandering mice converged on the goodies. The harvest mice popped straight in and helped themselves, while those whose girth prevented them found small problem in nibbling the holes a little bigger to accommodate their own vital statistics. The following morning the experimenter had established the presence only of 'some sort of rodent', and that he already knew, after having 14 out of 14 live-traps sprung in a single night!

The next step was to insert an unchewable 15 mm. plastic collar around the entrance to each ball. The harvest mice proceeded as before; the field mice and voles had to have another think. They spent a night or two chewing quantities of fluff from the outside of the tennis balls with competent little incisors, but these were not sharp enough to penetrate the rubber. Its resilient substance merely dented, with maddening persistence in response to every type of pressure. Expectation turned to frustration and the foragers had to content themselves with seed spilling from the orgy above; crumbs from the table of the favoured ones. There are obvious advantages to being small.

Having established the presence of harvest mice, the next stage was to seek the summer nests. These spheres of shredded grass with almost invisible entrance holes materialised well above ground closer to the pool, where the rodents had converged towards the end of the drought, in search of better feeding. They occurred in water horsetail, mint, fleabane, sallow, reeds and grasses, woven around the stalks like reed warblers' nests: one was an unusual spoon shape. No nest seems to be occupied for more than about a couple of weeks, so there were more nests than mice.

As the year matured these were overtaken by the rising waters, but the makers would have withdrawn well before this, to utilise the seed crops of the sands beyond. Nests built after September are at ground level, to forestall the winter nakedness of leaf loss and the ensuing collapse of brittle supports. So secretive are these wee beasties and so few naturalists sufficiently skilled to find them, that more than we suspect may be moving into the tangle of grasses in the remaining wild-scape, as modern harvesting methods make the cornfields less suitable.

The delicacy of tread, which enables them to seek seeds in tall drying vegetation, separates them from the rabbit populations, which prefer the fresh green growths of the shorter swards. As we learn more about the part played by feromones in the rabbits' social system, it is easier to appreciate the reason for their 'latrines' on prominences such as ant-hills, which form the link between members of local communities. The oval dung pellets collecting at these sites are poor in plant nutrients, having been through the digestive tract twice, so that little of any value is returned to the sward from whence it came.

Hares are most often seen in the wet vegetation complex behind the pool, fanning out over the dunes during the flush of spring growth when plants are not desiccated by summer drought or winter wind. They are big-hearted animals, with a highly efficient circulation permitting them to outpace almost every other. The great heart muscles and pounding blood-stream make them messy animals to clean for the pot, but they excite more interest bounding over the dunes than jugged.

Only the young are likely to fall prey to foxes, which are as numerous here as elsewhere in Glamorgan, although this is usually only apparent from the liberal spread of long twisted scats and the pungent whiff of fox smell where their tracks cross the footpaths (not to be confused with the similarly powerful odour of herb Robert crushed under-foot).

They are out by day as well as night and it is always a thrill to see a debonair Reynard trotting over the dunes on the alert for prey, the sun gilding the ruddy coat and highlighting the white shirtfront when he sits back on his haunches to contemplate the next move. The winter toll of foxes can be high, but all is recycled. A rock pipit has been watched catching flies bred in a fox carcass at Sker Point and the carrion goes to feed others—from buzzard to burying beetle.

Similarly patterned in rufous and white are the two small Mustellids, stoat and weasel. These excavate burrows in the firmer sands, but also enjoy more solid nooks and crannies. Either may be seen weaving among upshore beach boulders and tide-borne debris at Sker and they are notoriously inquisitive, a suitable squeak from the watcher sometimes stimulating a closer approach, with the sinuously raised body one big question mark as the quivering snout is thrust upwards to test the scent.

When the wardens were based in the farmyard caravan, before construction of the Nature Reserve Centre in 1979, a weasel came habitually to play in a pile of planks alongside, approaching so close that adherent sand grains were visible on the twitching whiskers. There would be plenty of mice for it to chase around the farm buildings. Stoats were hunting in the brown rat colony by the pool soon after this was founded and their dung was observed among the harvest mouse nests on the opposite shore.

Creatures which may be polecats have been seen, but there are feral polecat-ferrets about which could easily be mistaken for the genuine article in an area such as this, where ferreting has been carried out and domesticated animals may have gone to ground. So far no mink are suspected, and it will be advantageous if they stay away. The pool has plenty of small rudd to sustain them, but only half their normal diet is of fish and they have an unfortunate liking for nestlings.

Badgers have no sett on the nature reserve proper but are present on Kenfig Common and sometimes wander in to feed. Two families a little to the north, at Barlas, near Cornelly, gave enormous pleasure to badger watchers through the early seventies, but have now been displaced by the M4 motorway.

The two setts here were close together, among gnarled tree roots on the twenty foot banks of two old marl pits, 'The Horseshoe' and 'The Pool'. The depressions were overgrown with ash, elm, hazel and hawthorn, while elders had sprung up around both sett entrances, as so often in areas intensively disturbed by mammals. Badger watching sessions were instituted by Arthur Morgan in 1971, when it became known that the Stormy Down section of the motorway would destroy the sites. It seemed advisable to assess the status of the animals so that they could be got away before the holocaust—either by persuasion or physical means.

Many who witnessed the exploratory, shambling emergence of sow and boar which heralded the appearance of the rough and tumble, roly-poly cubs had never seen badgers before. How many of us have? Some were youngsters, who quite forgot the crackly bag of crisps confiscated beforehand, in the enthralment of close encounters with curiously sniffing furry noses. And how like those of the children themselves were the cubs' waddling playtime frolics—the games of tag among the tree roots, the somersaults and the mock fights, which brought suppressed chuckles from the most hardened badger watchers. Both setts contained cubs in those first four years of the seventies.

The Pool family lent itself to observation by parties settled quietly downwind—themselves watched by a ring of fascinated cows on one occasion! The Horseshoe site could only accommodate one and it was such lone watchers who experienced a more complete picture of the nocturnal activity on Stormy Down. Arthur Morgan has told of such an evening.

In the twilight hours the hunting paths of a late sparrow hawk and early barn owl crossed, the first meditating on the day's activities among the branches as the second sailed, ghost-like, across the hollow. The torch beam caught another of the night hunters—a spider dangling on a silken thread to intercept night-flying insects.

A living pendulum, swaying ever so slightly in the zephyr breeze, it was itself temptation to other hunters, the pipistrelle bats on their routine flights among the poolside bushes. 'Red in tooth and claw?' Perhaps, but there is plenty to go round—or was, before the arrival of the crashing bulldozers.

Moorhens called occasionally from the pool, awake still, for all the lack of visibility, and the occasional teal and mallard splashed down to roost after spells of feeding under cover of darkness. A fox loped by, relaxed and expectant of picking up some rodent scent. But no, that was man scent! Ears and nose came up, alert, tense. He cared not whether this was friend or foe: he may well have seen the corpse of a fellow fox strung on the fence of a nearby estate. He took no chances. The man had saved the mice this time.

Badgers have been bodily removed from threatened setts by conservationists, but they cleave instinctively close to the paths of their ancestors and are great travellers. It seemed best to discourage them, so that they would choose to go elsewhere of their own volition. To this end Arthur started his campaign at Christmas 1974, soaking old newspapers in a proprietary brand of repellent and stuffing them down the holes, which were lightly blocked outside. At this time of year there would be no young cubs underground and it was imperative to prevent any being produced there in the 1975 season.

During January, February and March activity at the setts fell off, but badgers still came and went at intervals. Each time they re-opened the holes Arthur re-plugged them with more repellent. One adult was still about, sometimes visiting two nights in succession, in Mid-April, when hole treatment ceased, but no old bedding had been cleared from the nesting chambers nor new bedding added. If cubs had been produced, they should have appeared above ground by now: it appeared that there were none.

One of the sows had travelled an ancient badger-track to a lay-by on the A48 half a mile away and got herself run over on the night of 10th/11th February. Examination showed that she was still carrying her litter of cubs. These would not be born at Barlas—nor anywhere!

Highway contractors moved in on 21st May, 1975. Arthur reported wistfully on a scene of utter desolation: a great bonfire throwing up showers of sparks: two smaller fires glowing dully in the evening sunlight. A broad swathe of trees and bushes was squandered, the Pool was filled, the Horseshoe excavated. Everything was ground to dust or buried under tons of hardcore.

The thousands who bowl along that stretch of motorway, to savour the rural assets of Gower or Pembrokeshire, know nothing of the rural assets that were sacrificed to get them there—nor of those which will be lost further west because of their presence. This is one of the prices our fellow creatures have to pay for our more affluent way of living.

More people in the countryside are inevitable, and desirable if people are to learn what the countryside is all about, but we have to share it. Tracts must be left for the true countryman to go about his business in harmony with natural populations which have learned to live with a muted level of human activity, avoiding face to face encounters, but unable to evolve rapidly enough to discover that all men are not their foes.

It is fashionable to pay lip service to conservation and to decry the guns and traps of human predation, but we sanction the heavy machinery which is ripping up the earth at a truly alarming rate and creating more devastation than all the guns and traps. Those take only the current generation; the bulldozers take the means of survival of future generations as well.

Part Eight

Rock Pools, Headlands and Downs Around Porthcawl

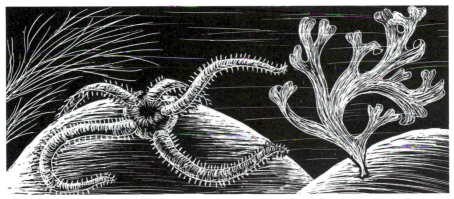

Brittle star and carragheen 'moss'

Even those who profess to know Britain well, who throughout much of their lives have taken pleasure in seeking out its abundant resources, will be the first to maintain that this abundant inheritance of ours is inexhaustible in its variety and wealth of treasure. This is part of the accepted magic of Britain.

Garry Hogg in "The Shell Book of Exploring Britain."

'Fetch' and shoals. Fishermen's fish. Animals of pools and foreshore. Seaweeds.

IT was a combination of wind and waves which brought Kenfig Borough to its knees, and the further away these two elements enter into partnership, the greater is the devastation that they can achieve. Local swells may be generated within the Bristol Channel, or further out in the Celtic Sea off Southern Ireland, but it is the oceanic swells originating way beyond which have the most potent impact.

This eastern flank of Swansea Bay faces into the teeth of the prevailing south-westerlies and the effective 'fetch', in which the long waves of the Atlantic ground swells can build up, stretches unobstructed to the Caribbean. When springs and swells coincide, tides 6-7 feet higher than the ordinary 'high' can be anticipated and it is time for the citizens of Newton and Porthcawl to get busy with the sandbags to protect their homes. Periodically the press releases pictures of what happens when they are insufficiently quick off the mark.

Sea fog lying thickly over the water has caused many Dutch ships plying from the West Indies to mistake the mouth of the Bristol Channel—wide open to the south-west—for the English Channel, and the timbers of some still protrude starkly from the sands where they foundered. The Scarweather Sands off Porthcawl and the North Kenfig Patches of gravelly material disturb the waves, and a clockwise flow of sediments around the first has been established by Dr. Michael Collins and others of the Swansea University Oceanography Department.

Looting and pillaging was rife in the eighteenth century, the locals converging with horses and carts from as far afield as Aberdulais, Llanharry and Llantrisant, to plunder the cargo, caring nothing whether the shipwrecked sailors lived or died. 'Le Vainqueur' was looted at Sker in 1753: The 'Planter's Welfare' lost her cargo of sugar, coffee, cocoa and cotton bound from Surinam to Amsterdam in 1770, when she foundered a little further east on Newton Sands. The 'Caterina' met her fate off Sker Point in 1781, and the local markets became flooded with cotton. The casks of wine and brandy did not get that far! Sker House and its barns made a useful storage depot for contraband—or confiscated goods.

Wrecks of a different kind come wafting in from the tropics at times—Portugese men-o'-war (*Physalia physalis*), with sting-loaded

350

83

84

Plate XXI BIRDS OF THE SHAGGIER
GRASSLANDS—*Keri Williams*

83. Left: Wheatear carrying larva
84. Top right: Dunnock feeding young cuckoo
85. Bottom: Tree pipit at nest

85

Plate XXII   MARINE LIFE AT
PORTHCAWL—*Author*

86. Top left: Beadlet anemone in barnacle-
     crusted pothole
87. Top right: Sandy rock pools
88. Mid right: Mussels and winkle in
     Sabellaria sand reef
89. Mid left: Wave-sculptured Carboniferous
     Limestone
90. Bottom right: Sponge-like sea-mat,
     Alcyonidium gelatinosum

blue streamers, by-the-wind-sailors (*Velella spirans*), with their membraneous hemisphere sail less inflated than the last's, and goose barnacles (*Lepas anatifera*), which ride in on drifting timber, the length of the black hose-pipe-like 'foot' indicating the degree of protection from hot sun achieved in their normal abode.

Warm-blooded orphans of the storm have included porpoises, grey Atlantic seals, shearwaters, petrels and other pelagic wanderers blown, helpless, onto the lee shore. High winds may bring these waifs far inland. These are legitimate casualties: the victims of oil spills at sea are in a different category.

The regular 'beached birds surveys' yield few corpses, but February 1980 saw no less than sixty oiled birds washed up along the Kenfig to Porthcawl stretch, following a tanker spillage off Cornwall. 56 of these were auks (36 guillemots, 11 razorbills and 9 too fouled for identification). Auks are not often seen this far up channel unless windblown or under stress. Their preponderance among the victims is not just chance. A glistening oil slick can appear like a fish shoal to a flying auk flock, so that the birds are tempted to settle and dive straight into trouble. Others found dead on this occasion were fulmar, kittiwake, cormorant and gannet.

But the sea yields generously of unsullied products and the rocks of Sker and Porthcawl give better opportunities to longshore fishermen than do the sands, where the water of the great tides is always ebbing or flowing beyond reach of the line. Rest Bay on the north-western flank of Porthcawl may provide fine skate (*Raja batis*) and thornback ray (*Raja clavata*), while plaice (*Pleuronectes platessa*) and flounders (*Platichthys flesus*) can usually be lured to a lugworm bait around the harbour. Cod (*Gadus morhua*) were particularly plentiful off Sker Point and Locks Common in January 1980. Mackerel (*Scomber scombrus*) usually move inshore about the beginning of July, unless the shoals are dispersed by storms, and can be caught from the rocks in summer as well as from boats.

Line fishermen gear their activities to the high tide, leaving the low tides to the shorebirds. Some drive south from the snowy hills of northern Gwent and Brecon to spend a January night on Porthcawl Pier or Breakwater—cool still, but not ice-bound like the hills of home. Whiting (*Merlangius merlangus*) shoal inshore to feed on the high tide and usually form the main catch, along with codling, pouting (*Trisopterus luscus*), sea bass (*Dicentrarchus labrax*) and the occasional grey mullet (*Crenimugil labrosus*) or dogfish (*Scyliorhinus caniculus*). 'Bass is best' is a fisherman's slogan as well as a brewer's, but they need to be small bass for the conoisseur: larger ones taste oily. Mullet make better eating than the smell produced within an hour of death indicates.

Fishermen leave the inner jetty on the ebb as the waves begin to break white over Tusker Rock offshore. Those on the outer breakwater,

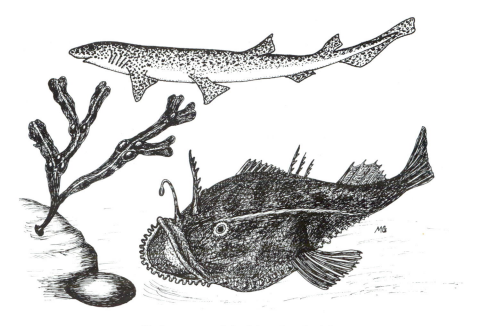

64. Lesser spotted dogfish and angler fish

which deflects the big seas from the little harbour, have a while longer before the tide withdraws to expose the mudflats within.

Sometimes laggard fish miss the tide and get stranded in pools among the rocks or peat beds of the sandier Kenfig Beach. Early May 1978 saw a portly and rather moribund angler fish (*Lophius piscatorius*) with deflated lure, breathing its last in a peaty pool. No longer would it gyrate that deceptive titbit enticingly above its ugly nose to lure some unsuspecting prey fish to its death. Teasing the prey, catlike, with that dangling bobble modified from the front of the dorsal fin, the angler fish suddenly flips this away and opens the great maw, so that the hapless fish is engulfed in the ingoing rush of water. Fishermen sell the hindmost parts of the predator as 'monk's tail' and culinary artists chop them up and pass them on as scampi!

The pinkish lesser spotted dogfish, cruising round like a small shark on the same occasion, was far from moribund, but had suicidal tendencies, running constantly aground. Sympathetic watchers pushed it repeatedly back, but each time its head came up and it slid ashore somewhere else. The secret of its blind persistence seemed to lie in the shallowness of the pool and that long, uptilted tail, which could gain no purchase on the water to propel the fish forwards unless the body was tilted, head up and tail down.

354

Huge rounded sunfish (*Mola mola*), which can weigh anything up to 80 pounds, sometimes cruise this way from the tropical South Atlantic and are caught fairly regularly off Porthcawl. Deep-bodied trigger fish (*Balistes carolinensis*) of a modest ten inches long, are others more typical of warmer waters—the Mediterranean in this case.

The ordinary beachcomber with no rod and line will see little of the sea-going fish, but has the chance of finding six or seven others in the rock pools. Eels and elvers (*Anguilla anguilla*) will be here, as almost anywhere else, fresh or salt, and the lesser sand eel (*Ammodytes tobianus*), with long dorsal fin and slender torso making it look a little like an elver, but the illusion is dispelled by the fishy forked tail. Butterfish (*Pholis gunnellus*) are also elongated, but stubbier, blunt both ends and with a row of black spots each side of the fin along the back. All three of these can be found in the open sea and the sand eels are particular favourites of the fishing terns.

Another with dorsal fin occupying the whole length of the back is the common blenny or shanny (*Blennius pholis*). This is yet stubbier, increasing in girth to the high brow of the squarish head. It has no scales and the front fins are tiny, like two little pegs on which to rest the chin, instead of being united into a sucker, as in the rock goby (*Gobius paganellus*). These little chaps are equally well camouflaged by their mottling and are similarly shaped but less 'high browed'. The sucker under the chin, break in the dorsal fin and presence of scales distinguish them.

Finally there are the rocklings, the three-bearded (*Onos tricirratus*) and five-bearded (*Onos mustellus*). The beard consists of a fleshy barbel dangling under the throat, with two and four tentacles respectively protruding from the snout—appendages matched in freshwater species by the catfish. The front fifth of the dorsal fin seems to have been trimmed short with scissors, nicking upwards at the front. Both have the usual cryptic patterning of dark above to blend with the pool floor and light below to blend with the sky, but the three-bearded is specklier.

A far cry from the fish in appearance, but regarded as the most closely related invertebrates present, because of their tadpole-like larval phase, are the tunicates or sea squirts. The free-swimming youngsters have muscles attached to something very like a backbone, but this disappears when they settle down to become star-spangled or double-necked 'vase' adults. The two necks are the inhalant and exhalant openings by which water enters and leaves and, when picked up, a sudden contraction of the body muscles squirts a jet of liquid out.

Sea squirts prefer still water, although common foulers of ships' bottoms, and the biggest may grow to 12 inches high in Swansea Docks. Of two which could be turned up around Porthcawl, the gooseberry sea squirt (*Dendrodoa grossularia*) is the more likely—in Pink Bay, where rocky overhangs get exposed only at low tide, half way between Sker Point and Hutchwns Point with its Coastguard Station further east. *Ascidiella aspersa* braves the greater turbulence west of Sker, but can only live at extreme low water.

In 1972 a spiny spider crab (*Maia squinado*) wandered in from deeper water bringing another sea squirt, *Styela coriacea,* on its capacious carapace. Examination by personnel from the Porthcawl Camp School revealed three other passengers, an encrusting sponge, *Oscarella lobularis,* a hydroid, *Nemertasia antennina* and an acorn barnacle, *Balanus crenatus.*

A smaller but equally exotic-looking spider crab is *Macropodia rostrata*, with long wispy legs radiating from a fragile, triangular body. So much more wispy and fragile as to have earned the name of sea spider is the common, reddish *Nymphon gracile*. Others of this group are the knobbly, more robust-looking *Pycnogonum littorale* and *Achelia echinata,* which is common at both Kenfig and Porthcawl.

More usefully solid is the edible crab (*Cancer pagurus*), which is quite abundant on the lower shore, but seldom worth taking for the pot. The big ones, like the blue lobsters (*Homarus vulgaris*), wisely live offshore, away from the prodding of weekend crabbers. The squat lobster (*Galathea squamifera*) is a jolly little fellow found skulking under rocks at Pink Bay, beady black eyes and greenish body preceded by formidable, far-reaching pincers.

Long clawed porcelain crabs (*Porcellana longicornis*) are smaller, rounder and commoner and venture further upshore. Broad-clawed porcelain crabs (*P. platycheles*), formerly present, have decreased along the whole coast since the hard winter of 1962-63. An infant circular crab (*Atelecyclus rotundatus*) only 4 mm across was found at Kenfig in 1972.

Velvet swimming crabs (*Macropipus puber*) and smooth swimming crabs (*M. depurator*) of the lower shore can deliver a sharp nip if tampered with. Crabs, like insects, shed their skins as they grow and these, resembling the dismembered prey of some hunter, can be picked up from the beaches. They make interesting specimens and demonstrate the flattening of the hind legs for use as oars, the bristly margins of the velvet crab increasing efficiency still further, as in the water beetles. The two swimming crabs were formerly in the same genus as *Portunus latipes,* which lives downshore among the Kenfig gravels. The blue crab (*P. holstatus*) sometimes gets stranded here. The reddish hairy crab (*Pilumnus hirtellus*) is so bewhiskered as to merge almost imperceptibly into the hollows and spongy growths were it lives.

Common shore crabs (*Carcinus maenas*) are the toughies of the shore, able to put up with long exposure to the air or immersion in non-saline water, and are much the most likely to be seen, scampering around on versatile legs having each joint functioning in a different plane, to give manoeuvrability.

356

Plate 22   SOME LOCALLY COMMON BEETLES—*Jack Evans*

109. Wasp beetle, *Clytus arietus*
110. A soldier beetle, *Cantharis rustica*
111. Cockchafer or maybug, *Melolontha melolontha*
112. Dor beetle, *Geotrupes stercorarius*
113. Strand beetle, *Nebria complanata*
114. Ladybirds mating, *Propylaea quatuordecempuncta*

357

Plate 23   ROCKS AND SEA LIFE AT PORTHCAWL—*Author*

115. Erosion of barnacle-clad boulder
116. Common starfish
117. Lesser sand eel
118. Common blenny
119. Sea bass

358

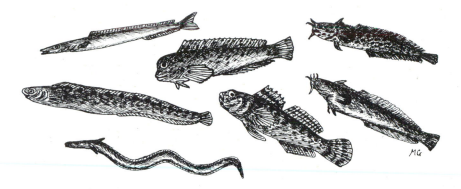

65. Rock pool fish from Porthcawl and Sker. First row: Lesser sand eel, blenny, three-bearded rockling. Second row: Butterfish, goby, five-bearded rockling. Bottom left: Elver

Opportunist hermit crabs (*Pagurus bernhardus)* meander around in droves at low water mark in their borrowed shells. These they appropriate after they have been vacated: the little soft-bodied pea crabs *(Pinnotheres pisum),* on the other hand, take up residence in shells still occupied by their rightful owners. Collectors of mussels for the pot may find that they have crabs as well living, not as parasites, but in harmony, in a symbiotic partnership. In filtering minute food scraps from the current of water being wafted into their hosts' gills, they may help to prevent these getting clogged by foreign bodies.

Mussels have more to fear from common starfish *(Asteria rubens),* which are always present in moderate numbers, but sometimes get washed inshore and die in hundreds when the tide leaves them stranded. Such mass mortalities among the rocks of Rest Bay can provide a bonanza for the gulls. Starfish habitats range from crevices among foreshore reefs to depths of as much as 1,200 feet, and their colour is almost as variable, from yellow to purple through shades of orange, red and pink.

Their myriad sucker feet can be likened to little squeeze bags. They are worked hydraulically, sea water being pumped from the circular body canal along a branch canal running the length of each arm and forced out into the tube feet. This causes them to elongate and muscles ensure that they push and pull in synchronised directions.

This method is used in feeding as well as locomotion, the suckers clamping to either side of the selected bivalve and the two shells being drawn inexorably apart. The starfish solves the problem of having no teeth by extruding its stomach into the victim and digesting it externally.

Mussels *(Mytilus edulis)* are its favourite food and once formed the basis of an important cockle and mussel fishery—but not since 1860. Now, since 1972, vast mussel beds have begun to form again at both Porthcawl and Sker. Individual mussels grow to considerable size but masses get ripped from the rocks and washed inshore, particularly when their streamlining is destroyed by barnacles growing on the shells. Guylines or byssus threads anchor them to the substrate and it was not these which had given way in the midden-like collections of empty shells accumulated in hollows east of Sker in February 1980. The threads were clamped grimly in death to the limey tubes of keel worms *(Pomatoceros triqueter)* and it was these which had broken from their hold.

Other starfish are too uncommon to make serious inroads on any prey animal. Sun stars *(Solaster papposus)* have been found well downshore on the Kenfig side of Sker and there is an old record of a brittle star *(Ophiothrix fragilis)*. Another paler brittle star *(Amphipholis squamata)* is quite common in rock pools. Not so the sea urchins, which are predominantly sand dwellers, the only record being of a green urchin *(Psammechinus miliaris)* in 1973.

Empty oyster shells *(Ostrea edulis)* are scattered through the mussel beds, but these are remnants of a former more vigorous population and few live ones are found nowadays, these at Rhych Point. Pearly saddle oysters *(Anomia ephippium)* are commoner and other bivalves, the rosy-nosed rock borers *(Hiatella arctica)* drill their incredible tunnels, slowly but surely into the rocks, as along most of Glamorgan's limestone coast. The two carpet shells *(Venerupis pullastra* and *V. saxatilis)* are about, but mostly the bivalve molluscs are sand dwellers, and drift into cavities between the rocks as empty shells.

Cephalopods are molluscs with a difference, the shells internal, and cuttlebones picked up on the beach can be much enjoyed by canaries. Live cuttlefish *(Sepia officinalis)* seldom come this far inshore, but spawn of the common squid *(Loligo forbesi)* does, as in July 1980, looking like bunches of black grapes, and an octopus *(Octopus vulgaris)* has been caught.

Other molluscs with no outer shells are the sea slugs, which are more attractive than their name suggests. A rare one found in Porthcawl is *Okenia elegans,* which is ornamented with black and orange spots. Others are *Acanthodoris pilosa* and *Doto fragilis*. A September gale in 1972 brought *Archidoris pseudoargus* ashore and September 1976 saw *Thecacera pennigera* very common at Porthcawl and Ogmore, although not seen at all on the Glamorgan coast previously. Sea slugs lay their eggs in ribbons of jelly which are frilled and crimped like curtain pelmets attached to the rock along one edge.

Beautifully iridescent sea mice *(Aphrodite aculeata)* are sometimes stranded on the shore, their scales hidden under golden green bristles. Generally mouse-sized, they are the most unwormlike of the fifteen or so species of bristle worm to be found here. Handsome catworms *(Nephthys cirrosa)* wriggle through the sand west of Sker Point and 6-8 inch long green leaf worms *(Eulalia viridis)* slide over mid-tide rocks and lay their eggs in March in conspicuous jelly blobs as green as themselves.

Worms are in intimate contact with their substrate and are quite choosy about where they live. Red ribbon worms *(Lineus ruber)* occur in soft mud accumulating in the shelter of Pink Bay. Greenish ragworms *(Perinereis cultrifera)* can reach to 10 inches and the brighter green king ragworm *(Nereis virens)* to 16 inches. These burrow in coarse sand on the lower shore, the first more commonly. Lugworms *(Arenicola marina)* also like rather more sand with their mud and the related *Audouinea tentaculata* swarms in muddy gravel half way down the shore. Sand mason worms *(Lanice conchilega)* are content in coarse shingly sand with plenty of shell flakes for building into their tubes. Honeycomb worms *(Sabellaria alveolata)* need sand to build their crusty reefs and rocks to fix them to.

The scale worms *Lepidonotus squamatus* and *Harmothöe imbricatus* skulk under stones in the eastern lee of Sker Point and *Polydora ciliata* burrows right into the limestone, which becomes pitted with narrow tunnels, a pair of tentacles protruding from each occupied hole when covered by the tide. Natural limestone forms the walls of their burrows; the *Spirorbis* worms, like the keel worms, build their little coiled tunnels with lime extracted from the sea water in solution. *Spirorbis borealis* cements its tubes to saw wrack and bladder wrack; *Spirorbis corallinae* is attached to coralline weed or one of the 'Irish mosses'.

Another rock tunneller is the boring sponge, *Cliona celata,* which will also work its way into big oyster and whelk shells, as will the worm, *Polydora.* Instead of tentacles, little blobs of yellow sponge show in the tube entrances. Sponges are colonial, their cells holding together but not very well organised. Cells parted by squashing will join up again in a loose mass and secrete spicules, which give the colony form. This structure is best seen in the purse sponges of the pools, the neat upright 'vases' of *Sycon ciliatum* and the flappier, dangling ones of *Grantia compressa.* The bright orange *Myxilla incrustans* and greenish-white bread crumb sponge *(Halichondria panicea)* are encrusting species, covered with little 'volcano vents'.

Hydroids or sea firs are also colonial, but the skeleton plays a more dominant role here, imparting shape, like little bouquets. Oaten pipes *(Tubularia indivisa)* grow on rocks west of Sker, sea oaks *(Dynamena pumila)* on saw wrack.

Flowerlike in a more solid way are the sea anemones, the beadlet *(Actinia equina)* predominant, as always. Dahlia anemones *(Taelia felina)* are quite common in pools, with gorgeous rosettes of pink, green or blue tentacles spreading from the warty column. *Sagartia elegans* from Pink Bay has a smaller rosette on a taller column and the daisy anemone *(Cereus pedunculatus)* has gone even more this way, the column spreading at the top like an orange chantarelle mushroom, with the tentacles frilling its margin. Both of these are south-westerly species.

Dead men's fingers *(Alcyonium digitatum),* which are of similar texture and structure, are soft corals, found but rarely, on Sker Point. Their general form is emulated by another, *Alcyonidium gelatinosum,* which is an unmatlike sea mat. This is the subject of some of the most spectacular strandings witnessed at Porthcawl, the branched fawn coloured masses half way between dead men's fingers and mermaid's glove sponges, and sometimes as big as a fist. It grows under rock overhangs too far downshore to be found except at very low spring tides.

The more typical mat of *Alcyonidium polyoum* grows at about the same level, on the branched holdfasts of oarweeds. Another, *A. hirsutum,* ventures up to midshore pools, encrusting the limey fronds of coralline weed on Porthcawl Point. Closely adherent to oarweed fronds as a delicate white honeycomb is the more familiar sea mat, *Membranipora membranacea,* while the less elegant *Flustrellida (Flustrella) hispida* wraps itself round the bases of brown wracks.

Each little white 'box' contains a single animal, which can be likened to a squeeze bag. Expansion of the body fluids causes the tentacles to pop out, their tiny cilia or hairs setting up a current wafting food particles into the darker gut below, the whole squashing down into the compartment when the tide ebbs away.

Best known of this group is the plantlike horn wrack *(Flustra foliacea)* whose communal skeleton is so light that it blows way inland, to float on the Sker Pools. *Bugula turbinata* is more finely divided, like a series of sweep's brushes. This lowly group has many members. Three other genera at Sker and Porthcawl are *Bowerbankia, Walkeria* and *Amathia.*

The shrimp, *Palaemon elegans,* is abundant in pools, winter and summer alike: another, *Crangon crangon,* is to be found from Kenfig east, while a skeleton shrimp *(Caprella ?hirsutum)* was recorded in 1957. Sideways flattened Gammarids, the shrimps of sandhopper type, are a familiar sight upshore. Flip a pile of decaying seaweed aside and showers of *Talitrus saltator* and *Orchestia gammarella* will spurt out, while *Gammarus locusta* is revealed by upturned stones (which please replace!).

Idotea granulosa, which lives among the brown wracks, is flattened the other way, like a woodlouse. Finest and commonest of this group is the sea slater *(Ligia oceanica),* which scurries round rocks well above tide level, sheltering in crevices. This is the home of the very few insect species adapted to life beside the sea—the bristle tail, *Petrobius maritimus* and the springtail *(Anurida (Lipura) maritima),* which has lost its spring but is so tiny as to walk effortlessly on the surface film of upshore pools without wetting so much as a whisker.

So rich an assemblage of animals implies a rich assemblage of plants and both are dependent on the broken nature of the intertidal terrain. The Porthcawl end of this stretch of shore forms an accommodating and delightful complex of silver limestone interspersed with golden sand. The Sker end is furnished with deep, narrow gullies in the red rock platform, stacks, arches and blowholes, with plenty of pebbles eroded from the Triassic puddingstone.

At Sker the cliff has been cut in the lower part of the intertidal zone, at Mumbles to the west in the middle part and at Nash Point to the east in the upper part. As pointed out by Dr. Chris Mettam, this means that the force of the waves is broken at Sker by the downshore cliff, so that the impact on the rest is smaller. Their remaining energy is expended in rolling up the long intertidal slope above, so there is no splash zone at the top and marine organisms cannot, therefore, extend above high water mark. The dwarf periwinkle *(Littorina neritoides)*, having none of its usual splash zone habitat, extends right across the shore platform at Sker, down to low-water of springs. The edible periwinkle *(L. littorea)*, which is usually distributed right across the shore, is unable to hang on to vertical surfaces effectively, so avoids the steep downshore zone.

Green seaweeds are represented by the usual green strings, grass kelp or gutweed *(Enteromorpha* species) and sea lettuce *(Ulva lactuca)*, with harsh tufts of *Cladophora rupestris* and softer ones of *C. glaucescens*. A charming little summer annual, seldom seen, is the feathery sea moss

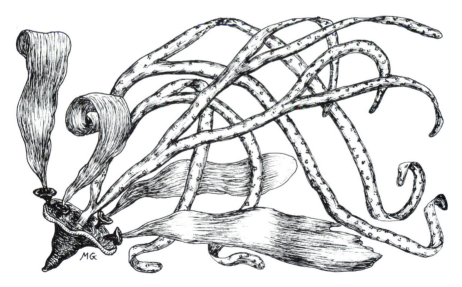

66. A strange growth form of thongweed *(Himanthalea elongata)* at Kenfig

(Bryopsis plumosa), contrasting with wiry filaments of *Chaetomorpha*.

Most of the oarweeds arrive only as drift, but one, *Laminaria digitata,* is common downshore and in the deeper pools, where thongweed *(Himanthalia elongata)* also grows. Gales in mid-September 1978 brought a lot of thongweed ashore, reproductive bodies oozing as orange specks from every pore. Among the drift were some very odd specimens—as illustrated in Figure 66. Some 'buttons' had either budded off from the old ones or germinated upon them—unusual in itself—but, instead of then producing ordinary reproductive 'thongs', these sprouted oarweed type fronds 8-10 inches long, up to 2 inches wide and delicate in texture, but not wrinkled like sugarweed *(Laminaria saccharina)*. Epiphytism (of one species growing on another) must be discounted, because oarweeds have branched hold-fasts at the base. Hybridisation must also be discounted because the two are in no way related, thongweed having more kin with the wracks or *Fuci*. Specimens went off to the experts, but no explanation has been forthcoming.

Asperococcus compressus and podweed *(Halidrys siliquosa)* are among the more interesting brown algae, the latter with fluffy tufts of *Sphacelaria bipinnata* growing upon it. *Pylaiella littoralis* and *Ectocarpus* habitually grow on bladder wrack here. The delicate summer annual among the browns is *Dictyota dichotoma*.

By the end of November 1974, after a very wet year, there was enough fresh water seeping out over the beach at Sker to cause a bloating of the fronds of a wide belt of spiral wrack. This normally happens only under estuarine conditions, the two faces of the frond separating between margin and midrib for lengths of 1-2 inches, to simulate true estuarine wrack, *Fucus ceranoides*. The blown up fronds of the upper shore and seepage zone were almost wholly sterile at this time: plants away from the land drainage were mostly fertile, with gametes oozing from the receptacles. The smaller channelled wrack suffered no swelling.

Red seaweeds are mostly to be found in the saw wrack zone and below, unable to withstand long periods of desiccation. Their area is necessarily restricted by the vertical nature of the lower shore at Sker and the turbidity of the Channel waters, which limits the depth at which they can photosynthesise. The edible ones, laver *(Porphyra umbilicalis)*, dulse *(Rhodymenia palmata)*, and less edible pepper dulse *(Laurencia pinnatifida)* are conspicuous.

Gelatinous *Dumontia incrassata* comes in as a summer annual, sharing the pools with *Furcellaria fastigiata* and the graceful *Plumularia elegans,* which is well named for its delicacy—a favourite with Victorian ladies fabricating seaweed pictures and Christmas cards. Plumes of *Halurus equisetifolius* grow at extreme low water with *Catenella repens,* which is usually much higher up, and woolly *Polysiphonia lanosa* confines its attentions, as always, to the egg wrack. Several softly undulant species of *Ceramium* afford cover for swimming inhabitants of the pools: crusty pink slabs of *Lithothamnion* serve in lieu of lino for the earthbound.

29 RED ROCKS AND GREY, AT SKER AND PORTHCAWL

Geology, brief history, plants of the Sker Trias and the Porthcawl Carboniferous. Waders of coast, farmland and pools, vagrants, migrants and residents

THE accompanying geology map shows a wedge of Triassic beds and Carboniferous limestone forming a series of headlands where the coast bends from south-east to east. The rock outcrops separate the two broad dune systems of Kenfig Burrows to the north (the southern stretch of Swansea Bay) and Merthyr Mawr Warren to the east (the western stretch of Glamorgan's 'Heritage Coast'), which continues south and east to Aberthaw in a succession of precipitous limestone cliffs.

These older rocks of the Porthcawl area are the only solid footing in the great sweep of mobile sand and saltings curving east and south from Swansea. They introduce a new element of rock plants and rock-frequenting birds such as rock pipit and purple sandpiper, which are seldom seen on the sands. Like them, they produce non-acid soils, any deficiency of the Triassic strata in this respect being offset by a covering of wind-born particles from the beach.

Sker Point, together with the downshore outcrop of Gwely'r Misgl to the north and an equivalent boss to the south, is composed of horizontal Triassic strata. Most is conglomerate or puddingstone, the rounded pebbles set in the sandstone matrix varying in colour, although mostly derived from the Carboniferous limestone which lies unconformable below. Some inclusions are more angular, forming a breccia.

Weathering enables the cemented fragments to escape and become loose pebbles once again. The suggestion that this is their second spell as

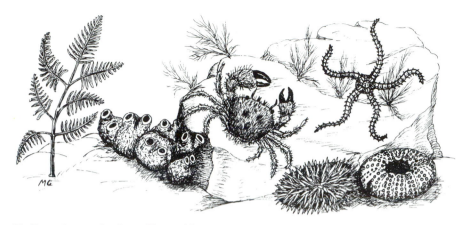

67. Downshore animals at Sker, with green *Bryopsis plumosa* (left). Gooseberry sea squirt (*Dendrodoa grossularia*), hairy crab (*Pilumnus hirtellus*), green sea urchin tests (*Psammechinus miliaris*) and brittle star (*Amphipholis squamata*).

a sea beach deposit rather than a collection of river-rounded stones washed in by floods when the Triassic rocks were forming, 200 million years ago, is strengthened by erosive features of the rocks beneath.

There is a time gap of 1-1½ million years between the formation of the Carboniferous limestone and the Trias directly above, a time-gap when any rocks deposited (during the era of the great coal forests) were worn away again. At the unconformity comprising the junction of the two remaining rock types there is evidence of coastal erosion, so fragments breaking from the old limestone sea cliffs would have been rounded up by the waves, to settle in the pink sand—as they do today. The weight of subsequent layers, now lost, compressed the pebbly sand into a conglomerate.

Areas where there were no pebbles, south-east of the point, have produced a granular sandstone, its colour purplish, like the much more ancient Old Red Sandstone beds of Skokholm Island in Pembrokeshire, rather than the contemporary orange Keuper beds of the Triassic rocks on Sully Island in South Glamorgan.

Much of the low headland of Sker Point lies between the tides and its joints have been eroded into fissures by the sea. Waves pounding up the walled corridors heighten as the passages narrow and spout skywards from the blowholes at the end when the tide is high. Others have cut arches and stacks, unsuspected by walkers who remain on the sanded terrain above. There is a wealth of salty pools with red seaweeds *(Chondrus, Ceramium* and *Corallina)* and a little laver on rocks marked by the zig-zag tracks of grazing limpets and the smoother trails of periwinkles.

Pebbles thrown up beyond wave-cut platform and water-smoothed sands have fabricated a series of pale storm beaches protecting the land within. One of these prevents the sea from flooding an extensive dip where wind-blown hornwrack and mermaids' purses accumulate, a hollow further guarded by a stone wall where most vulnerable. Grass has knitted the pebbles together over the back of the 8-10 feet high beach, to protrude seawards in places as a shaggy crest, undercut by the highest waves. A pool forms along the inner side of part in winter: elsewhere dark loamy soil is squeezed above the surface as innumerable worm casts and the turf is pitted with the beak marks of worm-eating birds.

Sker is a Scandinavian name, heritage, perhaps, from the days of marauding Vikings, and implies a rock face, scar or cliff. It turns up again in the offshore Tusker Rock, whose parallel wrack-covered ridges disappear beneath the sea twice daily and constitute a shipping hazard. A plaque commemorates the loss of the Mumbles lifeboat when on an errand of mercy here.

Sker House, site of R. D. Blackmore's celebrated novel, 'The Maid of Sker' and a new one by Alun Morgan, 'Elizabeth, Fair Maid of Sker', was incorporated in the 16th and 17th centuries into the fabric of the last remaining manor of Neath Abbey.

Bradley, writing in 1908, captures its aura of isolation: 'And in the midst of this solitude, far enough from any foliage, for trees mislike the furious, sand-laden blasts that smite this curious country, rises the old gabled house of Sker. . . . a tall, sombre, Tudor manor house dropped naked in the centre of miles of treeless pasture.'

The building has housed wreckers and pillagers of wrecks as well as monks and was used as a farmhouse until the mid-1970s, when the prohibitive cost of making good the ravages of time led to its abandonment. Now it is a ruin, with stored hay protruding from the disintegrating seaward wall. Crumbling in parts, it stands yet, four square to the winds in a bleak landscape, awaiting a saviour. Only the barn owls and field mice live on.

The Carboniferous limestone at Porthcawl reaches northwards towards Sker as a narrow belt, buried to landward by the sands of the Golf Course and to seaward by those of the beach. The three outcrops shown to the east on the Geological Map are Rhych Point (between Sandy Bay to the west and Trecco Bay to east), Newton Point (a favourite with longshore fishermen) and Black Rocks, where more Trias surfaces to landward before the rocks are overwhelmed by another vast spread of dunes.

The limestone is smooth-textured and pale gray, with fossil corals, sea lilies, brachiopods and sea mats, and calcite veins. It weathers into curvaceous solution pits and supports a better lichen growth than the Trias. *Caloplaca marina* paints many vertical faces with orange: the larger, more foliose and somewhat brighter *Xanthoria parietina* is

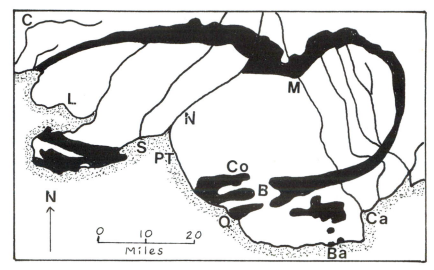

68. Map of Carboniferous Limestone in South-east Wales. Swansea Bay has cut into the southern rim of the saucer-shaped deposit underlying the Coalfield. L = Llanelly, S = Swansea, N = Neath, P.T. = Port Talbot, Co = Cornelly, O = Ogmore, B = Bridgend, Ba = Barry, Ca = Cardiff, M = Merthyr Tydfil

sparser and prefers horizontal faces where water and nutrients are more likely to collect. *Lecanora* produces white crusts; *Verrucaria* black stains, this last a different species from the common dark green skins of *Verrucaria maura* which appear in the intertidal zone. Here, too, are narrow fissures terminating in blowholes, but more fresh water seeps out here from the land, the runnels nurturing greenswards of salt-tolerant *Enteromorpha*.

A rudimentary saltmarsh spreads over the rocks south-east of Sker Point, where shingle, sand and silt have accumulated below storm beach and clifflet. Occupying the splash zone, this is often submerged in winter and sometimes washed away. Before final elimination fleshy white shoots of sea milkwort among sodden cushions of thrift get scoured free of silt, and salt marsh grass and sea couch are the only other survivors of the storms.

Sea milkwort occurs again among brookweed and bog pimpernel where fresh water trickles from the clayey, sand-covered edge of the golf links backing the beach. All are members of the primrose family, the pimpernel unusual so near the sea. With them is an uncommon liverwort, *Riccardia sinuata:* two others in dune slacks beyond are *Petalophyllum ralfsii* and *Moerckia flotowiana*.

The grazed and trampled turf above is clothed with ground-hugging thyme and rosettes of field daisy and buck's horn plantain. There is room for mosses, like *Climacium dendroides,* and small fungi, like the

368

frilly-edged *Psathyrella.* Fairy clubs, *Clavaria corniculata,* brighter than the foreshore lichens, push orange arms through the grass and *Hygrophorus psittacinus* toadstools grade from bright yellow to the pea green so seldom found in fungi. Puffballs fatten well, both the stalked *Lycoperdon* species and detachable spheres of *Bovista,* while mini umbrellas of *Panaeolus rickenii* sprout pertly from maturing pony dung.

Sker pools towards the farmhouse are cleared out at intervals to serve as drinking places for livestock and are then devoid of larger plants except where they spill out over the turf after heavy rain. Rapid recolonisation is ensured by generous helpings of cow dung and the rich aquatic flora yields a rich seed harvest for birds.

Elegant water crowfoot trailing among fool's watercress withers during summer droughts but its feathery seedlings germinate in thousands with the return of the water. Nodding bur marigold pushes through in concentric rings of diminishing diameter around the shrinking summer shoreline, so that the uppermost belt may be fruiting while the lowermost is scarcely beyond the seedling stage. These two epitomise the 'battle of the beaches'; rainfall favouring the persistence of the first, dry spells the downward advance of the second. Lax growths of broad-leaved pondweed and amphibious persicaria in the depths adopt a more chunky nature as their watery medium diminishes and throw up blunt spikes of green and pink flowers, which ripen into nutty titbits.

Out on the foreshore limestones of Rest Bay the plants are geared to physiological drought when their water supply gets too salty to drink, as well as to real drought in the scanty soil of the home crevices. Rock samphire, sea beet, thrift and sea plantain hold out tenaciously while orache and sea rocket germinate in sand and shingle pockets when the winter storms abate. Straying from above are rayed groundsel and Oxford ragwort, wallflower cabbage and perennial wall rocket, and the formidable 'scourge of Kent'.

Irregular leaching of minerals from the golf course sands has given rise to an acid flora of bell heather and ling mown to bristly doormat texture among swards of thyme and yellow bedstraw. Fairways are threaded between clumps of gorse and bramble, while bracken fronds get badly 'scorched' by salty gales where they encroach on the coast, with its sprinkling of sea holly, sea sandwort and sea bindweed.

Quite a few of the interesting species recorded around the links in the 1950s and 60s have lingered into the 1970s and 80s. The pathside blue-eyed grass (*Sisyrhinchium bermudianum*) remains and two new clumps were found on the Kenfig dunes in 1979. Pink and white motherwort *(Leonurus cardiaca)* may well be rearing four feet flower spikes on the farmland, as before. A nearby soil dump bore a good stand of crimson and pink opium poppies *(Papaver somniferum)* among scarlet field poppies in 1980, while scented agrimony *(Agrimonia procera)* and woolly thistle *(Cirsium eriophorum)* grew among the field scabious, greater knapweed and upright hedge parsley of the ungrazed grassland alongside.

The magnificent spread of meadow saffron or autumn crocus *(Colchicum autumnale),* sadly, was ploughed under during the 1970s. Such swards of pink 'naked ladies' still persist in a few parts of South Wales, but are poisonous to livestock and consequently unpopular with farmers.

Spring beauty (*Montia perfoliata*) had a tenuous hold among shaggy grasses and rest harrow until a few years ago, but the fleshy leaves encircling the stem were assiduously nibbled off by snails, so that few seeds were set, and it has not been seen lately. In the Scilly Isles (one of the few parts of Britain where the species is rampant) it is a weed of bulbfields and subjected to no such competition, but it may be tougher than it looks. It extends to the unlikely habitat of the western deserts of the New World—as in the Zion National Park—under the name of miner's or Indian lettuce.

The mile long belt of Lock's Common, with its silver rocks and golden furze, is a joy in spring, when drifts of blue spring squill and pink thrift mingle with crimson-tinted lemon-flowered kidney vetch. Some patches are golden with bird's foot trefoil and bulbous buttercup, some mauve with dove's-foot cranesbill and tares. All five plantains are here, the hoary plantain confined to such calcareous soils.

Botanically the common is rather special, some areas forming mini-limestone pavements; others being that odd anomaly of acid limestone heath. The 'pavement' system of clints or slabs dissected by grikes or crevices occurs in the higher part. Thyme, squinancy wort, rough clover and sea fern-grass grow in minor depressions on the clints; stemless thistle, salad burnet, eyebright and knotted hedge parsley in larger ones.

Lesser meadow rue *(Thalictrum minus)* is of particular interest in the grikes, which have their own moist woodland micro-climate, as in the more extensive and even more windswept limestone pavements of Aran, off Co. Clare, and contain mostly woodland plants. Among the herbs are wild arum, dog's mercury and perennial sow-thistle, among the woody species are wild privet, blackthorn and honeysuckle, but considerable lengths are occupied by ivy alone.

The limestone heath is a mixture of leached soil and rock outcrops where soil acidity is critical, varying seasonally and with rainfall, so that it sometimes favours germination of acid-lovers and sometimes of chalk plants. Chief colour-givers in July and August are fine-leaved heath and betony, which grows particularly well here: others are harebell and

370

centaury, with Scottish heather opening in September. Crested hair grass and golden oat give way here to grasses which demand less lime.

On the spray-washed lawns of the town the winter-scorched turf is dimpled with the saucer shaped depressions of buck's horn plantain, which sheltered something good to eat in January 1980 to judge by the hosts of foraging jackdaws and starlings. Sea purslane *(Halimione)* has invaded the walltop by the harbourside paddling pool—a plant of full saltmarsh and adequate testimony to the high incidence of salt spray crossing the promenade—and the need for that solid sea defence featured in Alun Morgan's historical novel, 'The Breakwater'. It grows eight feet above the plantain turf, with tree mallow, sea beet and rock samphire.

Porthcawl arose as one of four or five small ports shipping lime and other goods across the channel to North Devon and adjacent coasts. Then came a boom, with the construction of the breakwater and the queuing of ships to take on coal. But, at the beginning of the 19th century Bradley reports 'deserted docks, wharves and rusted tramlines, which tell a tale of blighted hopes and diverted trade.' He saw it change to become 'a flourishing watering place', but lamented that 'nothing but an earthquake and reconstruction could give Porthcawl a semblance of smartness'.

In this he was wrong. There was no earthquake, but the dereliction has been cleared, leaving only the picturesque stonework of the harbour and the infilled dock alongside the miniature railway awaiting development. The town has solved the problem of catering for all tastes as neatly as any. Rest Bay in the west is fashionable and spacious, opening onto the delectable green playground of Locks Common, (now backed by a frightening assemblage of new houses). Eastward, beyond the central promenade, is the opposite extreme of 'Coney Beach' with its rowdy funfair and crowded front and the great beaches of Sandy and Trecco Bays. Behind is what some claim to be Europe's biggest caravan site, much of which is discretely hidden in the ancient ragamuffin's haunt of Wig Fach Valley and visible only from across the dunes to the east, where distance, if not lending enchantment, at least hides a multitude of sins.

Greater black-backed gulls gather edible items washed ashore and air-lift them, sometimes laboriously, to the harbour to dunk in the fresh water trickle as they feed. Dapper turnstones move up from the rocks to explore the top of the breakwater, where palatable morsels are thrown into puddles by waves breaking against the outer wall. On the foreshore their tortoiseshell plumage merges with the seaweed until the short orange legs get busy and give them away. The accompanying redshank, in spite of a greater length of brighter leg, more often give themselves away by the plaintive whistling call.

Kenfig Pool

Beach Sand

Blown Sand

Alluvium

Boulder Clay

Glacial sand
and gravel

Lower Lias

Rhaetic

Trias

Carboniferous
Limestone

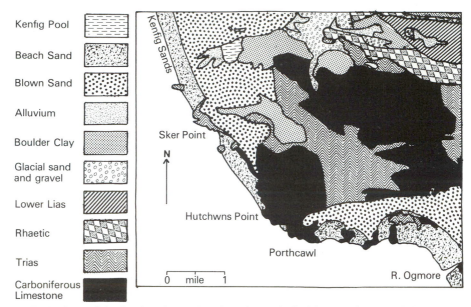

69. Geology of the Porthcawl area (Based on the Geological Survey of Great Britain, 1964)

The crimson extremities of the black and white oyster-catcher render it such a landmark on the sands that it is hard to reconcile its disappearance among the rocks. Sometimes it is the chinking sound of the all purpose bill chiselling limpets from their hold with powerful sideways thrusts that first draws the watcher's attention. Probing in the sands for cockles is achieved more quietly, but the scuffle marks where the tracks of unwary crabs stop short, show that little battles are being fought and won all the time.

Purple sandpipers are darker and the most difficult to spot of all, but should be looked for wherever there are weedy rocks. Flocks are usually smaller than those of turnstones, which can number thirty or so, while casual callers include grey and golden plover, black and bar-tailed godwit, dunlin, knot and whimbrel. Wintering ruff reach peak numbers in spring, when some of the north-bound host from the south drops in en route for far-off breeding grounds.

Little stint and curlew sandpiper may add spice to a bout of beach watching, with terns and other frequenters of the sands. Sanderlings can arrive on their way south while the year is still young, 38 appearing on 5th July in 1979 in their traditional beach habitat. Flocks had built up to 70 by 16th July, with 35 or so sprinting round the rocks in August. Ringed plover manage to bring off a few clutches of chicks most years and enjoy the old gravel workings, where a pair of shouting oyster catchers may occasionally be seen mobbing a buzzard. Turnstones find plenty of stones to turn here, revealing woodlice not so very different

372

from the sandhoppers of their more usual habitat. On the beach they flick showers of sand ahead with their beaks, as though still turning stones, instead of probing directly like other waders.

A sea watch on a summer dawn at Sker has yielded as many as 300 gannets and 196 manx shearwaters in a few hours. These are probably birds from the Pembrokeshire Islands and sightings of this magnitude were formerly regarded as bad-weather movements, but have proved too regular for that. The once sizable offshore flocks of common scoter and eider duck have been seen less frequently of late, while shelduck prefer muddier shores and are scarce.

Occasionally a great skua passes through on autumn passage—part of a remarkable movement across the heart of England from the Wash to the Bristol Channel—which has been best observed in Glamorgan by Ted Jones from Lavernock Point, nearer Cardiff. Landlocked 'Brummies' could scarcely expect to see such pelagic arctic wanderers in a month of Sundays, but the overland flight is at too great an altitude for the birds to be spotted in the Midlands except by radar. Like their cousins the gulls, the seafaring skuas do not entirely spurn the land; but, unlike them, they defer 'landfall' until land meets sea again. Kittiwakes and petrels have been blown inshore and the odd little auk, which, like guillemot and razorbill, usually arrives spent.

The principal inland feeders, drawing ornithologists from miles around, are the golden plovers. Several thousands strong, the flocks combine with those of lapwings to form mobs from which the odd few picked off by peregrine falcons are scarcely missed. They arrive in August in more modest numbers than the lapwings and build up to a winter peak. Many golden plover in the August flocks are still resplendent in summer plumage and about half the lapwings are brown-feathered juveniles, lacking the polish of their elders.

New Year's day 1979 saw a mixed flock of 5,000 birds off Sker with 1,600 golden plover on the sands the same day and small parties flying over. Although the brightest of the feathers are lost, along with the black breast of the breeding plumage, they are an unmistakable muted golden colour throughout their stay and are quite magnificent when flying into the horizontal rays of a winter sunset.

Lapwings are equally splendid under these circumstances, the iridescence which gives them their alternative name of green plover, offset by the splash of rufous, as in the shelduck—another which appears merely pied from a distance. They feed over the fields of Sker Farm, often in the poorer parts of a cereal or brassica crop, where it is logical to assume there may be a heavier infestation of insect pests. Soil here is a dark sandy loam, rich in earthworms, and these undoubtedly supply a major prey item.

Black-headed gulls also like earthworms and sometimes find it easier to steal these from the lapwings than to extricate their own. They are usually fewer than the plover and tend to space themselves out, perching on clods in the ploughlands and anthills in the pastures. From there they keep a watchful eye on the foragers, swooping when a lapwing starts hauling out a worm. If the victim abandons the prize, the gull will take over and pull it free: if it flies off with the worm dangling it will be chased and harried until it drops it. Small food items can be swallowed by the lapwing in flight, so it is not worth the gull's while to pursue. Larger prey they prefer to bring back to base to eat, otherwise, with their broad wings and erratic flight, they might easily outmanoeuvre a gull.

A lapwing has been observed pulling out a maximum of four worms per minute: a gull stealing 160 worms per day—more than enough to supply its needs. Victimised lapwings have to make up the deficit by feeding at night, when their persecutors are sleeping. If sufficiently well fed, they can be seen moving off the golf course just before dusk to muster in a communal roost on the beach.

The piratical method of feeding, as with skuas robbing terns and frigate birds robbing boobies, is a case of cleptoparasitism. Cuckoos are here in plenty, practising their own brand of cleptoparasitism, by foisting illegitimate offspring onto feathered foster parents. Both are parasitic modes of life, but cannot be equated with true parasitism in the biological sense.

There is a wealth of bird food at Sker Pools. Seeds of greater water plantain are sometimes more abundant than the favoured pondweed nutlets. They are produced in circular 'cakes' which break into wedge-shaped sections. Some sink in the shallows to nourish bottom feeders, some float to be scooped up by water fowl and some drift ashore to tempt the winter flocks of greenfinch, goldfinch, linnet, siskin and farmyard sparrow.

Two species of newt inhabit the pool and supply more ambitious feeders, great crested newts and either smooth or palmate, and there is an average aquatic fauna of ramshorn snails and smaller life. In the mild February of 1980 the true aquatics were supplemented by yellow-haired cluster flies *(Pollenia rudis)* sunning themselves on the ground and drifting over the water surface after a larval phase as a parasite of earthworms. Small yellow dung flies *(Scathophaga)* were also 'walking the waters' and taking off from them with no problems. In summer either might have been scooped up by swallows or martins: in winter every protein morsel is a welcome addition to a more frugal diet.

Another slightly out of its element on the pool surface at this time was a redshank. It is always a surprise to see a wader swimming, but this one took automatically to the water instead of the air when disturbed.

120

21

122

Plate 24　PORTHCAWL
　　　　　AND ITS PLANTS—*Author*

123

120. Lock's Common, Porthcawl, view East to distant Heritage Coast cliffs
121. Salt-scorched dog's mercury in the woodland micro-climate of a grike
122. Lesser meadow rue bitten off flush with surface of limestone pavement
123. Betony in the limestone heath

375

Plate 25   SKER AND SOUTH CORNELLY—*Author*

124. Sker Point at high tide
125. Female great green bush cricket
126. Spring beauty (*Montia perfoliata*)
127. River Kenfig meandering across the beach in November 1972
128. South Cornelly Quarry and chromium-tinted pool with broad pondweed
129. Wall germander on cliff with ivy

376

Not only did those inappropriately non-webbed feet propel it fast enough to produce a fine wake, but they enabled it to take flight from a running start half way across the larger pool—then much swollen by flooding.

Phalaropes are among the few waders which swim traditionally and these are furnished with lobes on their toes equivalent to the partial webs of the avocet. Six grey phalaropes blown in by gales in September 1974 took refuge on Sker Pools and caused some excitement among bird watchers. Waders more to be expected at the pools are greenshank, common sandpiper and the first of the wintering ruff. Rarities include spotted redshank, which have already donned their dark breeding plumage by early May, green sandpiper and woodcock.

Partridges are birds of the fields, and in a healthier state of numbers than in many parts of the country. Huge gatherings of greenfinches, feeding out over the farmlands and finding refuge in the widely spaced hedgerows, come to the pools to drink in winter. Twittering linnet flocks arrive in gusty disorder on windy days to slake their thirst, returning to the lee of the dunes, where foraging is less rumbustious. Yellowhammers, reed buntings and the usual hedgerow birds drop by for extra titbits and starlings come in hundreds from the thirsty feeding of the burrows.

A corn bunting turned up in 1977, fat, streaky brown and undistinguished, but a rare sight, with its chinking, dipping finch flight and unmusical call, so often likened to the rattling of a bunch of keys. Equally unusual was the wryneck passage which went through in September 1976, one bird remaining in a Porthcawl garden for a fortnight.

70. Pale overwintering shoots of sea milkwort washed free of sand by waves. Old shoot (right), thrift, edible periwinkle and limpets

Early August 1974 saw swallows massed on the ground, scarcely able to rise in the teeth of the gale then blowing. These were almost certainly migrants, which had been battling into headwinds on their way from northern breeding grounds and were so exhausted that rest was temporarily more important to them than food. Grounded swallows are more to be expected in spring, when, along with house martins, they come to scoop up little pellets of mud for their nests.

Pied and white wagtails linger here on migration and there are resident pieds at Sker House, with blue and great tits. Small birds tend to peel off from Sker Point as they do from Lavernock Point, which is a first-class site for observing migration. They feed up a little before passing on, in spite of the lack of bushes which are in such good supply at Lavernock.

Short-eared owls hunt over Sker in winter and little owls are usually about, sometimes causing consternation among the small birds of the old Trias quarry near the house when they fly in there to rest. Sparrow hawks quarter the area in early spring and the occasional hen harrier, peregrine and merlin in winter.

30 QUARRYING COUNTRY. CORNELLY AND STORMY DOWN

Carboniferous limestone outcrops, quarries and their vegetation. Plants of pure limestone and dolomite. Gulls, rooks and jackdaws in quarries and territory-holding birds of Stormy Down. Summer wildlife on the plateau heath.

CARBONIFEROUS limestone, laid down in a coral sea some 350 million years ago, forms a mighty saucer beneath the South Wales Coalfield. The rim of the saucer surfaces all round, the north crop bordering the Brecon Beacons National Park, the south crop bordering the Vale of Glamorgan. Swansea Bay has bitten deeply into this southern rim and the massive beds of the Gower Peninsula, which terminate on Mumbles Head, do not reappear eastwards until the North and South Cornelly region in the hinterland of Porthcawl. Here they support some huge quarrying enterprises.

Limestone is a tremendous asset, however it is regarded, adding scenically, biologically and economically to any landscape. Glamorgan has a great deal, dispelling at once the Englishman's traditional idea of Wales as a land of wet, acid peats. The limestone hills and vales are dry, basic and non-peaty, and support a greater variety of plant and animal life than any other rock type, including many special rarities. Nowhere is this more true than on the cliffs of Gower, described in the first book of this series, but the limestones of the western Vale are not far behind. Unfortunately from the scenic and wildlife point of view, the stone itself is in great demand by today's industrial society and the rolling hills are scarred with quarry faces.

The bedrock around Porthcawl and Cornelly is fairly pure calcium carbonate, some crinoidal and some oolitic. Further east, around Cardiff, the south crop has been dolomitised, with some of the calcium replaced by magnesium. Certain lime-loving plants, common in the west, seem not to occur on the magnesian limestones of the east. Notable among these are common rock rose, hoary plantain and crested hair grass *(Koeleria cristata)*, while salad burnet is extremely rare on the dolomite.

Squinancywort and small scabious are found only on the non-dolomitised coastal limestones, but cannot owe this distribution to their need for salty winds, because their range on the chalks of South-east England is almost entirely inland. Perhaps they need the mitigating maritime influence when growing on the harder, less tractable mountain limestones of the west, or they may be sensitive to an overdose of magnesium in the soil.

Dr. John Etherington has shown experimentally that rock rose, for one, cannot grow where the amount of magnesium in the soil outweighs the calcium. Otherwise it has wide tolerances—from the rainy limestones of the Brecon Beacons to the drier shell sands of the coast.

In a document on the Carboniferous limestones produced in 1971, the Nature Conservancy Council states 'These limestones are a major source of ecological diversity in the environment of South Wales, and their large-scale exploitation as a mineral is now posing some of the major conservation problems in the region.'

Commercial use of limestone and its derivatives doubled during the 1960s, when the Welsh production of sixteen million tons per annum was higher than the annual output of coal. This trend has continued and will be even truer in the 1980s if the 'go slow' in the steel industry entails closure of pits producing coking coal. Although some of the limestone contributes to steel-making, there is a wide range of other outlets, due to the versatility of both chemical and physical properties. Much of what is used is hacked from Glamorgan's fairest acres.

With quarrying units getting steadily larger to stay economically viable, the product is often used wastefully for roadstone and river banking, where other rock types would suffice, in order to keep a steady flow going to the steel smelters. The South Cornelly Quarries near Pyle, when producing a million tons of stone a year in the early 1970s, supplied most of the building blocks for the Port Talbot deep water harbour. Since completion of this, needs have dwindled and plants are creeping back over some of the cliffs and spoil heaps.

Quarrying here is extracting poor grade limestone having 'gulls' or vertical wedge-shaped pockets of aluminium clay interposed across the beds. Stone is washed and the washing water, loaded with clay and aluminium, collects in big pools which become an attractive green due to dissolved chromium salts.

One, 100 feet deep in part, supported a thriving stand of broad-leaved pondweed in the '70s, rimmed white in summer with drifted feathers from moulting and preening gulls. By 1980 this had become polluted with oil and the water a deep chocolate brown, but the surface scum blew up against the cliff, which was still occupied by gulls, in and out of the nesting season, and birds on the water floated out in the clear, their feathers unsoiled. A more northerly pool, some 56 feet deep, where police cadets practise scuba diving, remains translucently turquoise and has been stocked with fish.

In splendid contrast to the clear green water are the sheets of yellow stonecrop which adorn the cliff brinks, to be followed by ragwort. Blue spikes of viper's bugloss push from ground speckled pink with centaury and rest harrow. This is one of very few sites east of Gower where small scabious *(Scabiosa columbaria)* can be found; the species brightening so many roadsides in the Vale being the large scabious *(Knautia arvensis)*.

More than seventy kinds of flowers grow on the broken clifftop and even the arable weeds which start the succession off include interesting ones like field spurrey, field madder and fairy flax. Six brands of thirstledown have floated in. Woolly thistle and nodding thistle are handsome by any standards, and the first quite rare; slender thistle is more often found on sea cliffs and carline thistle on sand dunes.

This is an agricultural landscape, but plenty of calcicole or limeloving species find refuge in the hedge bottoms and are available to speed this succession on its way to limestone grassland. Banks of sweet marjoram and wild carrot move in and agrimony pushes up from close swards of thyme and eyebright.

One of the most prolific nectar bearers is winter heliotrope, which starts flowering early in January when there are few insects to benefit. Early flies and bumble bees visit it later on. Two of the most popular flowers with flying insects are yellow parsnip and woolly thistle. Green bottles, blow flies and soldier beetles favour the first at South Cornelly, bees and cuckoo bees the second.

This is one of the county's best butterfly sites, with peacocks and commas showing a preference for corn sow thistle and hemp agrimony.

380

Ringlets are among the less common—as in similar terrain by Ruthin limestone quarry east of Bridgend.

One long abandoned cliff of the South Cornelly quarry complex is a much prized site for wall germander *(Teucrium chamaedrys)*. Only a narrow belt of gorse, bracken and blackthorn separates the cliff brink from an encroaching tip of overburden above, but assurances have been given that the colony will not be violated.

'The Atlas of the British Flora' shows only fourteen sites in the whole of Britain for wall germander—eleven in the East, two in Cornwall and one at South Cornelly. No doubt the freely draining nature of the vertical rock face helps it to survive in this area of higher-than-average rainfall. Its native heaths are in South and Central Europe, Morocco and the Orient.

Over one hundred different flowers grow within 50 yards. Wall germander dominates part of the face with ivy and part of the brink with gorse, which is cut back periodically by Naturalists' Trust volunteers to give it a sporting chance. It seems to have profited and is holding its own very adequately, straggling out from the thorny barrier and throwing a fine crop of purple flowers each autumn.

Related dead nettles are calamint, wild basil and a hybrid mint, *Mentha x dumetorum*. Burnet rose, fennel, salad burnet and common gromwell seem to have strayed in from the dunes. Variegated canary grass, aggressive, as always, has escaped from a garden and established itself on the quarry floor with the intensely blue-flowered green alkanet nearby.

Trees growing up the face of the cliff are beginning to produce a woodland micro-climate in the germander site, in which such a sun lover may not long survive. The loftier shattered limestone cliffs of the working quarries are of different calibre—getting quite hot if facing the sun—and the big aggregations of birds use the shady north-facing cliffs above the bathing pools.

Jackdaws have lived in crevices throughout the last decade and were present to the extent of about 100 birds in January 1980, in spite of the big gatherings then at the nearby Tythegston Quarry. A pair of ravens nest regularly, bringing their family off so early in the year that an opportunist herring gull couple usually appropriate the substantial nest for rearing their own brood when the ravens have done with it.

Herring gulls have bred on the 150-feet cliffs since the early 1960s, increasing to sixty pairs by the end of their first decade, but any nests accessible to small boys tend to get vandalised (not without loss of human life). Nevertheless, the population continues to increase, and lesser black-backs, too, were well established as breeders by the 1970s.

When the siren sounds to warn of blasting, the gulls and daws take to the air, returning after the 'all clear'. Pandemonium ensues when there

71. Oyster-catcher, carrion crow, weld and lesser celandine

is no prior warning and they are taken by surprise. Jackdaws behave similarly in the Little Garth Quarry near Cardiff. The gull and crow families have justly earned their place in our regard as the most intelligent and adaptable of birds.

Greater black-backed gulls were present in the South Cornelly Quarry throughout the summer of 1973, apparently assessing the food potential. In 1974 and 1975 they started nesting themselves. It looked as though they had been waiting for the two smaller species to build up to the very considerable population then existing, before it was worth their while to move in and plunder unguarded eggs and chicks: which would be available in plenty when most needed for the growing family.

Oyster-catchers lay their eggs in scrapes in two types of situation. Some opt for the uneven rock surfaces exposed after the bulldozers have removed the soil-cover and before the holes are drilled for blasting. Others take up residence on the levelled but still rubbly surface of fields being reclaimed from old spoil tips towards Porthcawl. They are vulnerable to drastic changes in both types of site, finding as insecure a haven here as in more traditional coastal terrain from which they have been ousted by holiday-makers, and their success rate is low. The quarry is two miles from the sea, an unusually long way for oyster-catchers in southern Britain, although inland breeding is becoming common in Scotland and the North.

Other waders visit the quarry pools, in spite of the noise and bustle of machinery and blasting. They are mostly common sandpipers but redshank come as well. Mallard and mute swan are also seen. Swans nest in quarry pools in various other parts of the county and the visitors may be contemplating moving in.

Arthur Morgan spent many hours watching kestrels, barn owls and little owls on the quarry cliffs. These three, and tawny owls, were also a feature of the nearby Tythegston Quarry towards Porthcawl through the late 1960s and early 1970s. Crop pellets produced by the barn owls were gathered throughout 1973. One, collected in the spring, told of a two-year-old song thrush which had been ringed in Heligoland and travelled the long miles south only to form a meal for a resident. The rose-flushed redwings which come in winter are readily recognised as strangers, but they bring some of the more familiar with them from the north.

Other victims of these barn owls were bats which hunted around the quarry cliffs. Pipistrelles were everywhere on the right sort of evening; the larger ones seen were probably either noctules or serotines. 1973 was a particularly good year for bats because there were so many moths about.

The soft muds and thin snow carpets of the 1979-80 winter held the imprints of a big population of rabbits among spoil heaps above the working quarries. Where the tracks were thickest the crinkled leaf rosettes of weld had been nibbled right back to centre, these proving especial favourites. The question as to whether the paw marks in the same areas belonged to fox or dog was answered in a number of places by a pungent whiff of fox scent wiped onto the rough herbage. The local aggregation of vole holes would yield other delicacies for prowling foxes.

Before rubbish-tipping started in the Tythegston Quarry in 1970 common sandpipers visited the pool there, trees were regenerating freely and it was a fine habitat for bee orchids and wild strawberries. But that halcyon phase is past. The quarry floor communities were doomed at once and the cliff communities are being driven upwards and cannot survive long into the eighties. By the start of that decade only 20-25 feet of the broken grey cliffs with their vertical shafts of red soil remained uncovered.

Conservationists are not among those who preach that the rough places should be made smooth and that holes are there for the filling. Any loss of land irregularities is a loss of scenery: any loss of bosky hollows and leafy dells a loss of wildlife habitats.

It could be argued that a man-made hollow might well be obliterated by man and no-one would question the excellent rehabilitation schemes undertaken by the National Coal Board after open cast mining. Certainly the filling of quarries is a less reprehensible practice than tipping in the fine ice-gouged corries of the Rhondda mountains.

The natural rehabilitation of old quarry cliffs can, however, reconstruct the whole limestone succession in a delightful and informative way. The rugged faces can offer fresh panoramas of yesterday to geologists, fresh challenges for today to climbers and fresh promise for tomorrow to biologists. We have already seen how many plants and animals can live in these sheltered declivites, even while stone is still being extracted. As the faces mellow and a living soil begins to collect in cracks, there can be some unexpected arrivals. Even the rubbish infills can contribute to the web of life.

Far from it being a 'dead' quarry, January 1980 saw Tythegston bustling with the most vociferous life of all, in the form of some 600 or so Corvids, perhaps 2/3 jackdaws and 1/3 rooks. In spite of 'soiling over', these evidently found plenty to eat on the dump, which they blackened with their bodies when settled. Perhaps they were picking grubs from the blanket of soil. Herring gulls usually precede the various crows on the tips, gobbling most of the goodies by the time the bulldozers arrive for the covering operation.

At disturbance only jackdaws sought refuge on the cliff face. Rooks and the rest of the daws withdrew to the twigless summits of the clifftop elms—long since dead of Dutch elm disease, with their bark almost peeled away. The bare Scots pine tops, killed by the constant comings and goings, showed that these, too, were used—more so than the Corsican pines which were the chief element in the north woodland.

The birds breed here, as well as roosting. Peter Lansdowne, reporting on Glamorgan's part in the countrywide rookery census of 1975-76, states Tythegston Quarry to have been at that time the triple county's third largest rookery, with 90 nests. (Oxwich in West Glamorgan was largest, with 107, St. Andrew's Major in South Glamorgan second with 103).

This was at a time when the number of breeding pairs was 43% (or 36 pairs) less than 10 years before, although there were 30 more rookeries. Evidence suggests that numbers are now building up again on the rich farmlands of the south, although very few nest among the Coalfield hills. Many of Glamorgan's 126 rookeries, with their 3,091 nests, were located in elms, so there will need to be more changes as these become unsafe after succumbing to Dutch elm disease.

So much guano raining from the treetops inevitably affects the plants beneath. The lushness of red campion and dog's mercury is apparent even in January, the first a very characteristic plant of bird colonies from the South Wales sea bird islands to the Orkneys. Brittle nettle stems spike up among wintergreen hart's tongue, broad buckler and male ferns and the shrub layer is of elder, which appears so often as a result of disturbance by birds or mammals.

Buddleja is established along the cliffward fringe of the wood, where lanky gorse straggles to 15 feet under the trees, but the biggest surprise plantwise is the white stonecrop. Outsize succulent leaves of this cover several hundred square yards of marginal terrain and rubbly path, but shoots become spindly and die away as shade deepens under the tree canopy. This is unlikely to be native here, where yellow stonecrop is the expected species in what is still a rich limestone flora.

91

92

93

94

95

Plate XXIII   PORTHCAWL AND
STORMY DOWN—*Author*

91. Top left: Coast scene with Lock's Common mini limestone pavement
92. Top right: Adder on Stormy Down anthill
93. Mid left: Rock samphire on coastal limestone
94. Mid right: Woolly thistle, a local limestone species
95. Bottom left: Large scabious in rough calcareous grassland

385

Plate XXIV BIRDS OF THE
NIGHT—*Keri Williams*

96. Top left: Barn owl carrying vole
97. Top right: Tawny owl at nest hole
98. Bottom left: Nightjar on post
99. Bottom right: Little owl carrying beetle

So much extra fertility will nurture a big invertebrate population. Even on 20th January, 1980, when the site commanded panoramic views over a snow-covered Exmoor to the south and a snow-covered Coalfield to the north, steam was rising in a soft haze in this sun trap and drifting seaward down the Wig Fach Valley—ancient home of gipsies and vagrants and modern home of caravanners. Winter gnats danced in vertical columns—a temperature-induced activity—their wings scintillating in the slanting sunrays, and small relatives of the common dungfly basked on the leaves, in unaccustomed warmth.

The main effect which the big group of quarries around South Cornelly has on the bird life is to boost the number of nesting gulls and jackdaws, supply food for rooks and nesting shelves for raven and kestrel. Derek Wells's 'Common Breeding Bird Census' figures for the Carboniferous limestone of Stormy Down immediately to the north, show the composition of the bird life in a quarry-free zone. His census area comprised 200 acres of brackenny heath surrounded by dairy pasture.

Altogether 38 species held territories there in four years before the beginning of motorway construction, but 28 was the annual average. Figures for the 11 commonest species are shown diagrammatically in Figure 72, where it will be seen that 1972 was a poor year for nesting.

Skylarks were much the commonest, with up to 26 pairs; blackbirds next, with up to 17, and meadow pipits, yellow hammers, willow warblers and wrens runners up, with up to 11, 12 or 13. Stormy Down is one of the county's few nightjar habitats, with two pairs breeding in 1971 and 1972, but only one pair in 1973 and 1974. Single pairs were present in the breeding season in 1975 and 1976, but only one bird was seen in 1977 and only one in 1978, when Stormy Down was one of a mere three nightjar sites in the whole of Glamorgan. It is touch-and-go whether this delightful rarity will survive the noisy combination of motorway and quarrying.

Other species nesting each year of the four include kestrel, partridge, cuckoo, green woodpecker, magpie, blue tit, goldfinch and chaffinch. Species missing out only in 1974 were moorhen, wheatear and starling, while carrion crow and great tit missed only 1973. Those of sparser occurrence were stock dove, little owl, jay, marsh tit, tree creeper, mistle thrush, stonechat, grasshopper warbler, garden warbler, white-throat, tree pipit, bullfinch and reed bunting. Add the others from the diagram and we have an impressive list, by any standards.

The wedge of land east of the M4-A48 intersection on Stormy Down epitomises the ability of the wildscape to persist within earshot of the restive roar of contemporary society. Here, at nearly 350 feet above sea level, and the highest point treated in this account, is a good place to end our story—on a sultry June afternoon in 1980, when the drowsy

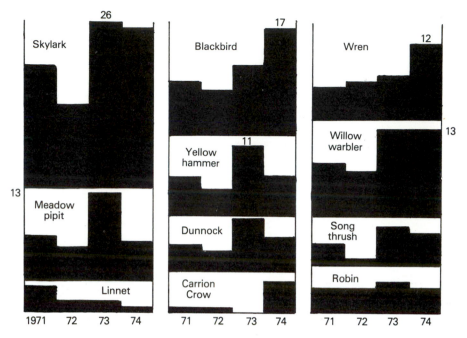

72. Birds of 200 acres of brackenny heathland on Stormy Down during the four years before construction of the M4 motorway. Numbers of nesting pairs of the eleven commonest species (after Wells)

hum of insects and thin screaming of swifts competed with the distant thunder of motorway construction and quarry extraction. Most visitors here will be unaware that any change has been effected since the initial felling of the trees to give open heathland, but the heavy hand of the industrial regime has imposed a fundamental change—which adds, rather than detracts from the whole.

With freshly green, ginger-whiskered bracken fronds uncoiling throughout, the summit plateau appears to be all of a kind, but it is far from that. Because of a superficial deposit of glacial till brought during the Ice Age, the virgin soil is as acid as any in our Swansea Bay region, except the ancient wave-cut hinterland where Margam Country Park climbs steeply to the Coalfield Hills. Nevertheless, 5-10 yard strips alongside the little unfenced roads receive repeated top dressings of limestone dust wafting from trundling quarry lorries, and could have been transplanted straight from the chalk downs of south-east England.

Instead of the general purple moor grass heath with its bell heather, ling, bilberry, tormentil, heath bedstraw and woodsage, the roadsides bore a sweeter greensward, bright with bird's-foot trefoil, cinquefoil and agrimony, bluebell, angelica and twayblade orchids. Only the wild strawberries, violets and red fescue strayed onto the summit heath, to find their niche where toiling ants had raised dry mounds of friable soil above the general level.

This was where the adders chose to sun themselves that summer afternoon, the sleekest and plumpest of all still coiled luxuriously to soak up the last of the warmth at well past 7 o'clock. At the falling of the human shadow the broad head came up, alert and curious, with questing tongue flicking in and out to taste the man scent. A tape measure stretched alongside as the jazzy zig-zag pattern glided into the heather, might have reached to 27 inches, but few could measure so independent a son of the wild in life.

Skylarks, trilling through the last of the heat haze, used the anthills as lookout posts and each mound held its little coils of lark dung, containing bright fragments of green nettle weevils and other beetles. Some also held the walking stick shapes of green woodpecker droppings, studded with the ant remains which showed their business here to be more crucial.

Larger, more fibrous droppings appeared on each of the low outcropping rocks, and sometimes a richly-hued, diamond-patterned feather to tell of the partridge that had left them there. Use of a hand lens showed an overwhelming preponderence of the shucks of woodrush seeds, which are borne, fat and shiny, three to a capsule. Some birds had voided nothing else, although the plant of their choice was quite uncommon, and they would have walked a long way to find that many seeds. Residual nutrients seeping from the discarded remains boosted the lichens which crusted the slabs.

Hard peas from the low gorse clumps, two to a pod, furnished more substantial fodder on the plateau, while more generous helpings in the spreading 'toes' of bird's-foot trefoil were to be had by the roadside. The cheery "chirrick-chirrick" coming at intervals from unseen foragers indicated that all was well in partridge land.

Little oak trees, chewed to the stature of bushes by sheep, and stagheaded from wind and fire, supplied four feet high twigs as stonechat song posts. Linnets sometimes joined them, tweaking invisible insects or eggs from the scaling bark. All the trees were heavily galled and many of last year's marble galls had been torn open by great tits, which will tap at the marble first to see if anyone is at home. A hollow sound, and they save their efforts, to rip open the artichoke galls on the same bushes.

These two infections are produced by Cynipid wasps, *Andricus kollari* and *Andricus fecundator*, but a third kind, less often seen, was commoner here than either. This was the curved leaf gall produced by *Andricus curvator*, whose unisexual generation takes the form of the less blatantly swollen collared bud gall. Woolly balls on the germander speedwell at their feet had been induced by the gall midge, *Jaapiella veronicae*, and each contained a number of larvae or pupae.

Gauzy-winged powder-blue lacewings moved silently through the sweet vernal grass, with its haytime fragrance of coumarin, and white Tortrix moths flitted between the rush clumps. A female pink and gold ghost moth *(Hepialis humuli)* skulked among the milkwort flowers awaiting the ghostly gyrations of a white male in the dusk, and a more cryptic heart and dart moth *(Agrotis exclamationis)* rose unwillingly when disturbed.

Leaf hoppers spurted over the sward and a shiny black ground beetle scurried into a mousehole, while half-grown grasshoppers leap-frogged round the pignut fronds. Spiders' eggs nestled snugly in silken balls in the brittle depressions of old bracken fronds.

Butterflies, though free as air, clung to their home terrain. Myriads of small pearl-bordered fritillaries had just emerged along the roadside strip, fattened on the leaves of violets, and were flirting busily, the unattached barging in on happy couples until the air was a whirl of fluttering orange wings. Common blues, nurtured on the roadside trefoils, were less interfering, pairs sitting peacefully, tail to tail, on buttercup and knapweed heads.

Over the heathland, small heath butterflies were much the commonest, with a sprinkling of wall browns and painted ladies. At this time of year, these last would be migrants, very likely from the Canary Isles or North Africa—come this far north to rear another generation in industrial South Wales. So long as it is worth their while to come, country lovers can take heart. Nature conservation and industry are not mutually exclusive. The essential need is for sufficiently wise planning to prevent the spread of a sterile, sub-urban No-Man's Land between the two.

Appendix

List of Flowering Plants and Ferns Mentioned in the Text

Briton Ferry, from an engraving made in 1804 by J. Laporte

The richness and beauty of the surrounding landscapes are not often equalled. It assembles round its retreat fine hills, woods, vales and rich pastures in the happiest style of Nature, with the Bristol Channel to the south. Neath River is the western boundary of the ornamented grounds. The woods literally run into the sea, and have in many places their roots in the salt water. This part of Wales is so mild in its climature, that myrtles, magnolias and other tender exotics, grow luxuriantly in the open air . . . . The scenery about Baglan is scarcely less delightful, nor can anything well be conceived more rural, tranquilized and fascinating than Baglan Hall.

Benj. Heath Malkin in "The Scenery, Antiquities and Biography of South Wales," 1804—writing of Briton Ferry

FLOWERS AND FERNS MENTIONED IN THE TEXT
Alphabetically under English names

Adder's-tongue fern—*Ophioglossum vulgatum*
Agrimony—*Agrimonia eupatoria*
Agrimony, fragrant—*Agrimonia procera*
Alder—*Alnus glutinosa*
Alder buckthorn—*Frangula alnus*
Alkanet, green—*Pentaglottis sempervirens*
Angelica, wild—*Angelica sylvestris*
Arrowgrass, marsh—*Triglochin palustris*
Arrowgrass, sea—*Triglochin maritimum*
Arrowhead—*Sagittaria sagittifolia*
(Arum, wild—*Arum maculatum*)
Ash—*Fraxinus excelsior*
Asphodel, bog—*Narthecium ossifragum*
Aster, sea—*Aster tripolium*
(Autumn crocus—*Colchicum autumnale*)
Avens, water—*Geum rivale*
Avens, wood—*Geum urbanum*

Barley, wall—*Hordeum murinum*
Bartsia, red—*Odontites verna*
Bartsia, yellow—*Parentucellia viscosa*
Basil thyme—*Acinos arvensis*
Basil, wild—*Clinopodium vulgare*
Beak-sedge, brown—*Rhynchospora fusca*
Beak-sedge, white—*Rhynchospora alba*
Bedstraw, fen—*Galium uliginosum*
Bedstraw, heath—*Galium saxatile*
Bedstraw, hedge—*Galium mollugo*
Bedstraw, lady's—*Galium verum*
Bedstraw, marsh—*Galium palustre*
Beech—*Fagus sylvatica*
Beet, sea—*Beta vulgaris* ssp. *maritima*
Bent, bristle—*Agrostis setacea*
Bent, common—*Agrostis tenuis*
Bent, creeping—*Agrostis stolonifera*
Betony—*Betonica officinalis*
Bilberry—*Vaccinium myrtillus*
Bindweed, field—*Convolvulus arvensis*
Bindweed, hedge—*Calystegia sepium*
Bindweed, large—*Calystegia sylvatica*
Bindweed, sea—*Calystegia soldanella*
Birch, downy—*Betula pubescens*
Birch, silver—*Betula verrucosa*
Bird's-foot—*Ornithopus perpusillus*
Bird's-foot trefoil, common—*Lotus corniculatus*

Bird's-foot trefoil, greater—*Lotus uliginosus*
Bird's-nest, yellow—*Monotropa hypopytis*
Bistort, amphibious—*Polygonum amphibium*
Bittercress, hairy—*Cardamine hirsuta*
Bittersweet—*Solanum dulcamara*
Black-bindweed—*Polygonum convolvulus*
Black mustard—*Brassica nigra*
Blackthorn—*Prunus spinosa*
Bladderwort, greater—*Utricularia vulgaris*
Bladderwort, lesser—*Utricularia minor*
Bluebell—*Endymion non-scriptus*
Blue-eyed grass—*Sisyrinchium bermudiana*
Bog asphodel—*Narthecium ossifragum*
Bogbean—*Menyanthes trifoliata*
Bog myrtle (or sweet gale)—*Myrica gale*
Bog rosemary—*Andromeda polifolia*
Bog-rush, black—*Schoenus nigricans*
Bog-sedge (or mud sedge)—*Carex limosa*
Bracken—*Pteridium aquilinum*
Bramble (or blackberry)—*Rubus fruticosus* agg.
(Brandy bottle (or yellow water lily)—*Nuphar lutea*)
Brome, barren—*Bromus sterilis*
Brome, false—*Brachypodium sylvaticum*
Brome, soft—*Bromus mollis*
Brooklime—*Veronica beccabunga*
Brookweed—*Samolus valerandi*
Broom—*Sarothamnus* (or *Cytisus*) *scoparius*
Broomrape, common—*Orobanche minor*
Buckler-fern, broad—*Dryopteris dilatata*
Buckler-fern, narrow—*Dryopteris carthusiana*
Bugloss—*Lycopsis arvensis*
Bulrush, greater (or reedmace)—*Typha latifolia*
Bulrush, lesser (or reedmace)—*Typha angustifolia*
(Bulrush, true—*Scirpus lacustris*)
(Bulrush, seaside—*Scirpus tabernaemontani*)
Bur-marigold, nodding—*Bidens cernua*
Bur-marigold, trifid—*Bidens tripartita*
Burnet, salad—*Poterium sanguisorba*
Bur-reed, branched—*Sparganium erectum*
Bur-reed, least—*Sparganium minimum*
Bur-reed, unbranched—*Sparganium emersum*
Buttercup, bulbous—*Ranunculus bulbosus*

Buttercup, celery-leaved—*Ranunculus sceleratus*
Buttercup, creeping—*Ranunculus repens*
Buttercup, meadow (or upright)—*Ranunculus acris*
Butterfly-bush—*Buddleja davidii*
Butterwort, common—*Pinguicula vulgaris*

Cabbage, Isle of Man—*Rhynchosinapis monensis*
Cabbage, Lundy—*Rhynchosinapis wrightii*
Cabbage, wallflower—*Rhynchosinapis cheiranthos*
Cabbage, warty—*Bunias ericago*
Calamint, common—*Calamintha ascendens*
Campion, bladder—*Silene vulgaris*
Campion, red—*Silene dioica* (or *Melandrium*)
Campion, sea—*Silene maritima*
Campion, white—*Silene alba*
Canadian pondweed—*Elodea canadensis*
Canary-grass, reed—*Phalaris arundinacea*
Canary-grass (variegated)—*Phalaris canariensis*
Carrot, wild—*Daucus carota*
Cat's-ear—*Hypochoeris radicata*
Cat's-tail, sand—*Phleum arenarium*
(Cat-tail (or bulrush or reedmace)—*Typha* spp.)
Celandine, lesser—*Ranunculus ficaria*
Celery, wild—*Apium graveolens*
Centaury, common—*Centaurium erythraea*
Centaury, lesser—*Centaurium pulchellum*
Chaffweed—*Anagallis minima* (or *Centunculus*)
Charlock—*Sinapis arvensis*
Chervil, rough—*Chaerophyllum temulentum*
Chestnut, sweet—*Castanea sativa*
Chickweed, common—*Stellaria media*
Chickweed, mouse-ear—*Cerastium* spp.
Cinquefoil, creeping—*Potentilla reptans*
Cinquefoil, marsh—*Potentilla palustris*
(Clematis, wild—*Clematis vitalba*)
Clover, alsike—*Trifolium hybridum*
Clover, crimson—*Trifolium incarnatum*
Clover, hare's-foot—*Trifolium arvense*
Clover, knotted (or soft)—*Trifolium striatum*
Clover, red—*Trifolium pratense*
Clover, rough—*Trifolium scabrum*
Clover, strawberry—*Trifolium fragiferum*
Clover, white—*Trifolium repens*
Club-rush, bristle—*Scirpus setaceus* (or *Isolepis*)
Club-rush, common (or true bulrush)—*Scirpus lacustris* (or *Schoenoplectus*)

Club-rush, floating—*Eleogiton fluitans*
Club-rush, grey (or seaside bulrush)—*Scirpus tabernaemontani* (or *Schoenoplectus*)
Club-rush, sea (or sea sedge)—*Scirpus maritimus*
Club-rush, slender—*Scirpus cernuus* (or *Isolepis*)
Cock's-foot—*Dactylis glomerata*
Colt's-foot—*Tussilago farfara*
Comfrey, Russian—*Symphytum x uplandicum*
Cord-grass, common (or rice grass)—*Spartina anglica*
Cord-grass, small—*Spartina maritima*
Cord-grass, Townsend's—*Spartina x townsendii*
Cornsalad, common (or lamb's lettuce)—*Valerianella locusta*
Corn spurrey (*Spergularia arvensis*)
Cottongrass, common—*Eriophorum angustifolium*
Cottongrass, hare's-tail—*Eriophorum vaginatum*
Cottongrass, slender—*Eriophorum gracile*
Couch, common—*Agropyron repens*
Couch, sand—*Agropyron junceiforme*
Couch, sea—*Agropyron pungens*
Cowslip—*Primula veris*
Cranesbill, dove's-foot—*Geranium molle*
Cranesbill, hedgerow—*Geranium pyrenaicum*
Cranesbill, long-stalked—*Geranium columbinum*
Cranesbill, meadow—*Geranium pratense*
Cranesbill, shining—*Geranium lucidum*
Cress, hoary (or Scourge of Kent)—*Cardaria draba*
Cress, thale—*Arabidopsis thaliana*
Crested dogstail—*Cynosurus cristatus*
Crosswort—*Cruciata laevipes* (or *Galium*)
Crowfoot, ivy-leaved—*Ranunculus hederaceus*
Crowfoot, round-leaved—*Ranunculus omiophyllus*
Crown vetch—*Coronilla varia*
Cuckooflower (or lady's smock or milkmaid)—*Cardamine pratensis*
Cuckoopint (or wild arum)—*Arum maculatum*
Cudweed, common—*Filago vulgaris*

Daisy, field—*Bellis perennis*
Daisy, ox-eye—*Leucanthemum vulgare* (or *Chrysanthemum*)
Dandelion, common—*Taraxacum officinale* agg.
Dandelion, lesser—*Taraxacum erythrospermum*

Dewberry—*Rubus caesius*
Dittander—*Lepidium latifolium*
Dock, broad-leaved—*Rumex obtusifolius*
Dock, curled, maritime variety—*Rumex crispus* var. *trigranulatus*
Dock, great water—*Rumex hydrolapathum*
Dock, sea—*Rumex maritimus*
Dog's-tail, crested—*Cynosurus cristatus*
Dog-violet, heath—*Viola canina*
Dogwood—*Swida sanguinea* (or *Cornus* or *Thelycrania*)
Duckweed, common—*Lemna minor*
Duckweed, ivy-leaved—*Lemna trisulca*
(Dutch-rush (or rough horsetail)—*Equisetum hyemale*)

Elder—*Sambucus nigra*
Enchanter's-nightshade—*Circaea lutetiana*
Evening primrose, common—*Oenothera biennis*
Evening primrose, fragrant—*Oenothera stricta*
Evening primrose, large-flowered—*Oenothera erythrosepala*
Evening primrose, small-flowered—*Oenothera parviflora*
Everlasting, pearly—*Anaphalis margaritacea*
Eyebright—*Euphrasia officinalis* agg.

Fennel—*Foeniculum vulgare*
Fen-sedge, great—*Cladium mariscus*
Fern, hard—*Blechnum spicant*
Fern, lemon-scented (or mountain)—*Thelypteris limbosperma* (or *oreopteris*)
(Fern, lady—*Athyrium filix-femina*)
Fern, marsh—*Thelypteris palustris*
Fern, royal—*Osmunda regalis*
Fern-grass—*Catapodium rigidum* (or *Desmazeria*)
Fern-grass, sea—*Catapodium marinum* (or *Desmazeria*)
Fescue, dune—*Vulpia membranacea*
Fescue, meadow—*Festuca pratensis*
Fescue, rat's-tail—*Vulpia myuros*
Fescue, red—*Festuca rubra*
Fescue, sheep's—*Festuca ovina*
Fescue, squirreltail—*Vulpia bromoides*
Fescue, tall (or giant)—*Festuca arundinacea*
Field madder (*Sherardia arvensis*)
Fig—*Ficus carica*
Figwort, water—*Scrophularia auriculata*
(Fiorin grass—*Agrostis stolonifera*)
(Flag, yellow (or yellow iris)—*Iris pseudacorus*)
Flax, fairy—*Linum catharticum*

Fleabane, blue—*Erigeron acer*
Fleabane, Canadian—*Erigeron canadensis*
Fleabane, common—*Pulicaria dysenterica*
(Floating Scirpus—*Eleogiton fluitans*)
Flowering-rush—*Butomus umbellatus*
Forget-me-not, field—*Myosotis arvensis*
Forget-me-not, water—*Myosotis scorpioides* (or *palustris*)
Foxglove—*Digitalis purpurea*
Foxtail, marsh—*Alopecurus geniculatus*
Frogbit—*Hydrocharis morsus-ranae*

Gentian, Autumn (or felwort)—*Gentianella amarella*
Germander, wall—*Teucrium chamaedrys*
Gipsywort—*Lycopus europaeus*
(Gladdon (or foetid) iris—*Iris foetidissima*)
Glasswort—*Salicornia ramosissima*
Glasswort—*Salicornia pusilla*
Goat's-beard—*Tragopogon pratensis*
Golden-rod—*Solidago virgaurea*
Golden-saxifrage, opposite-leaved—*Chrysosplenium oppositifolium*
Gold-of-pleasure—*Camelina sativa*
Goosefoot, red—*Chenopodium rubrum*
Gorse, common—*Ulex europaeus*
Gromwell, common—*Lithospermum officinale*
Ground-ivy—*Glechoma hederacea*
Groundsel—*Senecio vulgaris*
Groundsel, sticky—*Senecio viscosus*
Guelder-rose—*Viburnum opulus*

Hair-grass, crested—*Koeleria cristata*
Hair-grass, early—*Aira praecox*
Hair-grass, grey—*Corynephorus canescens*
Hair-grass, wavy—*Deschampsia flexuosa*
Hard fern—*Blechnum spicant*
Hard-grass—*Parapholis strigosa* (or *Lepturus*)
Hard-grass, curved—*Parapholis incurva* (or *Lepturus*)
Harebell—*Campanula rotundifolia*
Hart's-tongue—*Phyllitis scolopendrium*
Hawkbit, Autumn—*Leontodon autumnalis*
Hawkbit, rough—*Leontodon hispidus*
Hawkweed, mouse-ear—*Hieracium pilosella*
Hawthorn—*Crataegus monogyna*
Hazel—*Corylus avellana*
Heath, fine-leaved—*Erica cinerea*
Heather (or ling)—*Calluna vulgaris*
Hedge parsley, knotted—*Torilis nodosa*
Hedge-parsley, upright—*Torilis japonica*
Helleborine, broad-leaved—*Epipactis helleborine*

Helleborine, marsh—*Epipactis palustris*
Hemlock—*Conium maculatum*
Hemp-agrimony—*Eupatorium cannabinum*
Hemp-nettle, common—*Galeopsis tetrahit*
Hemp-nettle, red—*Galeopsis angustifolia*
Henbane—*Hyoscyamus niger*
Henbit—*Lamium amplexicaule*
(Herb Bennet (or wood avens)—*Geum urbanum)*
Herb Robert—*Geranium robertianum*
Hoary mustard—*Hirschfeldia incana*
Hoary pepperwort—*Cardaria draba*
Hogweed (or cow parsnip)—*Heracleum sphondylium*
Holly—*Ilex aquifolium*
Honeysuckle—*Lonicera periclymenum*
Horned-poppy, yellow—*Glaucium flavum*
Hornwort, rigid—*Ceratophyllum demersum*
Horsetail, field—*Equisetum arvense*
Horsetail, great (or giant)—*Equisetum telmateia*
Horsetaii, marsh—*Equisetum palustre*
Horsetail, rough (or Dutch rush)—*Equisetum hyemale*
Horsetail, variegated—*Equisetum variegatum*
Horsetail, water—*Equisetum fluviatile*
Hound's-tongue—*Cynoglossum officinale*
Hutchinsia—*Hornungia petraea*

Iris, stinking—*Iris foetidissima*
Iris, yellow (or flag)—*Iris pseudacorus*
Ivy—*Hedera helix*

(Jack-go-to-bed-at-noon (or goat's beard)—*Tragopogon pratensis)*
Jack-in-the-pulpit (or lords and ladies)—*Arum maculatum*

Kingcup (or marsh-marigold)—*Caltha palustris*
Knapweed, common—*Centaurea nigra*
Knapweed, greater —*Centaurea scabiosa*
Knotweed, Japanese—*Polygonum cuspidatum* (or *Reynoutria)*

(Lady's smock (or milkmaid or cuckoo-flower) —*Cardamine pratensis)*
Lady's-tresses, Autumn—*Spiranthes spiralis*
Lime, large-leaved—*Tilia platyphylla*
Lime, small-leaved—*Tilia cordata*
Liquorice, wild—*Astragalus glycyphyllos*
Loosestrife, purple—*Lythrum salicaria*
(Loosestrife, woodland (or yellow pimpernel)—*Lysimachia nemorum)*

Loosestrife, yellow—*Lysimachia vulgaris*
Lords-and-ladies—*Arum maculatum*
Lousewort, marsh (or red rattle)—*Pedicularis palustris*
Lucerne—*Medicago sativa*
Lyme grass—Elymus arenarius

Maiden pink—*Dianthus deltoides*
Male fern—*Dryopteris filix-mas*
Mallow, musk—*Malva moschata*
Mallow, tree—*Lavatera arborea*
Maple, field—*Acer campestre*
Mare's-tail—*Hippuris vulgaris*
Marjoram—*Origanum vulgare*
Marram grass—*Ammophila arenaria*
Marsh foxtail (*Alopecurus geniculatus)*
Marsh-marigold (or kingcup)—*Caltha palustris*
Marsh-orchid, early—*Dactylorhiza incarnata* ssp. *coccinea*
Marsh-orchid, southern—*Dactylorhiza praetermissa*
Marshwort, lesser—*Apium inundatum*
Mayweed, scentless—*Tripleurospermum maritimum* ssp. *inodorum*
Meadow-grass, annual—*Poa annua*
Meadow-grass, flattened—*Poa compressa*
Meadow-rue, lesser—*Thalictrum minus*
Meadowsweet—*Filipendula ulmaria*
Medick, black—*Medicago lupulina*
Medick, sickle—*Medicago falcata*
Melilot, white—*Melilotus alba*
Mercury, dog's—*Mercurialis perennis*
Mignonette, wild—*Reseda lutea*
Milfoil (or yarrow)—*Achillea millefolium*
(Milkmaid (or lady's smock or cuckoo-flower)—*Cardamine pratensis)*
Millet, wood—*Milium effusum*
Mint, corn—*Mentha arvensis*
Mint, hybrid—*Mentha* x *dumetorum*
Mint, hybrid—*Mentha* x *verticillata*
Mint, water—*Mentha aquatica*
Montbretia—*Crocosmia* x *crocosmiflora*
Moonwort—*Botrychium lunaria*
Moor-grass, purple—*Molinia caerulea*
Motherwort—*Leonurus cardiaca*
Mountain fern, lemon-scented—*Thelypteris oreopteris*
Mouse-ear chickweed, common—*Cerastium holosteoides* (or *vulgatum)*
Mouse-ear chickweed, little—*Cerastium semidecandrum*
Mouse-ear chickweed, sea—*Cerastium diffusum* (or *tetrandrum* or *atrovirens)*

Mouse-ear hawkweed—*Hieracium pilosella*
Mudwort—*Limosella aquatica*
Mudwort, Welsh—*Limosella australis* (or
  subulata)
Mugwort—*Artemesia vulgaris*
Mugwort, sea—*Artemisia maritima*
Mullein, great—*Verbascum thapsus*
Mullein, hoary—*Verbascum pulverulentum*
Mustard, hoary—*Hirschfeldia incana*
Myrtle, bog (or sweet gale)—*Myrica gale*

Navelwort (or wall pennywort)—*Umbilicus*
  rupestris
Nettle, common—*Urtica dioica*
(Nightshade, woody—*Solanum dulcamara*)

Oak, pedunculate—*Quercus robur*
Oak, sessile—*Quercus petraea*
Oat-grass, false (or tall)—*Arrhenatherum*
  elatius
Oat-grass, yellow (or golden)—*Trisetum*
  flavescens
Orache, Babington's—*Atriplex glabriuscula*
Orache, common—*Atriplex patula*
Orache, frosted—*Atriplex laciniata*
Orache, spear-leaved (or sea)—*Atriplex hastata*
Orchid, bee—*Ophrys apifera*
(Orchid, early marsh—*Dactylorhiza incarnata*
  ssp. *coccinea*)
Orchid, early purple—*Orchis mascula*
Orchid, fen—*Liparis loeselii*
Orchid, fragrant—*Gymnadenia conopsea*
Orchid, green-winged—*Orchis morio*
(Orchid, heath spotted—*Dactylorhiza maculata*
  (or *ericetorum*))
Orchid, musk—*Herminium monorchis*
Orchid, pyramidal—*Anacamptis*
  pyramidalis
(Orchid, southern marsh—*Dactylorhiza*
  praetermissa)
(Orchid, spotted—*Dactylorhiza fuchsii*)
Osier—*Salix viminalis*

Pansy, wild—*Viola tricolor* ssp. *curtisii*
Parsnip, wild—*Pastinaca sativa*
Pea, tuberous (or earth-nut)—*Lathyrus*
  tuberosus
(Pea, yellow (or meadow vetchling)—*Lathyrus*
  pratensis)
Pearlwort, knotted—*Sagina nodosa*
Pearlwort, procumbent—*Sagina procumbens*
Pennywort, marsh—*Hydrocotyle vulgaris*

(Persicaria, amphibious (or water bistort)—
  Polygonum amphibium)
(Persicaria, common (or redshanks)—
  Polygonum persicaria
Persicaria, pale—*Polygonum lapathifolium*
Pimpernel, bog—*Anagallis tenella*
Pimpernel, scarlet—*Anagallis arvensis*
Pimpernel, yellow (or woodland loosestrife)—
  Lysimachia nemorum
Pine, Corsican—*Pinus nigra* var. *maritima*
Pine, Scots—*Pinus sylvestris*
Plantain, buck's horn (or stag's horn)—
  Plantago coronopus
Plantain, greater—*Plantago major*
Plantain, hoary (or lamb's tongue)—*Plantago*
  media
Plantain, ribwort—*Plantago lanceolata*
Plantain, sea—*Plantago maritima*
Ploughman's spikenard—*Inula conyza*
Polypody fern—*Polypodium vulgare* and
  P. interjectum
Pond-sedge, greater—*Carex riparia*
Pond-sedge, lesser—*Carex acutiformis*
Pondweed, bog—*Potamogeton polygonifolius*
Pondweed, broad-leaved—*Potamogeton natans*
(Pondweed, Canadian—*Elodea canadensis*)
Pondweed, curled—*Potamogeton crispus*
Pondweed, fennel—*Potamogeton pectinatus*
Pondweed, perfoliate—*Potamogeton*
  perfoliatus
Pondweed, shining—*Potamogeton lucens*
Pondweed, small—*Potamogeton berchtoldii*
Poplar, white—*Populus alba*
Poppy, common—*Papaver rhoeas*
Poppy, opium—*Papaver somniferum*
(Poppy, yellow-horned—*Glaucium flavum*)
Primrose—*Primula vulgaris*
Privet, wild—*Ligustrum vulgare*
Purple-loosestrife—*Lythrum salicaria*

Quaking grass—*Briza media*

Radish, sea—*Raphanus maritimus*
Ragged robin—*Lychnis flos-cuculi*
Ragwort, common—*Senecio jacobaea*
Ragwort, marsh—*Senecio aquaticus*
Ragwort, Oxford—*Senecio squalidus*
(Rattle, red (or marsh lousewort)—
  Pedicularis palustris)
Rattle, yellow—*Rhinanthus minor*
Redshank (or persicaria)—*Polygonum*
  persicaria

Reed, common—*Phragmites australis* (or
  communis)
(Reed-canary grass—*Phalaris arundinacea*)
(Reedmace, great (or bulrush)—*Typha
  latifolia*)
(Reedmace, lesser (or bulrush)—*Typha
  angustifolia*)
Restharrow, common—*Ononis repens*
(Rice grass (or cord grass)—*Spartina* spp.)
Rhododendron—*Rhododendron ponticum*
Rock-cress, hairy—*Arabis hirsuta*
(Rocket, annual wall—*Diplotaxis muralis*)
(Rocket, perennial wall—*Diplotaxis tenuifolius*)
Rocket, sea—*Cakile maritima*
Rose, burnet—*Rosa pimpinellifolia* (or
  spinosissima)
Rose, dog—*Rosa canina*
Rose, Japanese (or salt spray)—*Rosa rugosa*
Rosemary, bog—*Andromeda polifolia*
Rush, blunt-flowered—*Juncus subnodulosus*
(Rush, Dutch—*Equisetum hyemale*)
(Rush, flowering—*Butomus umbellatus*)
Rush, jointed—*Juncus articulatus*
Rush, saltmarsh (or mud)—*Juncus gerardii*
Rush, sea—*Juncus maritimus*
Rush, sharp—*Juncus acutus*
Rush, sharp-flowered—*Juncus acutiflorus*
Rush, soft—*Juncus effusus*
Rush, toad—*Juncus bufonius*

Saffron, meadow—*Colchicum autumnale*
Sage, wood—*Teucrium scorodonia*
St. John's-wort, creeping—*Hypericum
  humifusum*
St. John's-wort, elegant—*Hypericum pulchrum*
St. John's-wort, marsh—*Hypericum elodes*
St. John's-wort, perforate—*Hypericum
  perforatum*
St. John's-wort, square-stalked—*Hypericum
  tetrapterum*
Sallow, goat—*Salix caprea*
Sallow, grey—*Salix cinerea*
Saltmarsh-grass, common—*Puccinellia
  maritima*
Saltmarsh-grass, distant—*Puccinellia distans*
Saltwort, prickly—*Salsola kali*
Samphire, golden—*Inula crithmoides*
Samphire, rock—*Crithmum maritimum*
Sandwort, sea—*Honkenya peploides*
Sandwort, slender—*Arenaria leptoclados*
Sandwort, thyme-leaved—*Arenaria serpyllifolia*
(Saw-grass—*Cladium mariscus*)
Saxifrage, mossy—*Saxifraga hypnoides*

Saxifrage, rue-leaved—*Saxifraga tridactylites*
Scabious, devil's bit—*Succisa pratensis*
Scabious, field—*Knautia arvensis*
Scabious, small—*Scabiosa columbaria*
Scorpion-grass—*Myosotis arvensis*
(Scourge-of-Kent (or hoary cress)—*Cardaria
  draba*)
Scurvy-grass, common—*Cochlearia officinalis*
Scurvy-grass, Danish—*Cochlearia danica*
Scurvy-grass, English—*Cochlearia anglica*
Sea-blite, annual—*Suaeda maritima*
Sea-buckthorn—*Hippophaë rhamnoides*
Sea-holly—*Eryngium maritimum*
Sea-lavender, common—*Limonium vulgare*
Sea lavender, rock—*Limonium binervosum*
Sea-milkwort (or black saltwort)—*Glaux
  maritima*
Sea-purslane—*Halimione* (or *Obione*)
  portulacoides
(Sea-sedge (or sea club-rush)—*Scirpus
  maritimus*)
Sea-spurrey, greater—*Spergularia media* (or
  marginata)
Sea-spurrey, lesser—*Spergularia marina* (or
  salina)
Sedge, bog (or mud)—*Carex limosa*
Sedge, brown—*Carex disticha*
Sedge, bottle (or beak)—*Carex rostrata*
Sedge, dioecious—*Carex dioica*
Sedge, distichous—*Carex disticha*
Sedge, false-fox—*Carex otrubae*
Sedge, glaucous (or carnation grass)—*Carex
  flacca*
Sedge, hairy (or hammer)—*Carex hirta*
Sedge, long-bracted—*Carex extensa*
Sedge, prickly—*Carex muricata*
Sedge, sand—*Carex arenaria*
(Sedge, sea—*Scirpus maritimus*)
Sedge, tufted—*Carex elata*
Sedge, tussock—*Carex paniculata*
Sedge, yellow—*Carex serotina*
Self-heal—*Prunella vulgaris*
Sheep's fescue—*Festuca ovina*
(Sheep's sorrel—*Rumex acetosella*)
Shoreweed—*Littorella uniflora* (or *lacustris*)
Silverweed—*Potentilla anserina*
Skullcap, greater—*Scutellaria galericulata*
Skunk cabbage—*Lysichiton americanus*
Sneezewort—*Achillea ptarmica*
Soapwort—*Saponaria officinalis*
Sorrel, common—*Rumex acetosa*
Sorrel, sheep's—*Rumex acetosella*
(Sorrel, wood—*Oxalis acetosella*)

(Southernwood (or field wormwood)—
    Artemisia campestris)
Sow-thistle, perennial (or corn)—*Sonchus
    arvensis*
Spearwort, greater—*Ranunculus lingua*
Spearwort, lesser—*Ranunculus flammula*
(Speedwell, field (or Buxbaum's)—*Veronica
    persica*)
Speedwell, marsh—*Veronica scutellata*
Speedwell, slender—*Veronica filiformis*
(Speedwell, water, blue—*Veronica anagallis-
    aquatica*)
(Speedwell, water, pink—*Veronica catenata*)
Spike-rush, common—*Eleocharis palustris*
Spike-rush, slender—*Eleocharis uniglumis*
Spotted-orchid, common—*Dactylorhiza fuchsii*
Spotted-orched, heath—*Dactylorhiza maculata*
    (or *ericetorum*)
Springbeauty—*Montia perfoliata*
Spurge, Portland—*Euphorbia portlandica*
Spurge, sea—*Euphorbia paralias*
Spurrey, sand—*Honkenya peploides*
Squill, Spring—*Scilla verna*
Squinancywort—*Asperula cynanchica*
Star-of-Bethlehem—*Ornithogalum umbellatum*
Stitchwort, greater—*Stellaria holostea*
Stock, hoary (or gilliflower)—*Matthiola incana*
Stock, sea—*Matthiola sinuata*
Stonecrop, biting (or wall pepper)—*Sedum acre*
Stonecrop, white—*Sedum album*
(Stoneworts—*Chara* and *Nitella* species, are
    algae, not flowering plants)
Stork's-bill, common—*Erodium cicutarium*
Stork's-bill, sea—*Erodium maritimum*
Sundew, great—*Drosera anglica*
Sundew, oblong-leaved—*Drosera intermedia*
Sundew, round-leaved—*Drosera rotundifolia*
Sweet-flag—*Acorus calamus*
Sweet gale (or bog myrtle)—*Myrica gale*
Sweet-grass, floating (or flote-grass)—
    Glyceria fluitans
Sweet-grass, plicate—*Glyceria plicata*
Sweet-grass, reed—*Glyceria maxima*
Sweet vernal grass (*Anthoxanthum odoratum*)
Sycamore—*Acer pseudoplatanus*

Tamarisk—*Tamarix anglica*
Tansy—*Tanacetum vulgare*
Tare, hairy—*Vicia hirsuta*
(Tare, purple—*Vicia sativa*)
Teasel—*Dipsacus fullonum*
Thistle, carline—*Carlina vulgaris*
Thistle, dwarf (or stemless)—*Cirsium acaule*

Thistle, noddingg—*Carduus nutans*
Thistle, slender—*Carduus tenuiflorus*
Thistle, woolly—*Cirsium eriophorum*
Thrift (or sea pink)—*Armeria maritima*
Thyme, basil—*Acinos arvensis*
Thyme, wild—*Thymus drucei*
Timothy, sand—*Phleum arenarium*
Toadflax, common—*Linaria vulgaris*
Toadflax, ivy-leaved—*Cymbalaria muralis*
Toadflax, pale—*Linaria repens*
Toadflax, purple—*Linaria purpurea*
Toadflax, small—*Chaenorhinum minus*
Tormentil—*Potentilla erecta*
Traveller's joy (or old man's beard)—*Clematis
    vitalba*
Tree-mallow—*Lavatera arborea*
Trefoil, hop—*Trifolium campestre*
Trefoil, lesser (or yellow suckling clover)—
    Trifolium dubium
(Trefoil, bird's-foot—*Lotus corniculatus* and
    L. uliginosus)
Tufted-sedge—*Carex elata*
Tussock-sedge, greater—*Carex paniculata*
Twayblade, common—*Listera ovata*

Vetch, common—*Vicia sativa*
Vetch, crown—*Coronilla varia*
Vetch, fodder—*Vicia villosa*
Vetch, horseshoe—*Hippocrepis comosa*
Vetch, kidney (or lady's fingers)—*Anthyllis
    vulneraria*
Vetch, narrow-leaved—*Vicia angustifolia*
Vetch, tufted—*Vicia cracca*
Vetchling, meadow (or yellow pea)—*Lathyrus
    pratensis*
(Violet, common dog—*Viola riviniana*)
Violet, hairy—*Viola hirta*
(Violet, heath dog—*Viola canina*)
Violet, marsh (or bog)—*Viola palustris*
Violet, sweet—*Viola odorata*
Viper's bugloss—*Echium vulgare*

Wallflower cabbage—*Rhynchosinapis
    cheiranthos*
(Wall pennywort (or navelwort)—*Umbilicus
    rupestris*)
(Wall pepper (or biting stonecrop)—*Sedum
    acre*)
Wall-rocket, annual—*Diplotaxis muralis*
Wall-rocket, perennial—*Diplotaxis tenuifolia*
Watercress—*Rorippa nasturtium-aquaticum* (or
    Nasturtium officinale)
Watercress, fool's—*Apium nodiflorum*

398

Water-crowfoot, brackish—*Ranunculus baudotii*
Water-crowfoot, common—*Ranunculus aquatilis* agg.
Water-crowfoot, hair-leaved—*Ranunculus trichophyllus*
Water-dropwort, hemlock—*Oenanthe crocata*
Water-dropwort, parsley—*Oenanthe lachenalii*
Water-dropwort, tubular—*Oenanthe fistulosa*
Water-lily, white—*Nymphaea alba*
Water-lily, yellow (or brandy bottle)—*Nuphar lutea*
Water-milfoil, alternate—*Myriophyllum alterniflorum*
Water milfoil, spiked—*Myriophyllum spicatum*
Water milfoil, whorled—*Myriophyllum verticillatum*
Water onion—*Aponogeton distachyos*
Water-parsnip, lesser—*Berula erecta*
Water-pepper—*Polygonum hydropiper*
Water-plantain—*Alisma plantago-aquatica*
Water plantain, floating—*Luronium natans*
Water-plantain, lesser—*Baldellia ranunculoides*
Water-purslane—*Peplis* (or *Lythrum*) *portula*
Water-speedwel, blue—*Veronica anagallis-aquatica*
Water-speedwell, pink—*Veronica catenata*
Water-starwort, common—*Callitriche stagnalis*
Water-starwort, intermediate—*Callitriche intermedia*
Water-starwort, various-leaved—*Callitriche platycarpa*

Waterweed, Canadian (or Canadian pondweed)—*Elodea canadensis*
Weld—*Reseda luteola*
Whitlowgrass, common—*Erophila verna*
Wild Columine (*Aquilegia vulgaris*)
Wild strawberry (*Fragaria vesca*)
Willow, creeping—*Salix repens*
Willow, goat (or sallow)—*Salix caprea*
Willow, grey (or sallow)—*Salix cinerea*
Willowherb, great (or codlins and cream)—*Epilobium hirsutum*
Willowherb, rosebay—*Epilobium* (or *Chamaenerion*) *angustifolium*
Wintergreen, round-leaved—*Pyrola rotundifolia*
Wood-rush, field—*Luzula campestris*
Wood-sage—*Teucrium scorodonia*
Wood-sorrel—*Oxalis acetosella*
Wormwood, field—*Artemisia campestris*
Wormwood, sea—*Artemisia maritima*
Woundwort, hedge—*Stachys sylvatica*
Woundwort, marsh—*Stachys palustris*

Yarrow (or milfoil)—*Achillea millefolium*
Yellow-cress, creeping—*Rorippa sylvestris*
Yellow-cress, marsh—*Rorippa islandica*
(Yellow pea (or meadow vetchling)—*Lathyrus pratensis*)
(Yellow rattle—*Rhinanthus minor*)
Yellow-sedge, small-fruited—*Carex serotina*
Yellow-wort—*Blackstonia* (or *Chlora*) *perfoliata*
Yorkshire-fog—*Holcus lanatus*

This list is based on 'English Names of Wild Flowers', produced by the Botanical Society of the British Isles in 1974. Well-known names other than the ones recommended in this text—whether vernacular or scientific—have been included, for ease of recognition where recent name changes have occurred, but are in brackets. (This leads to some plants having more than one entry.)
NB: This is not an exhaustive list for the region and few of the common plants receive specific mention.

Bibliography

Cross-leaved heath

No man can garner sunbeams, or commit his offspring to the wind for a journey of a thousand miles. A dandelion can. Science has far to go before it matches the ingenuity of a wayside weed.

Brendan Lehane in "The Power of Plants."

BIBLIOGRAPHY

ANDERSON, J. G. C. The concealed rock surface and overlying deposits of the Severn Valley Estuary from Upton to Neath. *Proc. S. Wales Inst. Engineers. LXXXIII,* 1, 27-47 (1968)

ANDERSON, J. G. C. The buried channels, rock floors and rock basins and overlying deposits of the S. Wales Valleys from Wye to Neath. *Proc. S. Wales Inst. Engineers. LXXXVIII,* 1, 1-17 (1974)

ANDERSON, J. G. C. and OWEN, T. R. The late quaternary history of the Neath and Afan Valleys, S. Wales. *Proc. Geol. Ass. 90,* 4, 203-211 (1979)

BAKER, J. Effects of refinery effluents on the plants of the Crymlin Bog. *Ann. Rep., Oil Pollution Res. Unit (1973)*

BASSINDALE, R. Studies on the biology of the Bristol Channel. 8. The distribution of amphipods in the Severn Estuary and Bristol Channel. *Jour. Animal Ecol. 11,* 131-144 (1942)

BRADLEY, A. G. *Glamorgan and Gower.* Archibald Constable, London (1908)

BOWERS, A. B. and NAYLOR, E. Occurrence of *Atherina boyeri* Risso in Britain. *Nature, 202,* 318, (1964)

BOYDEN C. B. *et al.* (1977). See under METTAM

BROWN, A. E. The effects of trampling on fauna with particular reference to soil arthropods in a sand dune ecosystem (Kenfig). Unpublished thesis. Zoology Dept., Univ. Coll. Cardiff (1976i)

BROWN, A. E. Environmental impacts on a sand dune eco-system with particular reference to the effects of human trampling. Unpublished thesis. Botany Dept., Univ. Coll. Cardiff (1976ii)

B.S.B.I. *Atlas of the British Flora.* Nelson, London 1962

CARDIFF NATURALISTS' SOCIETY, Ornithological Section. (1961-78) *Glamorgan bird reports,* published annually. Swansea.

CHATFIELD, G. D. P. A survey of birds in Swansea Docks, 1965-69. *Gower Birds, 1,* 3, 42-46 (1970)

COLLINS, M. B., FERENTINOS, G. and BANNER, F. The hydrodynamics and sedimentology of a high (tidal and wave) energy embayment (Swansea Bay), North Bristol-Channel. *Estuarine and Coastal Marine Science. 8,* 49-74 (1979)

COLLINS, M. B. *et al.* The supply of sand to Swansea Bay. *Industrial embayments and their environmental problems. A case study of Swansea Bay.* Pergamon, London (1980i)

COLLINS, M. B. and BANNER, F. T. Sediment transport by waves and tides. *The North European open shelf seas: the sea bed and the sea in motion.* Ed. Banner, Collins, Massie. Amsterdam (1980)

CRUTCHLEY, G. F. *Map of Railways of South Wales; Proposed and Constructed.* London (1840)

EDINGTON, J. M. and M. A. *Ecology and Environmental Planning.* New Ecol. & Env. Studies series, Chapman and Hall (1977)

EVANS, A. Leslie. Some eighteenth century wrecks. *Trans. Port Talbot Hist. Soc. 3,* 1, 90-94 (1967)

402

EVANS, F. *Tir Iarll, The Earl's Land.* Welsh County Series (1912)

FERNS, P. In *Joint Biological Excursion to N.E. Greenland 1974, Dundee and Wader Study Group.* Dundee (1974i)

FERNS, P. Wader counts in South Glamorgan. *Glam. Bird Report, 3,* 1, 6-7 (1974ii)

FONSECA, E. C. M. d'Assis and COWLEY, J. Insects and Spiders collected in Glamorgan June and July, 1952. *Trans. Cardiff Nats. (1950-52) LXXXI,* 66-74 (1953)

GEORGE, T. N. The geology of the Swansea main drainage excavations. *Proc. Swansea Sci. Field Nats. Soc. I* (1936)

GILBERT, O. L. An alkaline dust effect on epiphytic lichens. *Lichenologist 8,* 173-178 (1976)

GILLHAM, M. E. Various, in *Bull. Glam. Nats. Trust,* published annually (1963-80)

GODWIN, H. A Boreal transgression of the sea in Swansea Bay. *New Phyt. 39,* 3, 308-321 (1940)

HEATHCOTE, A., GRIFFIN, D. and MORREY-SALMON, H. *The Birds of Glamorgan.* Cowbridge (1967)

HIGGINS, L. S. An investigation into the problem of the sand dune areas on the S. Wales coast. *Arch. Camb.,* 26-67 (1933)

JENKINS, Ellis. *Neath and District: A Symposium.* Cowbridge (1974)

JEFFERSON, G. T. A note on some tropical and sub-tropical barnacles and other animals from the Bristol Channel. *Trans. Cardiff Nats. (1952-53). LXXXII,* 32-35 (1955)

JOHNSON, D. N. *The feeding habits of overwintering wildfowl on the freshwater lakes of South-east Wales.* Unpublished thesis, Zoology Dept., Univ. Coll. Cardiff (1975)

KAY, Q. *A Preliminary Survey of the Vegetation of Crymlin Bog.* Unpublished report. Bot. Dept., Univ. Coll. Cardiff (1971)

KING, P. E. and COPLAND, M. J. W. Occurrence of *Metoecus paradoxus* (Coleoptera, Rhipiphoridae) in Glamorgan. *Entomologists' Monthly Mag. 105.* 114 (1969)

LANSDOWNE, A. *Spartina* in Swansea Bay. *Bull. Glam. Nats. Trust. 11 1972*

LEES, A. *A survey of Crymlin Bog and Pant y Sais.* Unpublished report. Nature Conservancy Council (1980)

LEWIS, C. A. (Ed.) *Glaciations of Wales and Adjoining Regions.* Glaciation in South Wales, 197-223. Longmans, London (1970)

LIDDLE, M. J. and GREIG—SMITH P. A survey of tracks and paths in a sand dune ecosystem. I. Soils, and II. Vegetation. *Jour. Appl. Ecol.* I 893-903 and II 909-930 (1975)

MALKIN, B. H. *The Scenery, Antiquities and Biography of South Wales.* London (1804)

METTAM, C. in BOYDEN, C. B., CROTHERS, J. H., LITTLE, C. and METTAM, C. The intertidal invertebrate fauna of the Severn Estuary. *Field Studies, 4,* 477-554 (1977)

MORREY-SALMON, H. Ornithological Notes. *Trans. Cardiff Nats.* Published biennially (1920s onwards)

MORREY-SALMON, H. *A Supplement to the Birds of Glamorgan, 1967* (1st Jan. 1967 to 31st March, 1974.). Cowbridge (1974)

MORGAN, A. *The Breakwater.* A Novel of Porthcawl. Cowbridge 1975

MORGAN, A. *Legends of Porthcawl and the Glamorgan Coast.* Cowbridge (1978)

MORGAN, A. *Elizabeth, Fair Maid of Sker.* A novel. Cowbridge (1980)

NAYLOR, E. Marine biology in Swansea Docks. *Gower, 13,* 47-51 (1960)

NELSON, W. Kenfig Dragonflies. *Bull. Glam. Nats. Trust (1980)*

NELSON-SMITH, A. Ecology of Rocky Shores around Swansea Bay. *Rep. Working party on possible pollution in Swansea Bay. 2.* Tech. Reps. 55-70 (1974)

PARSON, R. Effects of refinery effluents on the freshwater animals of the Crymlin Bog, 21-28 Aug. 1972. *Ann. Rep. Oil Pollution Res. Unit (1973)*

PHILLIPS, D. Rhys. *A History of the Vale of Neath* (1925)

PURCHON, R. D. Studies on the Biology of the Bristol Channel XVIII Marine fauna at five stations on the northern shores. *Proc. Bristol Nats. Soc. 29,* 213-226 (1956)

PYATT, F. B. Lichens as indicators of air pollution in a steel producing town in South Wales (Port Talbot). *Env. Pollution. 1,* 45-56 (1970)

RAILWAY GAZETTE (Anon). New marshalling yard at Margam, Western Region. *The Rly. Gazette,* June 20th 1958, 712-714 (1958)

SOUTH GLAMORGAN. Outdoor Studies Centre, Porthcawl. *Sker: A list of Marine Flora and Fauna.* Cyclostyled leaflet in use at centre (1976)

TROW, A. H. *Flora of Glamorgan.* Cardiff (1911)

UNIVERSITY OF DUNDEE AND WADER STUDY GROUP. *Joint Biological expedition to N.E. Greenland,* 1974. Dundee (1974)

VACHELL, E. Botany. *The Natural History of Glamorgan.* Cardiff (1936)

VACHELL, E. The Limosella Plants of Glamorgan. Pt I. The history of their discovery. *Jour. Bot.* 65-71 (1939)

VON POST, L. A gothialogical transgression of the sea in South Sweden. *Geog. Ann. Stockh.,* 15 (1933)

WELLS, J. D. *The Birds of Kenfig.* Unpublished report (1972)

WELLS, J. D. Common birds census. Stormy Down. *Glam. Bird Rep. 3,* 1-8 (1974)

WESTON, W. Crymlin Bog. *Bull. Glam. Nats. Trust*

YOUNG, S. (Ed). *An Atlas of breeding Birds in Glam.* Cardiff (1975)

Index

Drawn by Mel Watkins, 1980

From the violence and tragedy of flood and earthquake we have been, in comparison with other lands, largely preserved. But the "Torrey Canyon" is a reminder of what unforeseen, man-made perils can beset a modern society.

From "Oil and Politics" in "The Sunday Times", March 1967.

INDEX

Plants are entered under their scientific names; for common names see the appendix commencing on page 392. Page numbers in heavy type refer to colour plates and those in italics to monochrome plates.

412

LIBRARIES

1		25		49		73	
2		26		50		74	
3	11-96	27		51		75	
4		28		52		76	
5		29		53		77	
6		30		54		78	
7		31		55		79	
8		32		56		80	
9		33		57		81	
10		34		58		82	
11		35		59		83	
12		36		60		84	
13		37		61		85	
14		38		62		86	
15		39		63		87	
16		40		64		88	
17		41		65		89	
18		42		66		90	
19		43		67		91	
20		44		68		92	
21		45		69		**COMMUNITY SERVICES**	
22		46		70			
23		47		71			
24		48		72			

96-1683AC\mT